P9-BJJ-235

MAXIMIZING
Performance
MANAGEMENT

Leading Your Team to Success

2ND EDITION

Susan A. Murphy, MBA, PhD

Medical Group Management Association
104 Inverness Terrace East
Englewood, CO 80112-5306
877.275.6462
mgma.org

Medical Group Management Association

Medical Group Management Association® (MGMA®) publications are intended to provide current and accurate information and are designed to assist readers in becoming more familiar with the subject matter covered. Such publications are distributed with the understanding that MGMA does not render any legal, accounting or other professional advice that may be construed as specifically applicable to individual situations. No representations or warranties are made concerning the application of legal or other principles discussed by the authors to any specific factual situation, nor is any prediction made concerning how any particular judge, government official, or other person will interpret or apply such principles. Specific factual situations should be discussed with professional advisors.

Library of Congress Cataloging-in-Publication Data

Names: Murphy, Susan, 1947- , author. | Murphy, Susan, 1947- . Aligning the team with practice goals. Preceded by (work): | Murphy, Susan, 1947- . Building and rewarding your team. Preceded by (work): | Murphy, Susan, 1947- . Leading, coaching, and mentoring the team. Preceded by (work): | Murphy, Susan, 1947- . Relationship management and the new workforce. Preceded by (work): | Medical Group Management Association.
Title: Maximizing performance management : leading your team to success / Susan A. Murphy.
Description: 2nd edition. | Englewood, CO : Medical Group Management Association, [2016] | Includes index. | Preceded by: Aligning the team with practice goals : a how-to guide for medical practices / Susan A. Murphy ; Building and rewarding your team : a how-to guide for medical practices / Susan A. Murphy ; Leading, coaching, and mentoring the team : a how-to guide for medical practices / Susan A. Murphy ; Relationship management and the new workforce : a how-to guide for medical practices / Susan A. Murphy. | This edition combines the four volumes of the previous edition into one.
Identifiers: LCCN 2016012805 | ISBN 9781568294889 (print)
Subjects: | MESH: Personnel Management--methods | Practice Management, Medical--organization & administration | Group Processes | Interpersonal Relations
Classification: LCC RT82 | NLM W 80 | DDC 610.7306/9--dc23
LC record available at http://lccn.loc.gov/2016012805

Item # 8957

ISBN-13: 978-1-56829-488-9

© 2016 Medical Group Management Association

Printed in the United States of America

10 9 8 7 6 5 4 3 2 1

Contents

Acknowledgments

Maximizing Performance Management may have my name on the cover, but it would not exist without the knowledge, enthusiasm, and expertise of many people. Space does not allow me to list everyone, but I want to publicly acknowledge a few colleagues who played especially important roles in the creation of the book you are holding in your hands. Acknowledgments always say "I could not have written this book without their help," but in this case it is absolutely true.

A number of current and former Medical Group Management Association colleagues had special roles in making this book a reality. Marilee Aust and Anne Serrano understood the importance of this topic during our initial conversation when creating the first edition. *Maximizing Performance Management* benefited greatly from their ideas, enthusiasm, and publication skills. Drew DiGiovanni and Peg McHugh made important contributions. I would like to thank Craig Wiberg, senior product manager at MGMA, who has been terrific and instrumental in the publication of this second edition.

Incentives and compensation are critical components in motivating and rewarding the team, and I turned to two leading experts for help. Laura Jacobs, president of GE Healthcare Camden Group, and her long-time colleague Mary Witt contributed this important chapter. Other experts deserve acknowledgment as well for their contributions to different sections of the book. They include generational guru Claire Raines (the chapter on generational differences); human resources expert David Milovich (content throughout the book); Matt Mulherin (success stories as well as the most up-to-date Press Ganey research statistics); Jasenka Sabanovic (life coach); and Lisa Goddard (editing skills). Real-world case studies make these concepts come alive, and I thank all of those involved, including Colleen Conway-Welch, RN, PhD; Deborah W. Royer, MGA; Gene Spiritus, MD; Christy Sandborg, MD; and Bill Zangwill, PhD. Dr. Pat Heim, my mentor and friend for 30 years, generously gave me permission to use information that we developed for our book *In the Company of Women*. Our coauthor, Susan Golant, challenges me by example to constantly improve my writing skills.

On the personal front, my husband Jim kept me sane and focused and laughing, which was no easy feat. He was my one-man management team helping me to maximize my own performance while I was writing. I am also blessed with another wonderful support team — my parents, Alice and Bill Applegarth, and my siblings Anne, Ginger, and Paul.

Finally, I am grateful to the thousands of colleagues, clients, friends, and associates with whom I have worked over the years. They have been my best teachers, and I am grateful to now share their real-world lessons with you, the reader.

About the Author

Susan A. Murphy, MBA, PhD, is president of Business Consultants Group, Inc., based in Rancho Mirage, California. Dr. Murphy's extensive professional background combines the worlds of corporate leadership, academia, and management consulting. She has served as an executive in two Fortune 500 corporations as well as on the graduate faculty at both the University of San Francisco and Vanderbilt University. She has also provided international management consulting for 20+ years to more than 300 healthcare organizations and businesses. Clients include Stanford University Department of Pediatrics, Kaiser Permanente, NASA Jet Propulsion Lab (JPL), Tenet Healthcare Corp., the U.S. Air Force, and the Medical Group Management Association.

Passionate about leadership, mentoring, and teaching individuals about gender and generational differences, Dr. Murphy thrives on serving as a catalyst for breakthrough team performance. She has coauthored numerous books, including *In the Company of Women; Conversations on Success; 4genR8tns: Succeeding with Colleagues, Cohorts & Customers*; and *Leading a Multi-Generational Workforce. In the Company of Women*, coauthored with Dr. Pat Heim, has been featured on *Good Morning America*, the British Broadcasting Corporation, and usatoday.com, as well as in *Time* magazine. The book was selected as Harvard Business School's "Book of the Month" and has been translated into several languages.

As a keynote speaker, Dr. Murphy is known for her "Wit and Wisdom." Audiences everywhere appreciate her humorous style and useful techniques, as she combines research and theory with real-life experiences. In 2004, Vanderbilt University honored Dr. Murphy with a Lifetime Achievement Award.

Introduction

As Michael optimistically walks into the Green Valley Medical Group building to report for his first day on the job, he can't help but feel excited: "I've worked so hard to get to this point in my career. I know that I can make a difference in this practice. After all, it used to have the reputation as the best in the city."

It's true that during the interview process, the seven physicians had described a very bleak view of their practice. However, Michael is sure that they were painting an overly negative picture because the last manager had glossed over so many of the problems with patient satisfaction and staff morale issues, and then, to add insult to injury, absconded with $500,000 in cash. Now with the practice on the verge of bankruptcy, the physicians wanted to find a strong manager who would permit them to return to taking care of patients. And Michael knows that he's the right choice. It couldn't be as bad as they represented it. Besides, he's ready for the challenge and has already paid his dues running much smaller practices for the past 15 years.

As Michael steps off the elevator onto the second floor and begins the trek to his new office, he imagines what it's like to be a patient here. Five patients are in the waiting area already, coffee-stained magazines are scattered throughout the room, and two of the patients are talking loudly on cell phones. Michael says "good morning" to the patients as he passes through the private entrance to his new office. Suddenly, Michael is hit by what seems to be a curtain of tension. Karen, the receptionist, has her nose to the computer and grunts at Michael as he greets her with a cheerful "good morning!" Two of the nurses, Ron and Jenna, can't seem to muster any more excitement for Michael's first day either — the two of them appear to be embroiled in their own brawl. "Maybe the physicians weren't exaggerating during my interviews," Michael thinks.

"I'll make the rounds and check on the physicians to see how they're doing on my first day here," thinks Michael. "They'll probably give me some ideas about where they want me to start." Michael starts with Dr. Samuels, one of the founders of the practice some 20 years ago. As Michael enters her office, he finds her buried under what looks like an explosion of charts, paperwork, personnel files, prescription pads, journal articles, and a plethora of things he can't even decipher. He's reminded of those pictures he's seen on the news of some developing nation after a major disaster has hit — people marshalling any small bit of strength to just make it through another day.

After Michael snaps back to the reality that is Dr. Samuels' office, and not a small village after a 9.0 earthquake, his fanciful ideas of riding into a practice on a white horse and cleaning up a few surface-level problems and then basking in the awe of all of his coworkers dies quickly. Michael realizes that he is walking into a workplace that is in need of a major overhaul and that to turn this practice around might be more difficult than building a new practice from scratch. This is no longer a "kick a couple of tires and change the oil" proposition; he has been hired to rebuild the car — but the catch is, he doesn't have the option of buying all the new parts and just putting it together. He has to decide which parts need the most attention first, take care of them, and then carefully rebuild this machine into a smooth-running, service-oriented, quality organization. And he doesn't have much time.

Throughout the morning, Michael stops by each physician's office, and most of them resemble Dr. Samuels'. As Michael talks to the physicians about their major concerns, many of his first impressions are confirmed by what they say: The office staff is disjointed and members are unwilling to work with each other. Ron and Jenna just can't seem to get over the different ways in which they communicate — leaving them to pass one another without as much as a glance — and the rest of the staff seems to have joined sides with either Ron or Jenna. More hiring needs to be done, but the physician partners are nervous about hiring any new employees and placing them into this toxic environment. More unhappy employees would make the culture even worse. Patient satisfaction is so low that they have stopped measuring it.

Where should Michael start? It seems like every system in this medical group practice is broken. There is high staff turnover; low morale, low productivity, and low quality; dissatisfied patients; bewildered physicians; and significant financial trouble. Michael decides to begin his journey by taking a systemwide approach that will align team member performance with medical practice goals. By using a systems thinking approach, Michael decides to assess the medical group as a large system with six subsystems that need to be in balance, congruent, and support the medical group's goals.

The subsystems Michael evaluates are from the Weisbord Six-Box model that is discussed in Chapter 1. These subsystems include:

- ▲ Purposes (Vision/Mission/Values/Norms/Goals);
- ▲ Leadership;
- ▲ Rewards (and Recognition);
- ▲ Structure;
- ▲ Relationships; and
- ▲ Resources and Helping Mechanisms.

Each of these subsystems communicates to each team member what is important and how to behave — each subsystem directly affects patient care. The first step is to define the purposes — the mission, values, and goals — of the medical group. Then Michael must determine which subsystems are not supporting them. Any deficiencies in these subsystems would then be addressed.

On that first day, Michael orders in pizza for the physicians for their lunch break. As he looks at the perplexed faces of his new team of physicians around the conference table, Michael takes a deep breath and officially begins his new job as medical group manager.

Michael begins, "Let's get to work and create a new and improved medical practice. One where you want to practice medicine, your staff wants to work, and your patients want to come for care. Let me start by asking you what you would like your organization to resemble."

"Well," Dr. Black speaks hesitantly, "I just want it to run smoothly."

"But *how exactly* would you like that to look? What are your goals for this practice?" prompts Michael.

"I'll be honest with you," confesses Dr. Samuels, "I don't think I've given it that much thought lately. Isn't that why we hired you?"

"I think it's important that we examine the problems that are affecting your practice currently," reasons Michael. "I know that you physicians are incredibly busy — that's one of the reasons you hired me — but at the end of the day, your names are on that office door. You need to be sure that your staff is a reflection of the type of practice you want to convey to your patients. Rather than mulling over how things haven't gone right, let's focus on the things that are going well in addition to those that need to be rectified so that you can be proud of the practice you've worked so hard to achieve."

Dr. Jordan exclaims, "We agree, Michael. Where do we start?"

Michael explains, "You need to start thinking about what you want your practice to reveal. We're going to rid this practice of its toxicity, and we're going to transform the culture into one that is focused, goal oriented, and people oriented."

Michael spent the next week observing the practice and interviewing every physician and team member about the mission, values, goals, leadership, rewards, structure, relationships, policies, and procedures. After the system assessment, Michael held a strategic planning session for the physicians, senior managers, and stakeholders. After the plan was developed, Michael set out to communicate the objectives to the rest of the staff. The next steps were to align the subsystems with the new goals of the practice.

LEADERSHIP ROLE IN EMPLOYEE ENGAGEMENT AND RETENTION

Michael voraciously researched the recent studies about employee engagement and retention. He was alarmed to read that the Gallup Poll in 2012 found that only 30 percent of the U.S. workforce is actively engaged, while 18 percent of the workforce is actively disengaged with productivity and quality costs of $445 to $550 billion per year![1] When leaders were actively engaged, there was a 14 percent higher engagement of employees and 19 percent higher employee retention — highly engaged employees are much less likely to leave organizations within the next year.

Additionally, the poll found that employee engagement strongly connected to business outcomes essential to an organization's financial success, including productivity, profitability, and customer engagement. Employee engagement dramatically decreases employee turnover, and patient safety and quality incidents. Michael eagerly shared this information with the physician leadership, insisting that they play an active role in engaging and retaining staff.

Michael continued his research and was surprised by the findings from the Center for Creative Leadership® (CCL) about employee engagement and retention. The CCL found that all generations want similar cultures in their workplace:[2]

- ▲ People want recognition and to feel valued;
- ▲ Development is the most valued form of recognition, even more so than pay raises and enhanced titles;
- ▲ Constant learning on and through the job is what people demand; and
- ▲ Almost everyone wants a coach or mentor, and most want their leaders to serve in this role.

Michael pleaded with the physician leaders to fill these needs for the physicians and team members.

During Michael's meetings with the physician leadership, he cited important research about the top four priorities for healthcare employees:[3]

1. Respect, including honesty, fairness, and trust;
2. Collaboration (employees want to know they are being heard and that their ideas are being taken seriously);
3. Growth, including knowledge, skills, and career development; and
4. A great leader who sets high standards for himself or herself.

Michael found that attracting and retaining younger physicians was one of the key areas of concern for the more-senior members of the medical staff. Michael provided the physicians with data that reveals factors such as cultural fit and family as driving forces in physician turnover: "Number three on [the] list consisted of three common problems: underutilized medical skills, the desire for upward advancement, and long and/or undesirable hours."[4] Michael emphasized the critical importance of developing a values-driven, relationship-oriented coaching culture where younger physicians receive mentoring support as they begin their medical careers.

Michael was encouraged to find research from Deloitte[5] that among physicians currently satisfied with practicing medicine, the majority found satisfaction with patient relationships (37 percent), protecting and promoting the health of individuals (32 percent), and intellectual stimulation

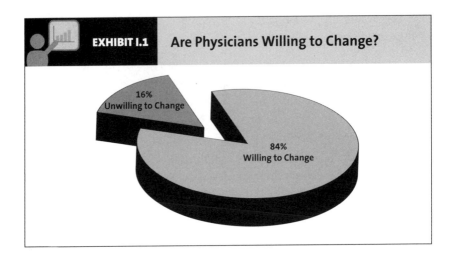

EXHIBIT I.1   **Are Physicians Willing to Change?**

16%
Unwilling to Change

84%
Willing to Change

(19 percent). To Michael, this showed that the physicians could buy into a compelling mission for their practice.

However, Michael felt the challenge of his new position as he reviewed the rest of this research, which found that the factors with lowest rankings among physicians were in interacting with colleagues (3 percent), leading a team of health professionals (1 percent), and running a business or administering a complex healthcare organization (1 percent). Michael smiled as he thought, "Now I see why they need me!"

Another survey that was encouraging to Michael found that most physicians (84 percent) are, in fact, willing to change as long as a reasonable argument could be made that change was necessary and a course set for that change (Exhibit I.1). Michael's challenge is to help the physicians see a new future and understand their role in creating and sustaining that new future. He needs to inform, engage, and inspire them.[6]

PATIENT SATISFACTION PRIORITIES

Michael has always measured patient satisfaction with the Press Ganey surveys and explained the indices of patient satisfaction to his new medical group. The top six patient priorities[7] include:

1. Sensitivity to their needs;
2. Overall cheerfulness of the practice;

3. Overall rating of care received during their visit;

4. Comfort and pleasantness of the exam room;

5. Waiting time in exam room before being seen by care provider; and

6. Amount of time the care provider spent with them.

ALIGNING EMPLOYEE PERFORMANCE WITH ORGANIZATIONAL GOALS

Although this book serves as a detailed manual for building a medical group practice for individuals like Michael, *every* organization has systems that can be improved. (Exhibit I.2 shows the flow from individual team member goals to vision, mission, and values, and back again.) So, even though your practice may not be suffering from poor patient satisfaction or enormous staff morale issues or on the brink of bankruptcy, the system-by-system diagnosis and prescriptions in this book will improve the performance of your practice.

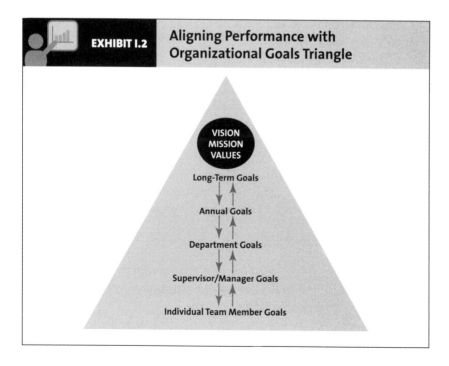

EXHIBIT I.2 — Aligning Performance with Organizational Goals Triangle

VISION
MISSION
VALUES

Long-Term Goals

Annual Goals

Department Goals

Supervisor/Manager Goals

Individual Team Member Goals

The six subsystems (purposes, leadership, rewards, structure, relationships, and resources and helping mechanisms) must be in balance to align team member performance with goals. Descriptions and exploration of these subsystems appear in Parts 1 through 4 of this book. A brief synopsis of these subsystems, including chapter contents of each part of the book, follows.

Purposes

Part 1 of this book is titled "Aligning the Team with Practice Goals." Chapter 1 explains the systems approach to aligning team member performance with organizational goals. Every medical practice is a dynamic system with six subsystems. For alignment to occur, each of six subsystems must be in balance and consistently support the medical practice goals. If one or more of these subsystems is weak and is not supporting the medical practice goals, the performance of team members cannot be effectively aligned with the goals. In Chapter 1, the six subsystems are explained, and diagnostic exercises clearly define areas of strength and weakness.

Chapter 2 explains how to develop the vision, mission, values, norms, and short- and long-term goals for your practice. Chapter 3 explains how to accomplish strategic planning, including the new model of Appreciative Inquiry. Chapter 4 demonstrates how to set specific, measurable, achievable, results-oriented, and time-bound (SMART) goals for each department and how to strategically link each goal to the overall medical practice goals. Managers are shown how to cascade the goals developed from the mission throughout the organization and into the individual team member performance plans.

Chapter 5 discusses the importance of customer service. With the power of social media, not only can customers leave a medical group when they don't feel cared about, they can take potential customers. In addition, now more than ever before, patient satisfaction scores play a role in reimbursement.

Leadership

Part 2 of this book is titled "Leading, Coaching, and Mentoring the Team." The medical practice leadership is crucial for keeping the other subsystems balanced. Part 2 focuses on the roles of the leaders in aligning employee performance with organizational goals. These chapters explore how leaders can effectively "walk the talk" every day and offer several methods for communicating the strategic plan and organizational goals to team members.

Chapter 6 describes the four leadership characteristics that are critical for successful leaders today and the role of emotional intelligence for leaders.

Chapter 7 examines the leader's role during change and the fact that although change is inevitable, growth is optional. The four stages for change are described in addition to the leadership actions needed at each stage so that team members can continue to be goal focused despite major changes.

Chapter 8 introduces the Situational Leadership® model that is a four-style process for orienting, training, and leading team members by focusing on how well they are aligning their performance with the organization's goals. The four styles are directing, coaching, supporting, and delegating. Through this process, the team member goes from being dependent on the leader for direction in the first style to being more independent by the fourth style, where the leader can both successfully delegate tasks and be assured that the organization goals and objectives are being met. This model ensures that team members know, from their manager, what their goals are and what is expected of them, and then the manager supports the team members as they advance through the development styles in their jobs, culminating in the delegating stage style.

Chapter 9 introduces managers to an innovative process whereby a manager can effectively communicate with a team member about his or her inappropriate, non-goal-oriented behavior in a manner that emphasizes both the goals and the performance the manager wants from the team member, and yet does not cause team member defensiveness. This innovative system will effectively address more than 95 percent of team members' inappropriate behaviors and get the team back on track toward goals — it effectively focuses on goals instead of mistakes. Additionally, this innovative system provides a consistent way for managers to discipline team members who are unable or unwilling to align their performance with organizational goals.

Chapter 10 focuses on how to run effective meetings. Without effective meetings, work does not get done, goals are not achieved, and staff members become demoralized and unproductive. If meetings are respectful, productive encounters, leaders and staff will exceed personal and professional expectations.

Chapter 11 explains how to create a coaching culture where leaders coach the individual team members using a multistep coaching model that includes setting and communicating SMART goals, training team members, building relationships, motivating and using positive reinforcement, monitoring performance, and giving feedback. The goal of the coaching system is to keep both managers and the team focused on aligning performance with organizational goals.

Chapter 12 illustrates how leaders establish a mentoring process for the team, focusing particularly on physician mentoring in both the clinical and academic settings. Young physicians want mentoring and will choose organizations that offer mentoring in order to enhance their skills in the most expeditious way.

Chapter 13 covers the critical topic of wellness for leaders. It is essential that leaders stay healthy physically, mentally, and emotionally for both themselves and their team. The same tools and processes for discovering an organization's purpose, values, goals, strengths, and obstacles can be applied to a leader's journey through life. Detailed in this chapter is a successful 10-step life-changing program for professionals titled "Add *Life* to Your Years."

Rewards and Structure

Part 3 of this book is titled "Building and Rewarding Your Team." Chapter 14 describes the importance of the rewards and recognition subsystem. It explains the role of compensation and incentives in engaging the team. This important chapter examines what physicians want, how to design an effective compensation system, and how to evaluate your current compensation system's effectiveness.

Chapters 15 through 17 demonstrate the importance of the structure subsystem. Chapter 15 includes how to interview, select, and hire the most appropriate candidate for the job to be performed. This includes Jim Collins' ideas of getting the right people on the bus and in the right seats.

Chapter 16 examines the importance of an excellent team member orientation process, including physician orientation. More than 25 percent of new employees leave within the initial three months; therefore, creating a sound orientation process is critical in aligning employee performance with organizational goals.

Chapter 17 explains the five important components for performance management and how to ensure that each team member's performance aligns with organizational goals. The significant connection between performance management and employee engagement is clarified.

Chapter 18 describes a performance appraisal process that directly measures and aligns team member performance with organizational goals. This chapter discusses the importance of preparation for the performance appraisal meeting through the evaluation to determine the effectiveness of the meeting.

Relationships

Part 4 of this book is titled "Relationship Management and the New Workforce." This part covers the critical subsystem of relationships among the team. Chapters 19, 20, and 21 examine the role of effective conflict management in the medical group practice.

Chapter 19 defines conflict and the cost when it is not managed effectively. Ways to decrease defensiveness are explained and effective conflict management guidelines are proffered to decrease the destructive nature of conflict. Chapter 20 introduces difficult conversation techniques, the difference between content and relationship conflict, as well as the five styles for managing conflict: collaborating, competing, compromising, accommodating, and avoiding.

Chapter 21 includes the role of effective conflict management in team development. The second stage of the team development process, storming, must include healthy conflict or the team development process could be thwarted. Groupthink is discussed, in addition to several types of difficult people who can interfere with aligning team performance with organizational goals.

Chapter 22 introduces gender differences and the importance for organizations to understand the physiological, genetic, and sociological differences between men and women. These differences are often invisible to us and can cause conflict in organizations because men and women often have differences in how they communicate, make decisions, manage meetings, and view the world.

Chapter 23 introduces generational differences and explains how the four generations in the workplace today have been raised on different planets in many respects. The World War II generation, Baby Boomers, Generation Xers, and Millennials have different viewpoints about leadership, work ethic, teamwork, technology, and many other areas. By understanding the different viewpoints of these generations, leaders can be more effective in maximizing team performance. Chapter 23 also reveals the actions that practices can take to attract and retain physicians and other team members of all generations.

Resources and Helping Mechanisms (electronic files*)

These files contain many resources and tools, including procedures for managing conflict, guidelines for customer service quality standards, policies for employee discipline, and employment process checklists. Also included are several case studies that demonstrate excellence in efforts to align team performance with organizational goals.

Press Ganey Award winners include practices that have decreased patient waiting time, increased patient education about radiation and chemotherapy, improved patient billing, and enhanced team member satisfaction and sense of ownership.

Vanderbilt University Medical Group; University of California, Irvine Medical Center; and Kaiser Permanente Medical Group in Northern California are highlighted in depth to demonstrate their successful efforts to align team performance with organizational goals.

The bottom line is that this comprehensive, results-oriented book provides a road map and prescriptions to take you and your medical practice to the next level and beyond. Whether you want to fine-tune your practice or manage a complete overhaul of the entire operation, this book provides the answers you need to align the performance of your team with your practice goals.

---

* Instructions to access the electronic files are available in Appendix A.

ENDNOTES

1   S. Sorenson and K. Garman, "How to Tackle U.S. Employees' Stagnating Engagement," *The Gallup Business Journal* (June 11, 2013), accessed June 15, 2015, www.gallup.com/businessjournal/162953/tackle-employees-stagnating -engagement.aspx.

2   R. Plettnix, *Emerging Leader: Implications for Engagement and Retention* (Brussels, Belgium: Center for Creative Leadership, 2006), accessed June 15, 2015, http:// iedp.com/Engagement_and_Retention#.

3   "4 Things Employees Want from Their Jobs and Leaders," CareerLink (Nov. 29, 2013), accessed Nov. 16, 2015, http://careerlink.com/lp/4-things-employees -want-from-jobs-and-leaders/.

4   Wendy Abdo and Michael P. Broxterman, "Why Physicians Change Jobs: Results from PHG's Second Annual Survey," Pinnacle Health Group, March 21, 2004, www.phg.com/2004/03/why-physicians-change-jobs-results-from -phgs-2nd-annual-survey/.

5   Deloitte, *Deloitte 2013 Survey of U.S. Physicians: Physician Perspectives About Health Care Reform and the Future of the Medical Profession*, accessed Nov. 16, 2015, http://www2.deloitte.com/content/dam/Deloitte/us/Documents/ life-sciences-health-care/us-lshc-deloitte-2013-physician-survey-10012014.pdf.

6   John Haughom, "Five Deming Principles That Help Healthcare Process Improvement," *Health Catalyst Insights*, accessed Nov. 16, 2015, www.health catalyst.com/5-Deming-Principles-For-Healthcare-Process-Improvement.

7   "Patient Surveys," Press Ganey, accessed Nov. 16, 2015, http://helpandtraining .pressganey.com/resources/patient-surveys.

PART 1

Aligning the Team with Practice Goals

CHAPTER 1

Systems Approach

Organizations are like humans. Both organizations and humans are systems made up of many subsystems — and each of these subsystems contributes to the overall health of the entity.

What exactly is a system? A system is a collection of things that interact with each other to function as a whole. There are many types of systems: biological, ecological, families, cities, the universe, businesses, governments, hospitals, and medical practices, to name a few.

Experts in healthcare are now taking a more holistic approach when assessing the health of a person by looking at all the systems in the body. And experts in organizations now look at all the systems in the organization to assess its overall health. This approach is known as *systems thinking*. Systems thinking is a holistic approach to viewing an organization, to understand how all parts of a system are linked together.

In our human bodies, each organ, bone, muscle, and nerve plays a unique part within the whole body. A strong contribution from one component can't make up for deficiencies in the others.

It's impossible to diagnose the overall health of a person by examining merely one component. Body functions are integrated and their interactions are as important as their individual roles. General practitioner physicians have become the gatekeepers in many medical practices, so all the systems of the whole body can be viewed in a more holistic manner. Specialists are often brought in later to treat individual components that are diseased.

This systems approach to the body can be applied to assessing the health of organizations. The model I like to use in my holistic diagnosis of organizations was developed by Marvin Weisbord and it's called the *Six-Box Organizational Model* (Exhibit 1.1). It provides a holistic view of an

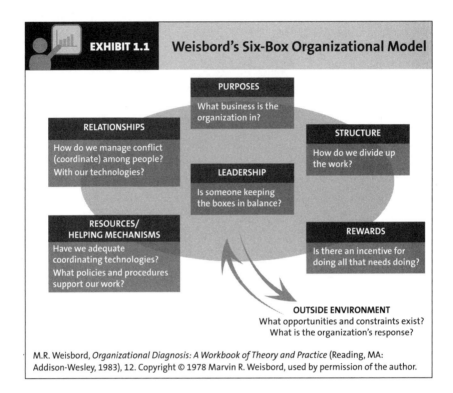

EXHIBIT 1.1   Weisbord's Six-Box Organizational Model

PURPOSES
What business is the organization in?

RELATIONSHIPS
How do we manage conflict (coordinate) among people? With our technologies?

STRUCTURE
How do we divide up the work?

LEADERSHIP
Is someone keeping the boxes in balance?

RESOURCES/ HELPING MECHANISMS
Have we adequate coordinating technologies? What policies and procedures support our work?

REWARDS
Is there an incentive for doing all that needs doing?

OUTSIDE ENVIRONMENT
What opportunities and constraints exist? What is the organization's response?

M.R. Weisbord, *Organizational Diagnosis: A Workbook of Theory and Practice* (Reading, MA: Addison-Wesley, 1983), 12. Copyright © 1978 Marvin R. Weisbord, used by permission of the author.

organization. I think of it as viewing the total system, and its subsystems, from an altitude of 35,000 feet.

The six subsystems are:

1. Purposes;
2. Leadership;
3. Rewards (and Recognition);
4. Structure;
5. Relationships; and
6. Resources and Helping Mechanisms.

As seen in the diagram, there's a seventh component that complicates these six internal interactions. That seventh component is the external environment. An organization is an *open system*, and it cannot be static. As we'll discuss in more detail later, leaders of organizations must be aware of what's occurring externally, that is, outside of their organizations, and these leaders must be proactive. Jack Welch, former CEO of General Electric, said, "If the amount of change inside an organization is less than the amount of change outside, then the end is in sight." The rate of change is accelerating and continuously affects what is occurring inside organizations.

THIS MODEL WORKS

I've been using the Weisbord Six-Box model to align organizational goals and behavior for 25 years. During the 1980s, I used this model as the organization diagnostic tool for 20 healthcare facilities when I worked at American Medical International, Inc. (AMI), as an internal consultant. This model can be used in any type of organization. In fact, in my current consulting practice, I've used this model successfully in many industries, including medical and legal practices, hospitals, manufacturing, technology, public relations, research, government, and academia.

In conducting my diagnosis, I analyze the organization using each of the six subsystems. I interview managers and team members and ask them questions about the mission and values, leadership, rewards and recognition, structure, relationships, and helping mechanisms throughout the organization.

Several years ago I was part of a *dream team* whose project was to work in a think tank and build the hospital of the future. This dream team consisted of six individuals — the CEO, four vice presidents, and an organization development consultant (me). Although I started as a consultant on this project, I was fortunate to join the team as a vice president when the medical center opened. We had the prodigious opportunity to build both the physical plant and the organization systems from the beginning. During the two years it took to build the physical structure, we meticulously created the organization building blocks one by one.

We started from scratch — all we had was a big chunk of land in Orange County, California. AMI was bankrolling this project.

We dreamed that our hospital of the future was to be a value-based organization that included systems designed so that everything about the organization — the people, building layout, medical staff, and volunteers — was aligned to meet our organizational goals. We created an organization based on values and then created systems so that those values were reinforced and communicated throughout every part of the organization, including goal setting, physician recruitment, patient satisfaction, conflict management practices, as well as hiring, rewarding, coaching, promoting, and firing employees.

We used a six-box organizational model as the framework for building our hospital of the future. Within the first year of operation, there was immediate quantifiable success. For example, our medical center received several top awards from the corporate office when measured against the other 125 healthcare centers throughout the United States:

- ▲ Number one in patient satisfaction;
- ▲ Number one in physician satisfaction; and
- ▲ Number one in employee satisfaction.

There were other signs of success: *Modern Healthcare* magazine named our CEO, John Gaffney, Administrator of the Year. The facility received a full three-year accreditation from the Joint Commission on Accreditation of Healthcare Organizations (JCAHO) during the initial year opening. We had been hoping for one year! JCAHO referred other hospitals to us for help. McGraw-Hill published a book about our hospital of the future, *The Orders of Change: Building Value-Driven Organizations*.[1]

OVERVIEW OF THE SIX-BOX MODEL

Let's examine each of these six boxes, or subsystems, in a generic way by demonstrating the kinds of questions that need consistent answers in order to align team performance with organizational goals. Later in this chapter, I'll elaborate and provide more examples about how to use these subsystems in medical practices.

Purposes (Vision, Mission, Values, Norms, Goals)

What *business* are we in? What are we attempting to accomplish? What values should guide our operating processes and are critical to our culture and our success? How are we going to treat each other and our patients?

What are our short- and long-term goals? Are the purpose, mission, values, and goals aligned so that they are clear and do not contradict one another?

Leadership

Is someone keeping the other subsystems in balance? Who is connecting the vision, mission, and values to the strategy, structure, and systems? Who is developing our culture and empowering, enabling, and energizing the team? Who is communicating the purpose, mission, values, and goals? Are all the leaders communicating similar messages through their actions and words? What happens when one of the leaders does not demonstrate that he or she agrees with the purpose, mission, values, and goals? Is there continual coaching and continuous improvement toward the goals?

Rewards

Is there an incentive for doing all that needs to be done? What's in it for the staff to support our purpose? Are we measuring the outcomes that tie directly to our mission and goals? Are we rewarding the values and behaviors that we want? For example, if we say that teamwork is one of our values, are we rewarding only individual accomplishments?

Structure

How do we divide the work? Is staffing adequate? Do we have enough staff members to provide quality work? How many sites do we need in order to achieve our purpose? Are people trained to do the work they are assigned to do so that we can achieve our mission and values? Are the roles and responsibilities clear? Is the workflow design efficient and effective with the most appropriate people performing the job assignments? Does the organizational design prevent duplication of efforts as well as stop assignments from falling through the cracks?

Relationships

How do we manage conflict among people? How do we manage conflict with our technologies? What are relationships like? Is communication open, authentic, and plentiful to align everyone toward the goals? Is teamwork encouraged at all levels? Does the culture of the organization foster trust and collaboration? How are conflicts dealt with among the constituents? For example, in healthcare, what happens when there are disagreements and conflict among physicians, staff, patients, or families? Is conflict ignored so that it continues to fester and damage relationships, or is it managed openly and professionally in a healthy manner?

Helping Mechanisms (Adequate Resources and Technology)

Do we have adequate equipment and technology to achieve the goals? Is our equipment in good working condition? Do we have policies, procedures, and processes that support achieving our goals? Do we have ample budget to achieve our goals?

Outside Environment, External Forces (*Everything Else*)

What constraints and demands does the outside environment impose? How are outside forces influencing the organization? How does the global economy help or hinder achieving the mission and goals? Have government regulations affected our ability to achieve the mission? Are unions having an effect on the organization? In the case of healthcare, what external forces play a role with patients, their ability to pay for services, and reimbursement for services from payers, such as insurance companies and the government? How has the Internet changed patients' access to medical information, and what effect does this have on medical practices? Who are the main competitors? Is there a parent organization that affects the organization?

Subsystems are in dynamic equilibrium. Change in any one subsystem has implications for the others. Every subsystem needs to be reexamined as they shift to ensure that they all still fit. For example, what are the implications if there is a shortage of resources and the income stream declines? What if conflict escalates among team members? What if some leadership members leave?

Careful monitoring of the subsystems is essential for ensuring that there is congruency among the subsystems. No subsystem can operate independently. If one subsystem changes, there will be changes in the others. For example, if there was a change in the relationships box in Exhibit 1.1 — reflecting a change in how conflict is managed among the team members — this change affects all the other internal subsystems and can strain the outside domains as well.

EXERCISE — What Else Is Going On? Scanning *Everything Else*

How satisfactory do you view current transactions between these external domains and your medical practice?

	Highly Unsatisfactory				Highly Satisfactory
Patient/Family/Visitor	1	2	3	4	5
Supplier	1	2	3	4	5
Competitor	1	2	3	4	5
Regulator	1	2	3	4	5
Parent organization	1	2	3	4	5

Do you have any influence over the situation?

Note: This exercise is available as an electronic file.*

---

*Instructions to access the electronic files are available in Appendix A.

> **⚙ EXERCISE** External Environment
>
> List three important environmental demands that influence your practice's strategic mission (major purpose for existing).
>
> 1. _____
> 2. _____
> 3. _____
>
> Note: This exercise is available as an electronic file.*

EACH SUBSYSTEM DIRECTLY AFFECTS OTHERS

When constructing the subsystems, it is imperative to understand that each subsystem directly impacts the strength of the other subsystems. For example, if you want to develop a high-performing team approach, it is critical that all six boxes facilitate and foster team behavior. The leaders would commit to work as a team, model team behavior, and train others how to behave on a high-performing team. The mission statement and values would include teamwork. The reward and recognition system would reward team-building behaviors and provide discipline for selfish, solitary ones. The team member relationships would receive a lot of focus, and members would be taught conflict management techniques and communication and collaboration skills. The organization structure would discourage *silos* and foster teamwork. The mechanisms would include state-of-the-art equipment in good working condition in order to facilitate productive effort and working relationships.

COMMUNICATING TO TEAM MEMBERS

It's through the six subsystems — purposes, leadership, rewards, structure, relationships, and helping mechanisms — that team members learn what is important and how they should perform. The leaders are responsible for ensuring that the messages the team receives are consistent and clear, and that they are focused on the customer as well as the vision, mission, and values. See Exhibit 1.2 for examples of the communications that come through loud and clear to team members.

---

*Instructions to access the electronic files are available in Appendix A.

EXHIBIT 1.2   Communications That Come Through Loud and Clear to Team Members

Reward systems
Verbal language
Body language
Office layouts
Working conditions
Decision-making process
Human resources policies
Benefits
Professionalism of leaders
Cues
Process improvement systems
Working relationships
Signals and codes that come from leadership actions
Types of feedback given — coaching/disciplining
Promotions
Demotions
Coaching, mentoring
On-boarding process
Actions by leaders

The way people dress
Style of leadership
Letters to customers
Formal communication
Informal communication
Website
E-mails from leadership
Treatment of customers
Respect displayed
Organizational structure
Work distribution
Conflict management
Training/Development opportunities
Where budget is spent
Value hiring
Values
Celebrations
Press releases to community

© 2016 Susan A. Murphy, MBA, PhD

CREATING AN ALIGNED AND CONGRUENT ORGANIZATION, ONE SUBSYSTEM AT A TIME

Asking the question, "If it were perfect, what would this subsystem look like?" can be an effective process for creating an aligned and congruent system. For example, if it were perfect, what would our mission be? If it were perfect, what would our leadership look like? What about our reward and recognition system? Our structure? Our relationships and how we manage conflict? Our helping mechanisms?

Throughout the chapters in this book, we'll be examining each of the subsystems, and we'll see that by strengthening each of the six boxes, we can strengthen the overall medical practice. See Exhibit 1.3 for the six-box model in input–output terms.

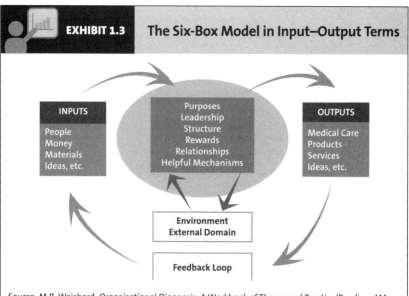

EXHIBIT 1.3 The Six-Box Model in Input–Output Terms

INPUTS

People
Money
Materials
Ideas, etc.

Purposes
Leadership
Structure
Rewards
Relationships
Helpful Mechanisms

OUTPUTS

Medical Care
Products
Services
Ideas, etc.

Environment
External Domain

Feedback Loop

Source: M.R. Weisbord, *Organizational Diagnosis: A Workbook of Theory and Practice* (Reading, MA: Addison-Wesley, 1983), 12. Copyright © 1978 Marvin R. Weisbord, used by permission of the author.

EXHIBIT 1.4 Benchmarking Your Team Effectiveness

20 CHARACTERISTICS OF HIGH-PERFORMING TEAMS

The 20 characteristics in this diagnostic tool are based on characteristics of high-performing teams. Distribute this questionnaire among your team members and have them complete it anonymously. The characteristics are in the Likert scale format to be scored 1 to 7, where 1 means this characteristic in not present in your team and 7 means it is very evident.

Collect the instrument from your team members and for each of the characteristics, calculate the mean score and the range. This will demonstrate where your organization is excelling and where you can focus on continuous improvement to increase your team's performance. The lower the mean score and the wider the range, the more attention the characteristic requires from you as the leader.

INSTRUCTIONS FOR EXERCISE

Indicate your assessment of your team and the way it functions by circling the corresponding number on a scale of 1 (low) to 7 (high).

Choose the number that you feel is most descriptive of your team.

(Exhibit continues)

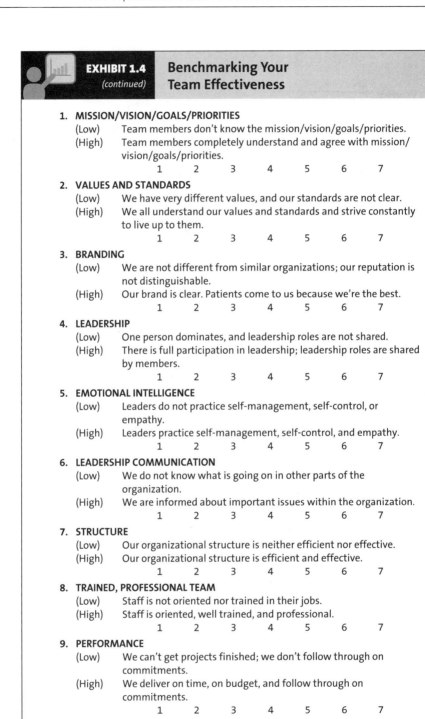

EXHIBIT 1.4 *(continued)*

Benchmarking Your Team Effectiveness

1. **MISSION/VISION/GOALS/PRIORITIES**
   (Low)   Team members don't know the mission/vision/goals/priorities.
   (High) Team members completely understand and agree with mission/vision/goals/priorities.

   1   2   3   4   5   6   7

2. **VALUES AND STANDARDS**
   (Low)   We have very different values, and our standards are not clear.
   (High) We all understand our values and standards and strive constantly to live up to them.

   1   2   3   4   5   6   7

3. **BRANDING**
   (Low)   We are not different from similar organizations; our reputation is not distinguishable.
   (High) Our brand is clear. Patients come to us because we're the best.

   1   2   3   4   5   6   7

4. **LEADERSHIP**
   (Low)   One person dominates, and leadership roles are not shared.
   (High) There is full participation in leadership; leadership roles are shared by members.

   1   2   3   4   5   6   7

5. **EMOTIONAL INTELLIGENCE**
   (Low)   Leaders do not practice self-management, self-control, or empathy.
   (High) Leaders practice self-management, self-control, and empathy.

   1   2   3   4   5   6   7

6. **LEADERSHIP COMMUNICATION**
   (Low)   We do not know what is going on in other parts of the organization.
   (High) We are informed about important issues within the organization.

   1   2   3   4   5   6   7

7. **STRUCTURE**
   (Low)   Our organizational structure is neither efficient nor effective.
   (High) Our organizational structure is efficient and effective.

   1   2   3   4   5   6   7

8. **TRAINED, PROFESSIONAL TEAM**
   (Low)   Staff is not oriented nor trained in their jobs.
   (High) Staff is oriented, well trained, and professional.

   1   2   3   4   5   6   7

9. **PERFORMANCE**
   (Low)   We can't get projects finished; we don't follow through on commitments.
   (High) We deliver on time, on budget, and follow through on commitments.

   1   2   3   4   5   6   7

(Exhibit continues)

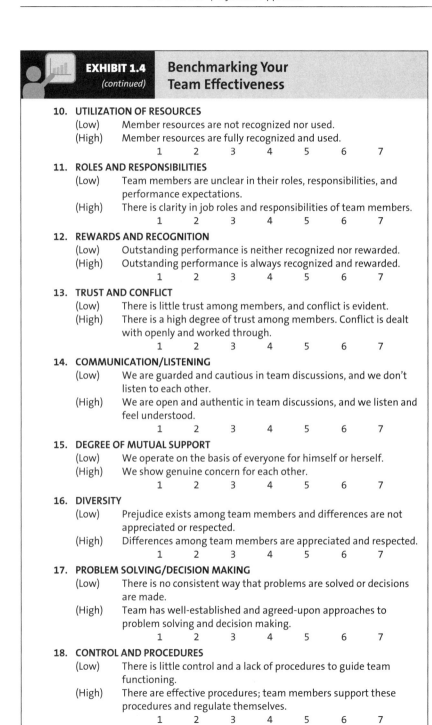

EXHIBIT 1.4
(continued)

Benchmarking Your Team Effectiveness

10. **UTILIZATION OF RESOURCES**
    (Low)   Member resources are not recognized nor used.
    (High)   Member resources are fully recognized and used.
                1   2   3   4   5   6   7

11. **ROLES AND RESPONSIBILITIES**
    (Low)   Team members are unclear in their roles, responsibilities, and performance expectations.
    (High)   There is clarity in job roles and responsibilities of team members.
                1   2   3   4   5   6   7

12. **REWARDS AND RECOGNITION**
    (Low)   Outstanding performance is neither recognized nor rewarded.
    (High)   Outstanding performance is always recognized and rewarded.
                1   2   3   4   5   6   7

13. **TRUST AND CONFLICT**
    (Low)   There is little trust among members, and conflict is evident.
    (High)   There is a high degree of trust among members. Conflict is dealt with openly and worked through.
                1   2   3   4   5   6   7

14. **COMMUNICATION/LISTENING**
    (Low)   We are guarded and cautious in team discussions, and we don't listen to each other.
    (High)   We are open and authentic in team discussions, and we listen and feel understood.
                1   2   3   4   5   6   7

15. **DEGREE OF MUTUAL SUPPORT**
    (Low)   We operate on the basis of everyone for himself or herself.
    (High)   We show genuine concern for each other.
                1   2   3   4   5   6   7

16. **DIVERSITY**
    (Low)   Prejudice exists among team members and differences are not appreciated or respected.
    (High)   Differences among team members are appreciated and respected.
                1   2   3   4   5   6   7

17. **PROBLEM SOLVING/DECISION MAKING**
    (Low)   There is no consistent way that problems are solved or decisions are made.
    (High)   Team has well-established and agreed-upon approaches to problem solving and decision making.
                1   2   3   4   5   6   7

18. **CONTROL AND PROCEDURES**
    (Low)   There is little control and a lack of procedures to guide team functioning.
    (High)   There are effective procedures; team members support these procedures and regulate themselves.
                1   2   3   4   5   6   7

(Exhibit continues)

EXHIBIT 1.4
(continued)

EXHIBIT 1.4
(continued)

Benchmarking Your Team Effectiveness

19. **INNOVATION/CHANGE/CREATIVITY**
    (Low)   The team is rigid and does not experiment with how things are done.
    (High)   The team experiments with different ways of doing things and tries new ideas.

1	2	3	4	5	6	7

20. **CELEBRATION**
    (Low)   Successes are not acknowledged or celebrated.
    (High)   Team acknowledges and celebrates successes.

1	2	3	4	5	6	7

© 2016 Susan A. Murphy, MBA, PhD

Note: This exhibit is available as an electronic file.*

DIAGNOSING POTENTIAL EXTERNAL DISRUPTIONS

Another way to think about the six subsystems is that each is continually being juggled to keep up with shifting and uncertain winds in the external domain, that is, with everything else outside. These external domains include the following:

- ▲ Customers (patients, families, visitors);
- ▲ Suppliers (of materials, pharmaceuticals, capital, equipment, space);
- ▲ Competitors (for both markets and resources);
- ▲ Regulatory groups (government, unions, trade associations, certifying groups); and
- ▲ Parent organizations (university, central headquarters, corporate office).

So, as we're building and strengthening a medical practice, it helps to discover how the external domain is straining the internal subsystems (relationships, rewards, leadership, structure, etc.) as well as how the internal issues may be straining relations with one or more important external domains. See Exhibit 1.4 for a diagnostic tool to benchmark your team effectiveness.

---

*Instructions to access the electronic files are available in Appendix A.

CHAPTER PRESCRIPTIONS

- Ensure that the leaders in your organization are aware of what's occurring externally (outside the organization) and become proactive leaders.
- Increase awareness by the managers as well as the team members about the subsystems and together work toward fulfilling the mission and values, leadership, rewards and recognition, structure, relationships, and helping mechanisms throughout the organization.
- Understand that each subsystem does not work independently of the other, but rather directly affects the strength of the others.

CHAPTER 2

Developing the Organization's Purpose

Asking the question "If it were perfect, what would this subsystem look like?" can be an effective process for creating an aligned and congruent system. So, if it were perfect, what would the purpose be?

PURPOSES — VISION, MISSION, VALUES, NORMS, SHORT- AND LONG-TERM GOALS

Developing the vision, mission, values, norms, and short- and long-term goals is a critical step in building an aligned organization. Without a clear purpose and direction, team members become confused, unproductive, and less motivated.

Two decades ago, I had the privilege of hearing Dr. Peter Senge describe visionary leadership. He drew three pictures (originated by David Peter Stroh) on a flip chart. The first picture (Exhibit 2.1) depicted a simple organization where each arrow represents a person.

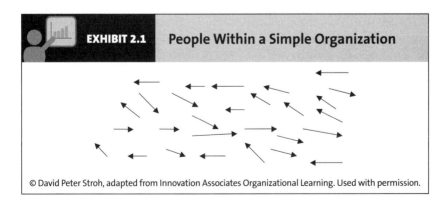

EXHIBIT 2.1 **People Within a Simple Organization**

© David Peter Stroh, adapted from Innovation Associates Organizational Learning. Used with permission.

Exhibit 2.2 demonstrates what happens when the manager sends the group to an empowerment course so they develop more energy and excitement about a project. The people become stronger and more determined, albeit going in different directions.

Exhibit 2.3 illustrates how people will energetically align themselves as they move toward achieving a shared vision, mission, values, and norms.

Looking down from 35,000 feet in the air, let's focus on the subsystems directly related to aligning the team's performance to organizational goals.

The purposes and goals box is where you want to be in the future. There are two categories of goals: broad (not measured) and specific (measured). The broad goals include the vision, mission, values, and norms. The specific goals include short- and long-term goals. These goals set the organization's direction.

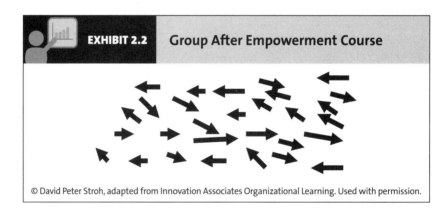

EXHIBIT 2.2   Group After Empowerment Course

© David Peter Stroh, adapted from Innovation Associates Organizational Learning. Used with permission.

EXHIBIT 2.3   People Align Toward the Vision, Mission, Values, and Norms

Vision
Mission
Values
Norms

© David Peter Stroh, adapted from Innovation Associates Organizational Learning. Used with permission.

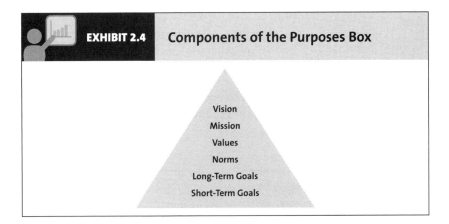

EXHIBIT 2.4   Components of the Purposes Box

Vision
Mission
Values
Norms
Long-Term Goals
Short-Term Goals

The compenents in the purposes box provides staff members in organizations with a shared vision, mission, and values, aligning their energies in one direction, therefore reducing conflict and harnessing everyone's energies toward the same end. Without shared focus and direction, people work at cross-purposes and act according to their individual inclinations. Without direction, the organization lacks purpose, and team members become ineffective, nonproductive, and confused as to where they are going. There are several components to the purposes subsystem (Exhibit 2.4), and each must relate easily to the others:

- The vision, as a goal, is a picture of what we want to look like in the future.
- The mission, as a goal, describes why we exist. What do we contribute to society? At all levels, the mission answers the following questions: Why do we exist? What do we contribute to the organization?
- Values, as goals, are what we preach, what we believe to be true, and what we stand for. Values have spiritual overtones.
- Norms, as goals, are the rules of conduct. They reflect how we behave and how we are observable. The mission and values give direction, whereas the norms give boundaries. The norms should be in sync with our values.

THE VISION FOR THE FUTURE

Let's first look at vision and mission. Developing a vision and mission injects a sense of purpose into the organization's activities. These tools provide long-term direction and give the firm a strong identity. In creating the vision and mission, you are collectively deciding who you are, what you are here for, what you believe in, what you want to be known for, and where you are headed.

The vision is a picture of where you want to be some time in the future. Some visions from well-known people include:

- ▲ Martin Luther King: "I have a dream" — describes his vision for a nonracist America.
- ▲ President John F. Kennedy: "By the end of the decade, we will put a man on the moon."
- ▲ American Red Cross chapter: "To be recognized as a compassionate organization setting the standard for alleviating human suffering."
- ▲ Walt Disney: "To Be the Happiest Place on Earth." There's a legend that goes with Disney's vision. Disney had died by the time Disney World opened. As the story goes, there was a private celebration for corporate executives at the park in Orlando, Fla., on opening day. During the festivities, one of the managers approached Mrs. Disney and told her that his only bad feeling that day was remorse that Disney did not live to see his creation. Her response was, "You fool! Of course he saw it. How do you think it got here?"

Another legend about visions concerns a couple touring an eastern European city where they came upon an immense construction site. At this stage the project was little more than a hollow opening in the ground, and the curious couple asked one crew member, "Excuse us, but this is a very impressive project. What are you doing here?" The abrupt and almost rude answer from the man who appeared to be in charge was, "We're digging a hole!" Not satisfied by that smug response, they asked another person the same question. This time the response was, "We're digging a foundation." Still lacking the information they hoped to get, they repeated the question to the third worker. This time they heard, "We're building a cathedral." So, is your team digging a hole or building a cathedral? If digging a hole, what have you done to allow team members to have such a limited view of their roles? How might you expand their view to include worthwhile and important work?

In creating your vision, it's important to aim high because you will never be greater than the vision that guides you. The vision is a statement about what the future of the organization will look like.

Some of the characteristics of a good vision include:

- ▲ Creating a mental picture of a future state (what success looks like);
- ▲ Focusing on *what* we do vs. *how* we do it;
- ▲ Engaging our heart and our spirits and capturing our imagination;
- ▲ By definition being "cloudy and grand," for if clear, it would not be a vision;
- ▲ Answering "Where are we going? Who and what will we be when we get there?";
- ▲ Providing meaning for the work people do;
- ▲ Being a living document that can always be added to; and
- ▲ Challenging and inspiring the group to achieve its mission.

Vision provides physicians and team members with an image of an ideal future state that is sensible and practical on the one hand, but emotionally uplifting and compelling on the other. As Jack Welch, the former CEO of General Electric, said, "Good business leaders create a vision, articulate the vision, passionately own the vision, and relentlessly drive it to completion."[2]

STRUCTURAL TENSION

Dr. Peter Senge, bestselling author of *The Fifth Discipline*,[3] taught me about the *structural tension* that occurs when you think about your vision (of where you want to be) and your current reality. The farther your vision is from your current reality, the higher the tension level — and the greater the discomfort. To decrease this structural tension, you can either move your current reality (your current state) toward your vision or lower your vision (your goals) to be closer to your current reality. We often will lower our goals because that's easier. I recommend that you keep your vision high and fight the temptation to lower your vision when the going gets tough. You will never be greater than the vision that guides you.

THE MISSION OF MISSIONS

The mission statement clarifies the purpose of the organization, why it exists, what the organization is seeking to do, and what it is trying to accomplish for its customers. Missions tend to be stable over time. A useful mission has some of the following characteristics:

- ▲ It is brief and sharply focused;
- ▲ It is clear and understood by everyone;

⬥ It is specific in that the mission tells why we do what we do and why we exist (patient care, provide jobs to the community, maximize shareholder value);

⬥ It is actionable in that we can use the mission to make decisions because it provides direction for doing the right things;

⬥ It inspires commitment;

⬥ It does not prescribe means;

⬥ It is sufficiently broad;

⬥ It addresses our opportunities;

⬥ It serves as the credo of the leaders;

⬥ It says what, in the end, we want to be remembered for; and

⬥ It involves daily decisions that should reflect the mission and vision.

Mission statements can fail if they:

⬥ Use fuzzy, nonspecific language;

⬥ Include interchangeable goals or visions that can be adopted by any company when only a few words are changed;

⬥ Lack true, prolonged leadership support — in action more than in words; and

⬥ Are poorly implemented.

Mission Statements

Following are three examples of mission statements:

1. Vanderbilt University Medical Center's mission is to "bring the full measure of human knowledge, talent, and compassion to bear on the healing of sickness and injury and the advancement of health and wellness through preeminent programs in patient care, education, and research."[4]

2. At Kaiser Permanente, "our mission is to provide affordable, high-quality, affordable healthcare services and improve the health of our members and the communities we serve."[5]

3. Our mission is to "serve the community with excellent, timely, and compassionate patient care, empowering people towards wellness in body, mind, and spirit."[6]

My own mission is "to serve as a catalyst in the optimum development and performance of people and their organizations." Values are beliefs the organization members hold in common and endeavor to put into practice.

THE VALUE OF VALUES

Values guide the organization members in performing their work. Values answer the question: "What are the basic beliefs that we share as an organization?" Strong values statements keep an organization on track. They help foster the right choices in both day-to-day and strategic decision making. Along with mission and vision, they provide the board, physicians, and team members a foundation for addressing new challenges, including financial crises and strategies to cope with changes in the environment. They help with tricky ethical questions that stray into gray areas. In periods of turbulent change, values provide stability.

Developing meaningful values can be an important investment in an organization because strong values provide the foundation for the culture and can positively affect the recruitment, retention, and commitment of staff and patients. Leaders must know what they care about, because you can only be authentic when leading others according to the principles that matter most to you. Otherwise, you're just putting on an act. Plus, if the leader's values are not the same as that of the organization, it is impossible to align performance with goals. Leaders who want to clarify their own values can ask themselves questions such as:[7]

- What do I stand for? Why?
- What do I believe in? Why?
- What causes me discontent? Why?
- What keeps me awake at night? Why?
- What am I passionate about? Why?
- What brings me suffering? Why?
- What makes me jump for joy? Why?
- Just what is it I really care about? Why?

Researchers have found that there are three central themes in the values of highly successful, strong-culture organizations:[8]

1. High performance standards;
2. A caring attitude toward people; and
3. A sense of uniqueness and pride.

I've done consulting work in several divisions of Johnson & Johnson (J&J), and whenever I sign a contract with a different division, I'm asked, "Have you read our credo?" From my experience with J&J, I've found that the credo is a fundamental part of the values of every J&J employee whom I've met. Students for decades have held class discussions about J&J's decision to remove Tylenol® from store shelves after finding that some were laced with poison. Although at the time it was expensive to destroy all that Tylenol, their credo dictated that destroying the Tylenol supply before another death occurred was the best action. Although J&J lost money one year because of that decision, by being true to their credo, employees, consumers, and Wall Street have remained loyal to them.

Some examples of values for medical practices include:

- Commitment to excellent services;
- Innovation;
- Diversity;
- Creativity;
- Honesty;
- Integrity;
- Teamwork;
- Trust;
- Accountability; and
- Continuous improvement.

As another example, the Vanderbilt University Medical Center's credo states: "We provide excellence in healthcare, research, and education. We treat others as we wish to be treated. We continuously evaluate and improve our performance."[9] And they go on to list their credo behaviors:

- I make those I serve my highest priority;
- I respect privacy and confidentiality;
- I communicate effectively;
- I conduct myself professionally;
- I have a sense of ownership; and
- I am committed to my colleagues.

MEDICAL GROUP MANAGEMENT ASSOCIATION

In 2008 I presented this information about vision, mission, and values to Dr. Bill Jessee, who was then executive director of MGMA, and his senior management team. As Dr. Jessee listened intently to the rationale behind the components of the purposes box, he quickly understood the benefits to an organization of having clear vision, mission, and values. MGMA at that time had several different statements. Under Dr. Jessee's guidance, MGMA created one clear mission, vision, and set of values.

MGMA's Mission, Vision, and Values

As posted on their Website, MGMA's consolidated mission, vision, and values are as follows:[10]

▲ *Mission* — To elevate the performance of medical practice leaders and their organizations by connecting members, building partnerships, setting the standards for certification, advocating for physician practice, and providing innovative solutions.

▲ *Vision* — To be the foremost resource for members and their organizations in creating and improving systems that complement the delivery of affordable, quality patient care.

▲ *Values* — Our commitment to support our members and their organizations as they provide outstanding patient care means that we are:

• Defined by administrator–physician leadership;

• Driven by data;

• Devoted to life-long learning and certification through ACMPE (American College of Medical Practice Executives, MGMA's certification body); and

• Dedicated to advocacy for better healthcare policy.

NORMS FLOW FROM THE VALUES

After developing meaningful values, the next step is to develop norms to go with the values. The norms are the behaviors that demonstrate the values. I sometimes call these *rules of conduct* or *codes of conduct*. Some successful organizations make these rules of conduct a part of the performance appraisal system and evaluate all team members by the same code. At our hospital of the future, 50 percent of every performance appraisal was based on how well the team member lived the values and norms on a day-to-day basis. Exhibit 2.5 is a sample of values and norms. Exhibit 2.6 shows more descriptive norms.

Exhibits 2.7 and 2.8 show samples of codes of conduct. For a sample credo, look at the Vanderbilt case study available as an electronic file.*

---

*Instructions to access the electronic files are available in Appendix A.

EXHIBIT 2.5   Sample Values and Norms

OUR VALUES AND NORMS

TEAMWORK — Accomplishing our goals through a collaborative focus.
Recognizes and demonstrates the worth and importance of others, preserving the emotional and spiritual dignity, confidentiality, and privacy of all external and internal customers.

ETHICAL STANDARDS — Doing the right thing to ensure compliance.
Conducts himself or herself in an honest, fair, and ethical manner.

QUALITY — Doing the right things consistently, correctly, and safely as they relate to all interactions provided by every team member.

1. Applies performance improvement principles and processes in individual and group activities to develop organizational systems and structures.
2. Uses resources (supplies, labor, and equipment utilities) in a cost-effective manner to remain within budget.

ACCOUNTABILITY — Taking responsibility for your own actions, both on a personal and professional basis.

1. Takes ownership of daily activities, processes, and outcomes.
2. Aligns behaviors of conduct and safety with organizational policies and mission.
3. Adheres to attendance standards.
4. Adheres to customer service house rules.

INTEGRITY — Committing to personal respect, honesty, and ethical actions in all situations.

Conducts himself or herself in an honest, reasonable, and straightforward manner.

DEDICATION — Consistently demonstrating a belief that teamwork involvement and follow-through are essential and used in all endeavors.

1. Responds to the feelings and emotional needs of all customers in gentle and caring ways.
2. Meets the individualized needs of our customers in a sensitive manner, including recognition of cultural diversity.
3. Meets commitments to all customers in a consistent, positive, and timely manner.

© 2016 Susan A. Murphy, MBA, PhD.

Note: This exhibit is available as an electronic file.*

---

*Instructions to access the electronic files are available in Appendix A.

EXHIBIT 2.6 | **Sample Values and Norms —**
More Descriptive Norms

OUR VALUES AND NORMS

Ethical: Our conduct is exemplified by honesty and integrity. This applies in all relationships (business and personal), internally and externally.

Respectful: We will communicate/interact with fellow team members, patients and families, visitors, and vendors as we would want them to communicate/interact with us.

Teamwork: We are players on a single team. We must work in unity to achieve our mission. We will develop and maintain strong internal relationships through open and constructive communication. We are expected to be part of the solution, not part of the problem.

Commitment/Dedication: We demonstrate commitment and dedication by doing our best and going the extra mile to get the job done. All team members have the responsibility to live up to the commitments we make in a timely manner, and to make every effort to present useful and accurate information in a professional way.

Proactive/Empowerment: Our behavior and actions should reflect a commitment to timeliness and a sense of urgency in dealing with patients, families, and other team members. This approach optimizes mutual efficiency and ensures that we make the most of our opportunities. We should also make decisions and proactively develop strategies designed to achieve our mission.

Professional: We shall be professional in all of our interactions, including our attire, appearance, conduct, and communications.

Fiscal Responsibility: We can only stay in business — and continue to service our patients — as long as we are profitable. Profitability requires fiscal responsibility. Each team member impacts our profitability and growth. We all have a shared responsibility to develop strategies, capitalize on opportunities, and use our resources wisely and efficiently.

Positive Environment: We are committed to maintaining an environment that breeds success. We believe in an atmosphere that encourages unity, innovation, and freedom to create. We celebrate, reward, and recognize one another when goals are met. We all must do our part to contribute to an enthusiastic, collegial, vibrant, and productive environment.

Strive to Exceed Expectations: All of us have the independent obligation to strive to exceed our patients' expectations. Our patients' positive perspective of their relationship with us is the key to our success. Every patient interaction has a definite impact on the success or failure of our commitment. Therefore, each team member has total authority and, with it, the obligation to make every effort to satisfy our patients while operating within our values.

(Exhibit continues)

EXHIBIT 2.6 *(continued)* **Sample Values and Norms — More Descriptive Norms**

Leadership and Management: Our managers' responsibility is to create an environment that promotes an organization-wide commitment to our values, mission, and goals. Effective leadership requires managers to exemplify the behavior that promotes teamwork, motivates productivity, and encourages personal development. Additionally, management provides guidance, consistent support, rewards, and appropriate accountability, which are all essential for our success.

© 2016 Susan A. Murphy, MBA, PhD

COMMUNICATING THE VISION AND THE MISSION

Some medical practices are now printing their vision and mission on the reverse side of their business cards. It feels quite reinforcing to have your name on one side of the card and the vision and mission on the other. It can make you feel as if you are tied more closely to those broad goals.

Additionally, some organizations have created brochures and other marketing materials that describe the vision, mission, and values. Often, these materials include pictures of what the values mean. For example, one practice showed teamwork as demonstrated by several people working together. Kindness can be shown by one person giving flowers to another. Caring can be depicted with one person wiping a tear from another's face.

Many facilities have framed the vision, mission, and values statements and placed them in visible positions around the offices.

Patchwork quilts have become popular images that represent the vision, mission, and values. Sometimes each department creates a section of the quilt, and when all the pieces are sewn together, patients and families get a sense that the whole campus works as one to create a quality and caring organization. Some facilities place the large patchwork quilt in the lobby so that everyone — physicians, other team members, patients, and visitors — can see what is important to the people who work there.

IF YOU BUILD IT, THEY WILL COME

Team members also want to contribute to success. A good example of this is a situation that happened with Gisela, a woman from Cuba who worked in housekeeping. One day when I arrived at my healthcare facility at 8:30 a.m.,

EXHIBIT 2.7 | **Sample Code of Conduct for Meetings and Interactions**

1. **Show Respect and Recognition** —Treat coworkers, customers, and vendors with dignity, empathy, and professionalism.
   * Make eye contact.
   * Avoid negative body language.
   * Be engaged in the conversation.
   * Employ direct communication of issues and concerns with the affected person(s). Do not talk about others behind their backs.
2. **Value All Opinions and Ideas** — All ideas should be listened to. Remember that the final solution is usually a compilation of previous ideas.
3. **Seek to Understand, Then Be Understood** — Before responding, make sure you understand what you are responding to.
4. **Seek to Understand Constructive Criticism** — Listen to the feedback, and respond professionally. Do not lash back.
5. **Share Information Openly and Provide Your Point of View** — Eliminate groupthink. Develop thoughts and convictions and contribute them to the team. Synergy comes from building on each other's ideas. The idea is king. If you have a suggestion or are in disagreement, say so with words.
6. **Refrain from Sidebar Conversations** — Do not participate in sidebar conversations, especially regarding a comment someone else in the meeting has just made.
7. **Solve Problems as They Arise** — Use initiative, energy, and creativity to tackle problems head-on. Do not let them fester.
   * Address concerns at the meeting. If this is not possible, address concerns with the individual.
   * Take ownership of a problem you identify and your response to it.
8. **Keep Discreet Information Confidential** — Discreet and confidential information must stay within the management team. No discreet information should leave the room.
9. **Involve Affected Groups/People in Decisions** — When making decisions, ensure that all affected decision makers are represented and/or involved. Be aware of them and include them in the decision-making process early on.
10. **Manage Meetings Effectively** —
    * Stick to the agenda at each meeting. If the agenda is met, bring the meeting to an end.
    * Come to the meetings with deliverables prepared; let the meeting owner know in advance if this will not be possible.
    * For each open issue at a meeting, identify an assignee and a due date to which he or she is willing to commit.
    * Follow through on action items.
    * Summarize decisions made and distribute to all impacted decision makers.

Note: This exhibit is available as an electronic file.*

---

*Instructions to access the electronic files are available in Appendix A.

| **EXHIBIT 2.8** | **Sample Code of Conduct** |

- When there is confusion about whose needs we are meeting, we step back and ensure that we are always putting our patients' needs first.
- We say only positive comments about our organization to others, and when we point out a problem internally, we try to offer suggestions about possible solutions.
- We keep sensitive information confidential.
- To resolve a conflict with someone, we go directly to that person first.
- We speak positively about others, and when someone complains to us about another person, we send him or her directly to the person involved to solve the issue.
- When a conflict has reached an impasse, we ask someone in Human Resources or other experts for assistance.
- When we make commitments, we follow through in a competent, timely, and professional manner.

Note: This exhibit is available as an electronic file.*

I was surprised to see Gisela waiting by herself in my office. Gisela always worked the evening shift, so I was concerned by her presence. As I entered, she started speaking with her thick, Cuban accent: "Susan, I know you'll understand, but I wanted to tell you. You always say to give care to our patients. Last night, a woman was in a car accident, came to our ER and needed emergency surgery. She couldn't speak English, only Spanish, and she was crying hysterically. I was supposed to clean all the meeting rooms, but checked the schedule for meetings for today and quickly cleaned only the ones that were needed. Then I sat with the patient for three hours to help her feel better until she went to surgery. But I didn't get to finish my cleaning assignment. Is that okay?" Gisela understood what the goals were — and took a risk to meet them.

CREATE A VISION THAT INSPIRES OTHERS

People will live *up to* or *down to* the vision that leaders create. In staff meetings during the building of our new hospital of the future, I frequently spoke about the vision we were creating. One day I said, "We aren't just going to be the flagship of AMI [American Medical International, Inc.], we are going to be the starship!" Because of my upbeat delivery of the message, several on the team smiled and some even laughed. However, on Boss's Day a few months later, I walked into my office to find a huge, laminated,

---

*Instructions to access the electronic files are available in Appendix A.

8-foot-long-by-4-foot-wide banner suspended from the wall behind my desk. The banner said, "We are the Starship!" People want to be a part of a vision that raises them to new heights and appeals to their greatness.

EXERCISE   Cash on the Spot

When working with groups of leaders, I often ask them to write down from memory the vision, mission, and values of their facility. Try it. My belief is that these should be on the tip of the tongue of everyone in the facility. See how you and your management team do!

To keep it fresh in everyone's mind, I've been known to walk around a facility, asking people, on the spot, to recite the organization's vision, mission, or values. If they get them correct, I reward them with cash on the spot — sometimes $1, sometimes $5! It's amazing how quickly they equate my visit with the vision and mission.

Note: This exercise is available as an electronic file.*

THE GOAL OF GOALS

Another component of the purposes subsystem is goals — both long term and short term. In the next chapter, we discuss strategic planning and business planning, which naturally lead to long-term and short-term goals. Short-term goals are manageable, often by fiscal years. For this discussion, long-term goals are those that may be reached after one year and often within one to five years.

What is a goal? A goal is an end toward which you direct specific effort. Where the vision, mission, values, and norms are general intents, goals are specific and measurable accomplishments to be achieved within a specified time and under specific cost constraints.

SMART GOALS

One of the best ways I've found for organizations to be successful is to set SMART goals. These are goals that are *specific, measurable, achievable, results-oriented*, and *time-bound*.

Specific means detailed, particular, and focused. A goal is specific when everyone knows exactly what is to be achieved and accomplished. If goals

---

*Instructions to access the electronic files are available in Appendix A.

are fuzzy, imprecise, and unquantifiable, you and your team will not know when you've reached the outcome.

Measurable goals are quantifiable and provide a standard for comparison that indicates when the goal has been reached. Doing something better or more efficiently does not provide the quantifiable measurement necessary to determine goal achievement. "Increase our patient satisfaction score by 10 percent" is a measurable goal.

Achievable means reachable, realistic, and possible. A goal can be a stretch goal as long as it is achievable. If goals are too lofty, we can get discouraged and lose the motivation to be goal oriented. For example, a goal to "eliminate staff absenteeism" is unachievable. A goal to "decrease staff absenteeism to 15 percent" would be more achievable.

Results-oriented means actively focused on an outcome or performance of an operation. SMART goals are action oriented and contain action verbs. Examples of action verbs are *create, increase, develop, produce, complete,* and *improve.*

Time-bound means that there is a deadline for reaching the goal. Without time constraints, people generally put off doing things. It seems that we can always find something else to do that appears to have higher priority. Imposing a deadline motivates us to be goal focused; the deadline must be precise to promote a sense of urgency. In fact, the more specific our deadline, the better chance there is for success. For example, a deadline for completing an assignment by "the spring" or "March 1" can accelerate the need for action.

EXERCISE   Name That Mission!

There's a country music song that declares, "If you don't stand for something, you'll fall for anything." When it comes to your practice, what do you stand for? How would you like to be remembered when your team talks about you? What would your team members say that you stand for?

During the past week, name one action you performed that demonstrated your belief in the mission and values? Did anyone see these actions? How did you promote the mission and values? Was it something you said? Something you sent out in an e-mail?

Note: This exercise is available as an electronic file.*

---

*Instructions to access the electronic files are available in Appendix A.

Three Types of SMART Goals

There are three main types of SMART goals: essential goals, problem-solving goals, and innovative goals. By understanding these three types, you will find it easier to identify the possible opportunities for setting obtainable goals and achieving desired results.

Essential goals are necessary for continued, ongoing progress. They identify activities needing improvement and are the types of goals that must be accomplished on a routine basis. An example of an essential goal is "By 4 p.m. each day, review list of patient phone calls to ensure that all patients have had their call returned by the end of the day."

Problem-solving goals identify a current problem or opportunity and the desired future situation. These goals pinpoint actions needed to improve performance. An example of a problem-solving goal is "Starting immediately, all insurance forms are to be completed in full and signed by the patient or guardian prior to seeing the physician."

Innovative goals identify ways to improve the current condition. These goals improve good activities by making them better — more efficient, easier, safer, faster, less expensive, or more profitable. An example of an innovative goal is "By January 1, create a two-page, streamlined patient questionnaire that includes patient and family health history plus insurance information."

Performance Goals

Performance goals for the entire organization are generated at the top of the organization, then cascade down through the departments, groups, and individual levels. Each of these goals supports the business strategy of the medical practice. Performance goals are often identified in terms of:

- ▲ Financial outcomes (for example, revenue, net income);
- ▲ Operational outcomes (for example, patient satisfaction, quality); and
- ▲ Behavioral outcomes (for example, performance by physicians, nurses, other team members, or application of knowledge).

DASHBOARDS FOR ORGANIZATIONS

Many medical practices are creating dashboards that measure how the practice is doing against the performance goals. When you peer at your car's dashboard, you can quickly assess how the car is functioning and receive timely alerts when something goes awry. Organization dashboards offer something similar — a consolidated view of key information about the goals, including alerts when trouble is looming.

These dashboards are essentially a snapshot of key indicators that provide a way to quickly identify and monitor important factors to ensure that the practice is on track toward its goals. Dashboard gauges can be created based on what's important to your organization. Some broad goals can include the following: quality, financial, patient satisfaction, team member satisfaction, productivity, ethics, compliance, continuous improvement and innovation, and growth in market share.

As these broad goal areas are developed into specific measurable categories, key indicators can be developed. For example, the financial goals can include measurement areas such as revenue, accounts receivable (A/R) days, collection percentage, charges on hold, lost charges, overtime costs, and staff productivity.

Just as it would be dangerous to take a coast-to-coast flight on a commercial airliner that had no instrumentation, running your practice without a dashboard could be just as dangerous. When one or more of the key performance indicators underperforms, you can drill down to the root cause and take corrective action.

The organization dashboard can do the following:

- Identify, track, trend, and correct problems as you evaluate the health of key areas in your organization;
- Promote more informed decision making and better results;
- Eliminate duplicate data entry;
- Continually identify operational efficiencies; and
- Proactively identify and apply corrective measures.

See Exhibit 2.9 for a sample dashboard of organizational goals.

Sample Dashboard Goals[11]

The following are sample dashboard goals for some broad goal areas:

- Patient satisfaction
  - Increase patient satisfaction score by 5 percent.
  - Decrease average patient wait time to 10 minutes.

EXHIBIT 2.9 | Dashboard of Organizational Goals

- Increase patient retention by 5 percent.
- Increase patient comments and notes by 5 percent.
- Increase patient referrals by 5 percent.
- Follow up patient visit with phone call.
▲ People commitment
  - Increase retention rate to 85 percent.
  - Increase team member satisfaction score by 5 percent.
  - Eliminate turnover during first three months.
  - Increase recruitment referrals by 5 percent.
  - Hold one-on-one coaching sessions monthly for each team member with his or her manager.
▲ Quality
  - Increase accurate prescription dosage by patient.
  - Increase score for quality indicators by 5 percent.
▲ Financial
  - Increase net operating revenue by 5 percent.
  - Decrease overtime by 5 percent.
  - Improve collection rate by 6 percent.
  - Decrease A/R over 60 days by 10 percent.
  - Increase productivity by 4 percent.

▲ Ethics and compliance

   • Complete charts within 24 hours of patient visit.

▲ Innovation and improvement

   • Improve three processes per year.

▲ Growth in market share

   • Increase physician visits by 5 percent.

   • Hire two new physicians this year.

   • Send a marketing mailer two times this year.

   • Call each patient before visit to reconfirm.

 EXERCISE   Purposes Critique

▲ Do we have formal vision, mission, values, and norms?
   • What documents concretely define our purposes?
   • Do we have SMART goals throughout our organization?
▲ How good is the fit between our stated purposes and patient needs?
▲ To what extent do most people in the organization understand the purposes?
▲ What are examples of behavior that show a strong connection between behavior of the team members and the values and norms that we espouse?
▲ What are examples of behaviors that tend to contradict our formal purposes, showing lack of clarity or lack of agreement?

Note: This exercise is available as an electronic file.*

 CHAPTER PRESCRIPTIONS

■ Define the purposes of your organization so that you can relay them to your team members, enabling all to work together to achieve them. Ensure that your vision is inspiring.

■ Compose a clear, purposeful, and attainable mission that will help delineate the purpose and goals for your organization.

■ Clarify the values of the organization in order to emphasize the particulars that set you apart from other organizations. These values will be essential in providing clear and strong leadership to your team.

■ Develop norms (rules of conduct) to reinforce the values so that behavior of all team members is consistent and supports the purpose.

■ Set short- and long-term goals that help you achieve and maintain the values, mission, and purposes of your organization.

---

*Instructions to access the electronic files are available in Appendix A.

CHAPTER 3

Strategic Planning

"If you don't know where you're going, any road will take you there," said the Cheshire Cat in *Alice in Wonderland*. If you're starting out on a road trip, it's imperative that you have a destination in mind. The same is true in organizations. The destination or goal must be clear before a successful strategy can be developed.

The first essential step is to develop the organizational goals and then develop the strategy that will align team member performance with those organizational goals. These goals flow from the medical group's strategic plan. Simply put, strategic planning is an ongoing process that determines where the medical group wants to go over the next one to five years, how it's going to get there, and how the group will know that it has arrived.

There are many models and approaches that can be used in a strategic planning process. First, I'm going to focus on the goals-based model that starts with the focus on the medical group's mission, vision, and values. Next, the focus of the plan is on developing goals that will support the mission, then the strategies to achieve the goals, and finally the action planning that delineates who will do what by when. Some plans are for 1 to 5 years, whereas some extend 10 years into the future. Some plans are only five to seven pages long, yet others may be much longer.

Many executives find that the strategic planning process itself is more important than the strategic planning document because during development of the plan, the key stakeholders and senior managers of the medical group clarify where they want the practice to go and how it will get there.

BENEFITS OF STRATEGIC PLANNING

What are the benefits of strategic planning for a medical group practice? Strategic planning serves many purposes for medical groups; for example, it:

- ▲ Clearly defines the purpose of the medical group and establishes realistic goals consistent with that mission;
- ▲ Communicates those goals and objectives to the medical group's constituents;
- ▲ Develops a sense of ownership for the plan, goals, and mission;
- ▲ Ensures that the most effective use is made of the medical group's resources by focusing the resources on the key priorities;
- ▲ Provides a baseline from which progress can be measured;
- ▲ Builds consensus about the vision and direction of the medical group;
- ▲ Builds a stronger team among the board, executives, and staff;
- ▲ Provides clearer focus for the medical group, producing more efficiency, effectiveness, and productivity; and
- ▲ Solves major problems.

CONSIDERATIONS PRIOR TO A FORMAL STRATEGIC PLANNING SESSION

The first step in strategic planning is for stakeholders and senior leaders to look externally and analyze the current situation by studying the healthcare industry and environment, and then to look internally and analyze the medical group. When I'm conducting strategic planning with an organization, I circulate questions prior to the initial meeting to encourage participants to get involved early on. Some of the questions concern the healthcare industry, external environment, and the medical group itself. To explore the medical group practice industry, questions include:

- ▲ What services does the medical group practice provide? Are there other healthcare services the organization is competing with?
- ▲ What is the size of the organization relative to others in the area?
- ▲ How does the medical group compare in terms of market share, sales, revenue, and profitability with other group practices?
- ▲ How does the medical group compare with others in terms of financial ratio analysis?
- ▲ What is the medical group's major competition? Who are the major constituents?
- ▲ What are the trends in terms of government control, political influence, or public atmosphere that could affect the healthcare industry?

To explore the medical group practice environment that encompasses the social, technical, economic, environmental, and political arenas, my questions include:

- ▲ Are there any trends in the environment (social, technical, economic, environmental, political) that could have a positive or negative effect on the medical group practice or current strategy?
- ▲ What is the state of the economy? Inflation? Recession? Depression?
- ▲ What is the cultural, social, and political atmosphere?

The next step is to explore the medical group practice itself, and my questions include:

- ▲ What is the organization's mission? Is it clearly stated? Is it attainable?
- ▲ What are the strengths of the medical group practice? Leadership and managerial expertise? Financial strength? Patient preference?
- ▲ What are the constraints and weaknesses of the organization? Are there any real or potential sources of dysfunctional conflict in the structure of the organization?
- ▲ What opportunities and/or potential threats are facing the medical group?

COMPONENTS OF STRATEGIC PLANNING SESSIONS

After the gathering of ideas and data in response to the questions, the next step is to begin meeting with the stakeholders and senior managers to continue the strategic planning process. The following is a 12-step process that I have used successfully for more than 20 years.

Step 1: Analyze the Environment

Analyze those existing and future conditions in the environment that have an influence on the medical group. The objectives in performing this step are to identify new opportunities for existing and new services and products and to identify major future risks to market position and profit margins.

Conditions of primary interest would include economic, competitive, technological, governmental, and market forces.

Step 2: Analyze the Internal Situation of the Medical Group

Analyze the group's balance sheet, operating statements from the past five years, profit and loss reports, capital purchases, human resource indicators, lawsuits, and so forth. Review measures of success.

Step 3: Identify Medical Group Strengths and Weaknesses

After an analysis of conditions in Steps 1 and 2, an orderly review of services, products, markets, processes, personnel, facilities, and certain strengths and weaknesses will emerge. Such resource analysis will not only serve to highlight possible competitive advantages available to the medical group but will also tend to focus on opportunities and risks.

Step 4: Consider Personal Values of Top Management

The aesthetic, social, religious, and personal values of top management and influential stockholders exert a significant influence on strategy.

Additionally, the emerging constraints of social responsibility and consumerism are factors to consider. Personal values represent both guides and constraints on the direction of the business.

Step 5: Refocus on the Vision, Mission, Values, and Norms

Review the vision, mission, values, and norms of the medical group. Reaffirm that they provide the right direction for the medical group.

Step 6: Identify Opportunities and Risks

The medical group should, at this point, be able to identify opportunities in the environment for it to fill a unique niche. These opportunities occur when there are specific needs for services and products that the group is uniquely able to supply because of its resources.

Step 7: Define Services, Products, and Market Scope

This task involves the explicit definition of the future scope of the group's activities. The main idea is to concentrate on a very limited number of carefully defined services, products, and market segments. These segments depend on the analysis resulting from the preceding Steps 1 through 6. Careful identification of the services, products, and market scope is advantageous because it (a) reduces the time and complexity of decisions regarding acquisitions, new investments, and other elements of the development plan; and (b) allows the organization to focus on decisions and actions that take advantage of its competitive edge.

Step 8: Define the Competitive Edge

This requires a careful evaluation of unique group skills, position, market advantages, and other competitive factors.

Step 9: Establish Goals, Objectives, and Measure of Performance

Quantitative specifications are required to describe many characteristics of the organization and to provide a clear definition of strategy. Quantitative goals may be established for such parameters as annual rate of revenue growth, profits, return on investment, market share, number of employees, values of assets, debt, standing in the industry, quality indicators, and so forth.

Step 10: Determine Deployment of Resources

Should resources be applied to growth from within or to acquisitions? In which areas should the medical group focus its resources? Readjusting the application of resources is thus established in a manner similar to the grand-scale shifts of personnel and materials in military conflicts. The senior leaders review professional staff and determine where to allocate human resources and where equipment and supplies need to be deployed in order to meet the goals.

Step 11: Communicate Plan Internally and Externally

Communicate plan internally and externally so everyone involved is clear regarding the goals, objectives, and measures of performance. Included in this step is ensuring that each department knows how the goals of the organization affect the performance of their departments.

Step 12: Develop Action Plans in Each Department

Develop action plans in each department and have managers and team members translate the medical practice goals into their performance and behavior. SMART goals are developed for all team members in the practice. As discussed in Chapter 2, SMART goals are specific, measurable, achievable, results-oriented, and time-bound.

TIPS FOR CONVERTING ISSUES AND PROBLEMS TO GOALS

The following are some tips to consider when converting issues and problems into goals: gain consensus on the top three to five issues and prioritize them. Additionally, deal with issues you can do something about and clearly articulate them. It is tempting to ignore current major issues in the interest of pursuing more creative, forward-looking goals. Many organizations fail because they focus too far into the future and do not address immediate issues. Also, when articulating the goals, ensure that all team members understand the objectives and that the goals, when achieved, will address each issue.

APPRECIATIVE INQUIRY MODEL IN STRATEGIC PLANNING

Appreciative Inquiry (AI)[12] is an innovative strengths- and values-based process that focuses on what works in an organization, not on what doesn't. It focuses on imagining possibilities and generating new ways of looking at the world.

There are two premises for AI:

1. *Social constructionism:* This occurs when we create our reality through our language and in dialog with others.

2. *Positive outcomes approach:* To the extent that we create a clear vision of what we desire, we act to make that vision a reality. Instead of asking what problems they are having, positive imagery forces stakeholders, leaders, and team members to ask what is working well around them. This approach is based on the assumption that inquiry about strengths, hopes, values, and dreams is itself transformational.

In strategic planning, AI invites all stakeholders to co-create their preferred future by discovering and valuing the best of the past and existing situation (discovery), envisioning a desired or potential state (dream), dialoguing about the potential state, and co-constructing the future (design and destiny). This *4-D* cycle includes:

▲ *Discovery:* The discovery phase starts with an appreciative interview in which people tell stories of their high points and uncover life-giving experiences in their group, department, or organization.

▲ *Dream:* The stories from the discovery phase are shared in a dream phase, bringing tremendous energy into the room. Various techniques are used to facilitate dialogue around the stories and reinforce positive thinking. Participants are able to envision the group's greatest potential.

▲ *Design:* Participants construct and align their ideals, values, structure, and mission in the design phase. They ask what the organization would look like if it were designed to maximize the positive core to realize the vision.

▲ *Destiny:* In the destiny phase, participants declare their intended actions and actual plans to realize the preferred future. They innovate what will be.

AI can result in substantial improvements in organizational productivity, efficiency, and effectiveness because team members are working to further improve what they already regard as beneficial to the organization. Their motivation can also be substantially improved through this process because it allows them to prevail over the frustrations that bog them down and encourages them to concentrate on what they really want to do — find their real purpose, that is, their vision and mission.

"Celebrate! Change Your Lens, Change Your Life" is an excellent resource for strategic planning using the AI approach. This is a 19-minute film narrated by a National Geographic photographer, Dewitt Jones, whose job was to travel the globe and find the best picture in that location. Sometimes he had to use a micro lens, and other times he needed a macro lens to capture the perfect photo.[13]

Two Approaches

Two different approaches can be used for strategic planning: problem solving and appreciative inquiry:

Problem Solving	Appreciative Inquiry
Define the problem.	Find existing solutions (what works).
Analyze the cause, and fix what's broken.	Envision what might be.
Find a solution, and develop an action plan.	Determine what should be.
Focus on decay.	Focus on life-giving forces.

The basic assumption in a problem-solving approach is that an organization is a problem to be solved, whereas in AI, the basic assumption is that an organization is a mystery to be embraced.

Possible Questions to Use for Appreciative Inquiry

Think of a situation where your organization was working at its inspired best, working just the way you dreamed it could, or where you were giving your best and the organization was working at its best. Then ask yourself the following questions:

- ▲ Who was involved? What happened?
- ▲ What was significant or special about what happened?
- ▲ What is there about the organization that makes this sort of thing possible? What are the core values? What are the essential qualities?
- ▲ What would need to be attended to for these qualities to be characteristic (of the organization) all the time?

THE STRATEGIC PLAN

When should strategic planning be done? The scheduling for the strategic planning process depends on the nature and needs of the organization and its immediate external environment. For example, planning should be carried out frequently in an organization whose products and services are in an industry that is rapidly changing.

Strategic planning should be done:

- ▲ When an organization is just getting started;
- ▲ In preparation for a new major venture; for example, when developing a new department, division, major new product or line of products, and so forth;
- ▲ At least once a year in order to be ready for the coming fiscal year; and
- ▲ Annually, at which time action plans should be updated.

In addition, during implementation of the plan, the progress of implementation should be reviewed at least on a quarterly basis by the board. The frequency of review depends on the extent of the rate of change in and around the organization. Exhibit 3.1 presents a sample outline of a strategic plan.

THE BUSINESS PLAN

The business plan is an important part of the process to align the strategic plan with goals and team member performance. A sample business plan outline is provided in Exhibit 3.2.

 **EXHIBIT 3.1 Sample Strategic Plan Outline**

1. Facts About the Organization — External and Internal
2. Trends and Where They Appear to Be Going
3. Stated Role of the Organization (Vision, Mission, Values)
4. Strengths/Weaknesses/Opportunities/Threats of the Medical Group. What There Is to Build on in Achieving Ambitions in the Next Five to Seven Years
5. Issues to Be Addressed
6. Problems That Must Be Solved to Achieve Mission in the Next One to Three Years
7. Opportunities to Be Seized
8. Alternative Planning Solutions for the Next One to Three Years
9. Recommended Course of Action for the Next Five to Seven Years: Timing and Action
10. Development of Financial Projections
11. Development of Process to Implement Plan: Budgets, Action Plans, Schedules, Resources Needed

Note: This exhibit is available as an electronic file.*

 **EXHIBIT 3.2 Sample Business Plan Outline**

EXECUTIVE SUMMARY
On one page or less, briefly describe the fundamental elements of the business. This is the most important part of the plan. Describe who the audience is, the present and planned products or services, the unique features of these products or services, what investments are required (that is, time, resources, and money) and the projected rate of return, and the management team.

This summary should be readable, concise, believable, and interesting. The primary function of this section is to whet the reader's appetite to read further.

TABLE OF CONTENTS, ILLUSTRATIONS, AND GRAPHS
The table of contents is a road map of the document that follows. Illustrations and graphs are not necessary but are often useful.

(Exhibit continues)

*Instructions to access the electronic files are available in Appendix A.

EXHIBIT 3.2 (continued)　**Sample Business Plan Outline**

DEFINE PRODUCT OR SERVICE

Spend as much time as necessary on a short, easy-to-read description that will explain your product or services to someone who is not an expert in your area. Cite specific reasons why a customer will want to buy the product or service. Relate the product or service to the mission statement.

Your description should answer these questions:

- What does the product/service do?
- What is the product/service (physical traits, etc.)?
- Who are the customers? Who makes the buying decision, and what is the relationship between buyer and end user?
- What makes this product/service different?
- How complex is the product/service from the user's point of view?
- Can the product/service be tried with little risk? How?
- What are the results of using the product/service? Does it make something faster, better, easier, cheaper?
- Why will the customer buy the product/service?
- What training is required to use the product/service?
- What regulations are relevant to using the product/service (liability, environmental, federal/state tax, etc.)?

DEFINE AND DESCRIBE YOUR MARKET

This task enables you to determine how much of your product or service you can sell, where you can sell it, at what price, and how to get it to market. Illustrate the total market and your segment of the market.

MANAGEMENT ANALYSIS

Roles in leadership, marketing, and finance are important to any business organization. Analyze the teams' skills and identify any gaps. Prepare an organization chart and define the responsibilities, authorities, and background of each key team member.

QUALITY ASSURANCE AND RELIABILITY PLANS

Describe the quality you plan to attain and how you will maintain and monitor it.

Note: This exhibit is available as an electronic file.*

THE FINANCIAL PLAN

A financial plan is an important part of the process to align the strategic plan with goals and team member performance. The components of a sample financial plan outline are provided in Exhibit 3.3.

---

*Instructions to access the electronic files are available in Appendix A.

EXHIBIT 3.3 Sample Financial Plan Outline

FINANCIAL ANALYSIS

The financial analysis section will reveal what your marketing and operational plans will cost. Provide numbers for three to five years of future operations, plus two or three years of past financial reports for an existing company.

Use monthly, quarterly, or annual time frames for:

- Sales (Unit) Volume and Returns: Use number of units to be sold.
- Sales Forecast and Pro Forma Income Statement: Use projected pricing to estimate future sales and expenses. Include:
  - Net sales (unit price times net unit volume, adjusted for collections)
  - Cost of sales (materials, labor, and overhead) — Use detailed bills of materials, price quotes, and time standards.
  - Gross margin (sales less cost of sales)
  - Operating expense (research and development; general and administrative expenses)
  - Operating profit (loss) (gross margin less operating expenses)
  - Miscellaneous income (non-sales sources, such as interest earned, consulting fees)
  - Net income (loss) before taxes (operating profit or loss plus miscellaneous income)
  - Taxes on income
  - Net income (loss) (net income before taxes less taxes)

CASH FLOW ANALYSIS

- Beginning cash balance
- Cash receipts
- Cash disbursements
- Net cash from operations
- Sales of stock
- Purchase of assets
- Funds invested
- Short- and long-term debt
- Ending cash balance

Note: This exhibit is available as an electronic file.*

THE BALANCE SHEET

A sample balance sheet is also provided (Exhibit 3.4) because it is an important component when aligning the strategic plan with goals and team performance.

*Instructions to access the electronic files are available in Appendix A.

EXHIBIT 3.4   **Sample Balance Sheet Outline**

Prepare a pro forma balance sheet for each year in the business plan. This will reflect the asset management and capital investment decisions and should include assets (current and fixed), liabilities, long-term debt, and any stockholder equity. It may be appropriate to include some key financial ratios:

▲ Return on equity (net income divided by total equity)

▲ Current ratio (current assets divided by current liabilities)

▲ Working capital (current assets less current liabilities)

▲ Debt to equity (total liabilities divided by total equity)

OBJECTIVES AND MILESTONES

Break down milestones and objectives into specific tasks and report the time and money to be expended per task plus the expected or actual date of achievement.

APPENDIXES

Use appendixes for data that are too detailed for the body of the plan but necessary for analysis. These may include product/service specifications, market research results, detailed market planning information, financial analyses, job descriptions, and responsibilities and tasks for team members.

Note: This exhibit is available as an electronic file.*

PERFORMANCE AND FEASIBILITY GRID

As you're prioritizing the actions in your strategic plan, consider allocating resources based on the performance and feasibility they can create (Exhibit 3.5).

Resources include money, people, time, materials, energy, knowledge, and so forth.

MONITORING AND EVALUATING YOUR STRATEGIC PLAN

Too many strategic plans end up collecting dust on a shelf. Monitoring and evaluating the implementation of the plan is as important as identifying the strategic issues and goals. After the plan is developed, it's crucial to ensure that your practice is following the steps in the plan.

Strategic plans are guidelines, not rules. So, it's acceptable to deviate from the plan, but it's also important that everyone involved in the planning knows the reasons for the deviations and then updates the plan to reflect the new direction.

*Instructions to access the electronic files are available in Appendix A.

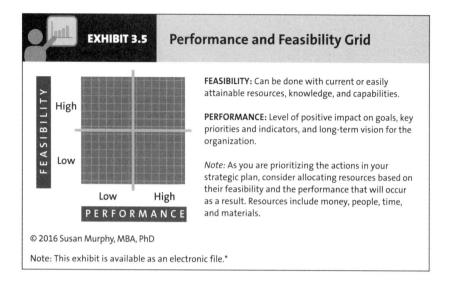

EXHIBIT 3.5   Performance and Feasibility Grid

FEASIBILITY: Can be done with current or easily attainable resources, knowledge, and capabilities.

PERFORMANCE: Level of positive impact on goals, key priorities and indicators, and long-term vision for the organization.

Note: As you are prioritizing the actions in your strategic plan, consider allocating resources based on their feasibility and the performance that will occur as a result. Resources include money, people, time, and materials.

© 2016 Susan Murphy, MBA, PhD

Note: This exhibit is available as an electronic file.*

Responsibilities for Monitoring and Evaluation

The strategic plan document should specify who is responsible for (1) the overall implementation of the plan, (2) achieving each goal, and (3) monitoring the implementation of the plan. The board of directors usually expects the medical practice manager to regularly report to them about the status of the plan's implementation, including progress toward each of the overall strategic goals. Simultaneously, the practice manager expects regular status reports from department managers regarding the progress in achieving their assigned goals.

Evaluating Plan Implementation

Key questions need to be asked when evaluating implementation of a strategic plan. First, are the goals being achieved? If they are, acknowledge, reward, and communicate the progress. If not, then consider the following questions:

▲ Will the goals be achieved according to the timelines in the strategic plan? If not, then why?

▲ Should the deadlines for completion be changed? (Be careful about making these changes — know why you're behind schedule before deadlines are changed.)

▲ Do team members have adequate resources — money, staff, equipment, training, supplies — to achieve the goals?

▲ Are the goals still realistic?

*Instructions to access the electronic files are available in Appendix A.

- Should priorities be shifted to put more focus on achieving the goals?
- Should the goals be changed? (Again, be careful about making these changes. Find out why you're not achieving the goals before actually changing them.)
- What can be learned from your monitoring and evaluation in order to improve future strategic planning efforts?

Frequency of Monitoring and Evaluation

Organizations, like medical practices, that are experiencing rapid change from inside and/or outside will want to monitor plan implementation at least on a monthly basis. Boards of directors should see the implementation status at least quarterly. Medical practice managers and the senior team should review the status at least monthly.

Reporting Results

It is important to write down the status of the monitoring and evaluating. Answer the key questions under the preceding "Evaluating Plan Implementation" section about the specific strategic goals and your progress toward achieving them. Document action that needs to be taken by management for those goals that are off track.

Deviating from the Plan

The strategic plan is not a strict road map that absolutely must be followed. It's all right to deviate from the plan. In fact, most organizations end up changing direction to some degree when there are changes in client needs, government regulations, availability of resources, and so forth. It's important that organizations stay flexible and vigilant so they can be proactive. The most important aspect of deviating from the plan is that you have a strong understanding of what's going on and the reasons why you're deviating from the plan.

Changing the Plan

Develop a procedure for changing the strategic plan. Include the following:

- Why the changes should be made;
- The changes to be made, including changes to goals, responsibilities, and new timelines; and
- Date the new plan and keep old copies of the previous plan.

Celebrating Success

Strategic planning takes a lot of hard work, negotiation, creativity, decision making, and teamwork. When your plan is completed, celebrate your success.

CHAPTER PRESCRIPTIONS

- Define goals that are directly in line with achieving and maintaining the organization's vision, mission, and values.
- Create strategies to achieve the desired goals, considering your specific organization (environment, employees, etc.).
- Develop an action plan that determines the specific ways these goals will become reality: Who needs to do what in order for this to occur? Remember that some goals will be achieved quickly; others may take years.

CHAPTER 4

What Good Are Goals?

Have you ever worked for someone who said, "I'm not sure what I want, but I'll know it when I see it"? I have; and trust me, this type of thinking creates a very frustrating culture. How can your team perform if they don't know where they're going or when they've reached the destination?

After a team creates its vision, mission, values, and norms (these are lofty, broad-spectrum goals), the next step is to actualize these high-level components into specific, measurable, achievable, results-oriented, and time-bound (SMART) long-term and short-term goals.

Other terms for a goal include *ambition, purpose, target, and aspiration.* A goal can also be an end that one strives to attain. Goals give you a road map to your future, and they provide something to strive for.

A goal is a dream with a deadline. There's a joke about people who don't set deadlines for accomplishing their goals. The joke says they're headed for "Someday Isle" because their life is a series of "Someday I'll do this ..." and "Someday I'll do that ..."

Why is it important to set goals? Because goals:

▲ Establish direction for ongoing activities;

▲ Identify expected results;

▲ Improve teamwork through a common sense of purpose; and

▲ Heighten performance levels by setting targets to be achieved.

If you or your organization never sets goals, how will you know where you're headed? If no goals exist for progress, how will you know how it's doing? If there aren't goals for achievement, how will you know when you're succeeding? Would you get on an airplane if you didn't know where it was going to land?[14]

SMART GOALS

As mentioned in Chapter 2, successful organizations create SMART goals. Examples of SMART goals are:

- ▲ "The physician will see patients within 15 minutes of the scheduled appointment time."
- ▲ "We will reach our revenue goal of $1.2 million by July 31."
- ▲ "Our practice adheres to the 'Sunset Rule,' which means all client calls will be answered before the end of the business day on which the client initially contacts us."
- ▲ "We will increase our patient satisfaction score by 10 percent by December 31."
- ▲ "All patients will be called at least 24 hours prior to their appointment to confirm the appointment."

When you set your goals, you'll want to be as specific as possible. Setting goals is a way to focus your attention on what you want in the future. If you're not specific, you and your team will never know where you are going. By setting SMART goals for your team, not only are you asserting, "I know what I want; have confidence in me," but you're also saying, "I believe you are capable of achieving these goals. I have confidence in you!"

SMART goals are action-oriented and involve an activity, a performance, an operation, or something that produces results. Examples of action verbs are shown in Exhibit 4.1.

As shown in Exhibit 4.2, goal setting is a dynamic process that includes resources, action verbs, and results in achievements. There is continuous feedback on your progress.

EXHIBIT 4.1	Examples of Action Verbs		
appraise	identify	interview	provide
authorize	identify	investigate	quantify
bill	implement	monitor	research
chart	improve	perform	restrict
create	increase	plan	review
document	influence	prepare	schedule
evaluate	inform	process	select

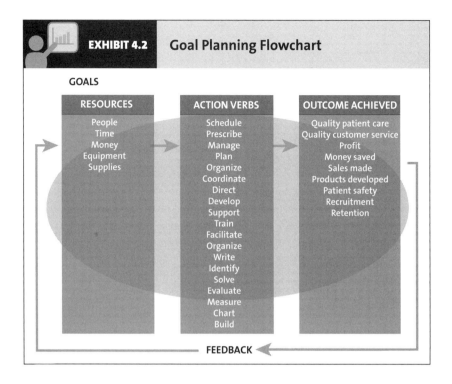

EXHIBIT 4.2 Goal Planning Flowchart

GOALS

RESOURCES	ACTION VERBS	OUTCOME ACHIEVED
People	Schedule	Quality patient care
Time	Prescribe	Quality customer service
Money	Manage	Profit
Equipment	Plan	Money saved
Supplies	Organize	Sales made
	Coordinate	Products developed
	Direct	Patient safety
	Develop	Recruitment
	Support	Retention
	Train	
	Facilitate	
	Organize	
	Write	
	Identify	
	Solve	
	Evaluate	
	Measure	
	Chart	
	Build	

FEEDBACK

THREE TYPES OF GOALS

There are three types of goals: essential, problem-solving, and innovative. By separating goals into these three types, it is easier to prioritize where to focus your time and energy.

- Essential goals are required for the operation of the business or for personal improvement. Essential goals must be reached.
- Problem-solving goals identify a less-than-ideal condition and propose a solution that should be done.
- Innovative goals are activities that will result in something better, faster, cheaper, easier, or safer. It would be a good choice to reach these goals.

CONTRIBUTING TOWARD A COMMON GOAL

Peter Drucker, a brilliant leadership guru, addressed the importance of having everyone in the organization focused on the overall goals:

Any business enterprise must build a true team and weld individual efforts into a common effort. Each member of the enterprise contributes something different but they must all contribute toward a common goal. Their efforts must all pull in the same direction, and their contributions must fit together to produce a whole — without gaps, without friction, without unnecessary duplication of effort.

Business performance therefore requires that each job be directed toward the objectives of the whole business. And in particular each manager's job must be focused on the success of the whole. The performance that is expected of the manager must be derived from the performance goals of the business; his results must be measured by the contribution they make to the success of the enterprise. The manager must know and understand what the business goals demand of him in terms of performance. And his superior must know what contribution to demand and expect of him — and must judge him accordingly.

If these requirements are not met, managers are misdirected. Their efforts are wasted. Instead of teamwork, there is friction, frustration and conflict.[15]

ALIGNMENT BY SETTING TEAM GOALS

To illustrate the importance of including every team member in the goal-setting loop, I'd like you to think about taking a family vacation. You and your spouse are the family leaders, so the first steps for you to take are that you'll need to agree on where to go and how to get there. Suppose you agree on the destination, but your spouse would choose to drive the car and you'd rather fly in order to get there faster. After everyone arrives, you might want to visit all the historical landmarks, but your spouse wants to take a bunch of books along and spend the whole time reading, and your kids want to hit the beach every day. Instead of a nice break, there will be lots of discord, frustration, and broken dreams.

This same type of misalignment can occur in organizations for many reasons, including:

- ▲ Fuzzy measures and targets;
- ▲ Unclear strategies and weak top-management commitments;
- ▲ A gap between organization goals and department goals, or department goals and individual team member goals; and
- ▲ Failure to connect individual or team accountabilities to rewards.

Research shows that less than 20 percent of employees know their organization's business strategy. Only two-thirds of vice presidents believe that their leadership team is in agreement on the business strategy. Consider the effect on employees and on an organization's ability to embed its strategic goals into department goals when less than 20 percent of organizations are fully aligned. Recent research finds that 15 percent to 25 percent of workforce time is wasted on low- or no-value activities.[16]

As discussed in Chapter 2, aligning every team member with the vision, mission, values, and goals is critical to success in all organizations, especially medical practices, where the health and wellness of patients is the purpose.

So, how do you start to set SMART goals and cascade them throughout the organization? Start by setting organizational goals for two to five years, and then set SMART short-term goals for one year. The key to successful goal-setting is for everyone on the team to accept and own the goals. When people actively participate in developing their goals, they become motivated to reach the target. The number of meetings depends on the size of your organization. You may need one goal-setting meeting if you're small. If your organization is larger, you may need several meetings to reach everyone in the organization — one with the practice management, another with each department manager, and then others with team members. I believe it's important to include your part-time team members too.

The following steps can be followed for setting aligned goals:

1. Review your vision, mission, values, and norms.
2. Review long-term and short-term goals for the entire organization.
3. Ask each person to set goals for his or her own area of responsibility.
4. As a team, discuss each team member's goals and determine the degree of fit with the team goals and broader (short- and long-term) goals of the organization.
5. Resolve any differences between the individual and the team, as well as team and organizational goals.
6. Modify team and individual goals based on the discussion.
7. Discuss and establish methods for reaching goals.
8. Identify ways to measure achievement and establish timelines for monitoring progress.
9. Check for understanding of everyone's goals.
10. As a group, establish times when performance will be reviewed.
11. Write down every goal.

WRITE DOWN YOUR GOALS

Several studies have shown that writing down goals increases your chances for success — it encourages you to focus on the goals and achieve success. A study of Harvard alumni 10 years after graduation looked at the correlation between written goals and success. Group A (83 percent of the class) had no goals and was making X dollars. Group B (14 percent of the class) had unwritten goals and was making three times the income of Group A. Group C (3 percent of the class) had written goals and was making 10 times the income of Group A.

After the goals are set, progress toward them must be constantly monitored. Don't just mention these goals once in January and expect that people will remember or adhere to them for the rest of the year. A football coach won't exhort the team, "We're going to the Super Bowl!" at the beginning of the season and then drop the topic. The coach repeats this goal over and over throughout the year to motivate the players. It's important to talk about the goals in meetings and during coaching sessions; visibly show how you're doing in moving toward them in your newsletter by graphing the progress. Then celebrate success as you reach the milestones.

VISUALIZE SUCCESS

The next step is to think positively about the goals and to encourage your team to do so as well.

When I'm working with organizations as they set goals, I often quote several famous philosophers from the past century who were convinced of our mind's power. For example, William James, the first great modern philosopher of the subconscious said, "The greatest discovery of my generation is that human beings can alter their lives by altering their attitudes of mind. If you wish to be rich, you will be rich. If you wish to be learned, you will be learned. If you wish to be good, you will be good. You must really wish these things and wish these exclusively …"[17] There are two other experts I like to quote.

Ralph Waldo Emerson said, "A man is what he thinks about all day long"[18] and "The ancestor of every action is thought."[19] Henry Ford, a visionary leader and inventor, said, "Whether you think you can or think you can't, you're right."[20]

Effective leaders can maximize the team's performance by encouraging their team to visualize success.

EXHIBIT 4.3 **Example of Cascading Goals**

GOAL: PATIENT SATISFACTION
INCREASE PATIENT SATISFACTION SCORES BY 5 PERCENT

The goal of the practice is to increase the patient satisfaction score by 5 percent. Effective leaders will ensure that they communicate this goal to every employee in the practice.

Leaders will talk about this goal in every staff meeting and every newsletter, and they will model behaviors that demonstrate that patient satisfaction is important. There will be strategy sessions to talk with every team member about how they can impact patient satisfaction.

Below are some examples of performance goals that could be developed so that every employee can participate in achieving higher patient satisfaction scores.

Physicians

- Every morning, each physician will call patients from the previous day to ensure understanding of prescriptions, treatments, and next steps, and to query if patients have additional questions.
- During patient visit, physician will sit down next to the patient and touch him or her at least once during the visit.
- After examining the patient, the physician will conclude the visit by asking the patient, "What other questions do you have for me?"

Entire Staff

- Every six months, each team member will sit in the waiting room for 15 minutes wearing eyeglasses smeared with petroleum jelly (as a means of developing empathy for patients who have cataracts) and cotton in their ears (empathy for those who are hearing impaired).
- Each team member will use service recovery skills when dealing with disgruntled patients who are tired of waiting and start to leave the office while angry. "I agree it is a long wait, and I would be frustrated too. I am very sorry for this delay; let me see how much longer until the doctor can see you." Or "I agree with you and I'm hoping you will stay. I am concerned about you and your [symptoms]. You have already waited this long and I would hate for you to leave and not get the care that you deserve."

Receptionists

- Check daily to ensure that current, relevant magazines are in the waiting room and patient exam rooms.
- When patients have waited 15 minutes, update them on the status of their appointment and apologize. If the wait is more than an hour, give them something "extra" as a part of service recovery (meal voucher, pen and message pad, flowers, health magazine).
- Conduct a pre-visit telephone call to verify that the patient remembers the appointment and plans to keep it. It has been shown that this pre-visit call reduces no-shows and tardiness.

© 2016 Susan A. Murphy, MBA, PhD

Note: This exhibit is available as an electronic file.*

*Instructions to access the electronic files are available in Appendix A.

CREATE CASCADING GOALS

Active participation by *all* team members is the surest method for success. When there is open discussion, collaboration, negotiation, and then agreement, you can create ownership and motivation for everyone in the organization. Exhibit 4.3 presents an example of cascading goals.

In Exhibit 4.4, each individual commits to the share he or she is capable of contributing to the overall organizational goals. These goals could involve finance, customer and patient satisfaction, quality, and so forth.

According to Tom Peters, a management guru for 25 years, 80 percent of an organization's projects fail. Businesses spend only 20 percent of their time planning how they are going to execute their projects.[21] Exhibit 4.5 is a planning tool that I frequently use to assist organizations in planning. It's a goal-planning document that outlines steps to take when developing SMART goals and involves the whole organization in the process of achieving them.v

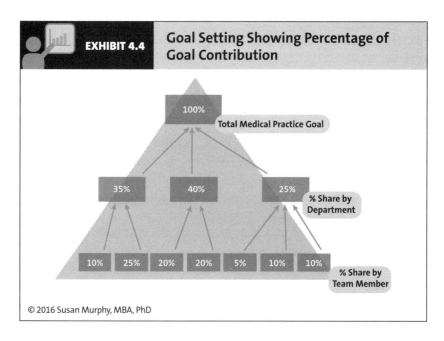

EXHIBIT 4.4   Goal Setting Showing Percentage of Goal Contribution

100% — Total Medical Practice Goal

35%   40%   25% — % Share by Department

10% 25% 20% 20% 5% 10% 10% — % Share by Team Member

© 2016 Susan Murphy, MBA, PhD

EXHIBIT 4.5 **Goal Planning Tool**

GOAL PLANNING

Goal (Specific, Measurable, Achievable, Results-oriented, Time-bound)

_____

_____

_____

_____

Benefits from Achieving This Goal

_____

_____

_____

Possible Obstacles   Possible Solutions

_____   _____

_____   _____

_____   _____

Action Steps	Who	Target Date	Date Completed	Resources Needed
1.				
2.				
3.				
4.				
5.				
6.				
7.				
8.				
9.				
10.				

Is it worth the time, money, and effort to reach this goal?   ___Yes   ___No

© 2016 Susan A. Murphy, MBA, PhD

Note: This exhibit is available as an electronic file.*

---

*Instructions to access the electronic files are available in Appendix A.

CHAPTER PRESCRIPTIONS

- Set detailed short- and long-term goals that work in conjunction with your vision and mission. Be sure to attach specific deadlines to each goal.
- Frequently reflect on the progress of each goal and create new deadlines if necessary. If a new deadline is set, be sure that you consider why you have to change it, and evaluate the new situation appropriately (learn from the adjustment).
- Determine who was responsible for the goal's success or collapse. Praise those who helped make the goal a reality, and talk with those who may have hampered its victory.

CHAPTER 5

Patient Satisfaction

"If you don't take care of your customers, someone else will!" Although the author is unknown, the sentiment is time-honored and even more significant today for two reasons: (1) With the power of social media, not only can customers leave a medical group when they don't feel cared about, they can take many of your potential customers with them; and (2) patient satisfaction scores play a growing role in reimbursement.

Prior to the explosion of social media, the frequency with which satisfied vs. dissatisfied customers shared their perception of their experiences was fairly straightforward. On average, one *satisfied* customer told four other people. One *dissatisfied* customer told 11 other people. Each of the 11 people told 5 others. Prior to the Internet, one bad healthcare experience spread to 67 people. Now with Healthgrades, Yelp, Facebook, Twitter, and Instagram, anyone can post comments and online reviews about your medical practice 24/7. Some new businesses exist for the sole purpose of helping physicians delete negative feedback from customers.

Now, more than ever before, patient satisfaction scores play a role in reimbursement. Both the federal government and private insurers tie payments to quality metrics. The Clinician and Group Consumer Assessment of Healthcare Providers and Systems (CG-CAHPS) program is a series of patient experience survey tools that were developed by the Agency for Healthcare Research and Quality to understand patients' perceptions of the quality of healthcare. The Centers for Medicare & Medicaid Services (CMS) develops, implements, and administers "several different patient experience surveys. ...Many of the CMS patient experience surveys are in the CAHPS family of surveys."[22] CMS's proposed rule revises the physician fee schedule to include CG-CAHPS in its new quality reporting measures on:

- ▲ Appointment availability;
- ▲ Physician communication;
- ▲ Courtesy and helpfulness of office staff; and
- ▲ Overall rating of physician.

Major insurers, including Aetna, Cigna, Humana, and UnitedHealth Group, are contracting with accountable care organizations, patient-centered medical homes, and other entities that tie physician pay to quality metrics and patient satisfaction scores.

WHO IS THE CUSTOMER?

A customer is someone who buys goods and services from a business.[23] *External* customers are people or organizations who purchase or use your products or services. In medical practices, external customers include patients, families of patients, referring physicians, group buyers, and vendors. Conversely, *internal* customers are individuals or other departments within your organization. In medical practices, internal customers include physicians, team members, and other departments. It is vitally important to know who your customers are. "If you're not serving the customer, you'd better be serving someone who is."[24]

MOMENTS OF TRUTH

My view of customer service was forever changed in 1985 by one book: *Service America!*[25] Prior to reading *Service America!*, I had thought of service as an intangible feeling that couldn't be measured. Karl Albrecht and Ron Zemke, the authors, showed me how service management can turn a company in any kind of service field into a customer-driven and service-oriented business. Service management is based on the idea of managing thousands of "moments of truth,"[26] which are the critical incidents in which customers come into contact with the organization and form their impressions of its quality and services.

The story of Jan Carlzon, the former president of Scandinavian Airlines (SAS) is highlighted in the book *Service America!* Carlzon defines a moment of truth as "Anytime a customer comes into contact with any aspect of a business, however remote, is an opportunity to form an impression."[27]

From this simple concept, Carlzon took an airline that was losing $8 million per year to a gross profit of $71 million in a year. In early 1984, Air Transport World awarded SAS "Airline of the Year" for 1983;[28] SAS was the most punctual airline in Europe. All of this happened while the rest of the airline industry was losing an aggregate of $1.7 billion per year. Carlzon credited most of the improvement to making "sure you're selling what the customer wants to buy."[29] Examples of moments of truth in Carlzon's airline business are:

- When you call to make a reservation to take a flight;
- When you arrive at the airport and check your bags curbside;
- When you are greeted at the gate;
- When you are taken care of by flight attendants onboard the aircraft;
- When the airplane arrives safely and on time; and
- When your luggage arrives with you.

Note that all these moments of truth are controlled by people. Carlzon's famous one-liner was, "We have 50,000 moments of truth out there every day." Carlzon often said to his front-line people, "SAS is *you*! In the mind of the customer, you are the company at that particular moment of truth. I want you to respond to the real need of the customer and not use some standardized procedure for getting rid of him."[30]

Moments of Truth in Medical Practices

Moments of truth for patients in medical practices take on a similar definition as that of Carlzon. A moment of truth is "Anytime a patient comes into contact with any aspect of a medical practice, however remote, is an opportunity to form an impression."

Opportunities to form good impressions abound in the medical practice. They begin before patients even arrive with *telephone etiquette*. Most patients would prefer to speak directly to a person. Many practices have automated answering because of the high volume of calls they receive during the day. An important moment of truth for patients that can make or break patient–practice relationships is how their phone calls are received.

Medical practices can offer patients a *welcoming reception*. Patients want attention when they enter the office. Staff members should be instructed to focus on the patient in front of them, welcome them, call them by their name with their proper honorific, Mr., Mrs., or Ms., and follow the office protocol regarding patient intake.

A waiting area that is clean, uncluttered, stress-free, and welcoming makes a good first impression. Comfortable chairs, soothing décor, soft background music, and even aquariums are moments of truth for patients. Provide water and tea for your waiting patients, make current magazines and periodicals available, and keep the TV volume low on a nonpolitical, nonviolent station.

Patients appreciate *shorter waiting times.* Patients do not like to wait in the waiting area and this moment of truth is increasingly important to younger generations. Patients want to be kept updated about wait times while they are in the waiting room as well as once they have been escorted to an exam room.

Patients frequently complain about the lack of attention they receive in medical practices. *Friendly, kind, and professional staff members* can overcome this perception. *Patients want you to introduce yourself, let them know who you are and how you can help them.* Patients want to feel cared about, listened to, and respected. They do not want to feel rushed, even if there are last-minute emergencies and complications. Patients want to feel comfortable enough to bring up issues that the doctor needs to know about and discuss with them during their examination and diagnosis.

Physicians who are competent, knowledgeable, and confident offer a moment of truth in the medical practice. Patients appreciate *physicians who are courteous, empathetic, respectful, and make patients feel they matter.*

Using clear, concise communication is appreciated by patients. *Patients want physicians to explain medical conditions, to listen and answer questions and spend appropriate amounts of time with them.* Patients welcome *feeling that their time is valued by the practice.*

Wall posters, hand-out brochures, three-dimensional models of body parts and systems, as well as interactive information on a TV screen, tablet computer, laptop, smartphone, or PC are all *educational materials* that medical practices can offer to patients.

Medical practices should prepare *written instruction sheets* that cover most of the information they provide to patients (preparation for tests, medication instructions, referrals to other providers) as a reference sheet once they return home. Don't embarrass patients by having them call the medical office because they didn't understand the directions of the physician or staff.

Easy access and parking, longer office hours, and appointment availability are all moments of truth for medical practices. *Easy, timely access to appointments for new patients, follow-up appointments, or well-patient preventive examinations* are all important to patients. If staff cannot schedule patients in a timely manner, physicians will lose these patients and word will get out that new patients cannot be accommodated. Medical practices might consider adjusting office hours to include weekends or one or more late nights or early days each week. Medical practices have increased competition from nontraditional care providers, such as walk-in clinics at Walgreens, CVS,

Walmart, and Target pharmacies because of patient demand for easy access to medical care.

FIVE SERVICE DIMENSIONS ALL CONSUMERS CARE ABOUT

As medical groups continue to search for effective ways to take care of their patients, I find the research by Leonard Berry and associates to be important in understanding what patients want. I was first introduced to these five dimensions 25 years ago by Berry and consider them fundamental in identifying the moments of truth for patients.[31]

- **Reliability**, which is the ability to perform the promised service dependably and accurately. Do what you say you are going to do.
- **Responsiveness**, which is the willingness to help customers and provide prompt service. Respond eagerly and quickly.
- **Assurance**, which is the knowledge and courtesy of employees and their ability to convey trust and confidence. It's important to communicate your expertise to customers.
- **Empathy**, which is the caring, individualized attention that the firm provides its customers. Customers need to feel that employees care about them, and that they are not just performing a job to expectations.
- **Tangibles**, which is the appearance of physical facilities, equipment, personnel, and communication materials. Service providers need to make sure everything in the facility looks good; is clean, organized, and up to date; and is working properly.

When customers are asked which of these are most important to them, the response usually includes reliability (32 percent) and responsiveness (22 percent), then followed by assurance (19 percent), empathy (16 percent), and tangibles (11 percent). To receive high scores in customer service, organizations should focus on all five areas.

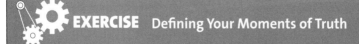

EXERCISE Defining Your Moments of Truth

A **moment of truth** is an episode in which a customer comes into contact with any aspect of your organization, however remote, and thereby has an opportunity to form an impression.

What are your moments of truth with your external customers?

What are your moments of truth with your internal customers?

Welcome Complaints

It's important to give customers the opportunity to complain. Half of unhappy customers don't bother to complain and you *do* want to know when your customers are unhappy. The old adage "no news is good news" is wrong when it comes to patient satisfaction. As soon as you hear of a complaint, it is important that you fight the temptation to become defensive. Instead, become alert and pay attention. Time is of the essence. Following are some interesting and important statistics that your entire team should know:[32]

- Organizations lose 20 percent of all customers who complain;
- Fifty percent of customers do not bother to complain;
- Forty-five percent complain only to the front-line representative;
- Less than 5 percent of customers reach management level to complain; and
- When complaints are resolved quickly, 95 percent of unhappy customers will come back to you again.

"Therefore, for every problem reported to corporate headquarters, you can assume there are at least 19 other similar incidents that simply were not reported or that were handled by the front line without being reported."[33]

Reasons That Customers Do Not Complain

In today's busy world, there are many reasons that customers don't take the time to complain. Here are some reasons why your customers do not:[34]

- Your customer believes that your product or service is not worth his or her time and trouble.
- Your customer believes that your company does not care or will not listen.
- Your customer fears argument and does not want to be further frustrated.
- Your customer believes you already know and have decided not to do anything about it.

Seven Deadly Sins of Service

Typically, patients cite service problems among their reasons for not returning to a particular medical group. Service problems include unsupportive staff behavior (coldness, impatience, annoyance, and runaround); appointment delays; and confusing and incorrect bills, combined with insensitive, condescending handling of financial questions.

Karl Albrecht describes "seven sins of service" as key criteria all customers use to explain their loss of loyalty to a particular service provider:[35]

1. Apathy;
2. Brush-Off;
3. Coldness;
4. Condescension;
5. Robotism (staff members who act like automatons);
6. Rule-bookism (performance via policy only, without human thought or judgment); and
7. Runaround.

HOW TO IMPROVE YOUR PHYSICIAN–PATIENT COMMUNICATION NOW

Let patients tell you their story without interruption. A study at Rochester Medical School found that 51 of 74 physicians interrupted their patients within 18 seconds of the patient's explanation of their symptoms.[36] This is important because patients take from 60 seconds to 150 seconds to tell their whole story when their doctors asks open-ended questions and do not interrupt.[37]

Patients are pleased with communication when the doctor does the following during their visit:

- Asks open-ended questions, rather than a series of yes-or-no questions;
- Listens to the patient's answers with guidance but not interruption;
- Asks the patient's opinion of his or her illness or condition;
- Demonstrates an open, honest relationship with the patient;
- Shows personal interest and concern with the patient, for example, by calling the patient by name;
- Takes time to read the answers if the patient was asked to fill out a medical history;
- Touches the patient; patients want the "laying on of hands";
- Sits down when talking with the patient because when the doctor sits down, time spent with the patient seems longer;
- Looks at the patient when speaking;
- Pays attention to body language;
- Tells the patient when to expect results; and

▲ Asks patients what they want, for example, "What is your goal for this visit?"

In general, most patients are satisfied when communication from their provider has the following elements:

▲ Information;

▲ Technical and interpersonal competence;

▲ Partnership building;

▲ Social conversation;

▲ Positive rather than negative talk; and

▲ Longer duration.

House Rules for Customer Satisfaction

Some medical practices develop team member norms for the entire practice. One way of developing house rules is the following process, which I've used successfully many times:

1. During a meeting of team members, ask participants to brainstorm consequences of positive vs. negative relationships among coworkers.

2. Ask team members to list behaviors by their team members that make them feel valued, supportive, and productive in their work. Next, have them identify coworker behaviors that have the opposite effect, depleting their energy and motivation to serve customers.

3. Break into smaller groups, asking each group to share its lists and identify five dos and don'ts that would have the most positive effect on coworker relationships.

4. Make a final, encompassing, streamlined list and adopt these behaviors as your house rules for customer service (Exhibit 5.1 shows a sample list of house rules).

Team Members Are the Key to Patient Satisfaction

"People don't care how much you know until they know how much you care."[38] This statement is true for both your internal and external customers. Your team members will not feel empowered to provide exceptional service if they do not feel that their leadership cares about them. For example, J. Willard Marriott Jr., CEO of Marriott Hotels, describes his role: "My job is to motivate them, teach them, help them, and care about them. If we take

EXHIBIT 5.1 House Rules

1. Recognize everyone. Break the ice, say "Hello," and make eye contact.
2. Make complaints and frustrations constructive. Go directly to the person involved and work together to solve problems.
3. Give attention to details. Focus on accuracy and quality.
4. Listen attentively when someone complains or voices opinions. Don't get defensive.
5. Show respect at all times. Treat others with professionalism, dignity, and empathy.
6. Initiate improvements. Take responsibility for continually improving our practice.
7. Say "Thank you." Show appreciation to others.
8. Become a telephone pro! Answer that call — the telephone is our lifeline.
9. Always serve our customers. Without customers, there is no practice.
10. Our team members are our practice. Make our positive, professional attitude contagious!

care of them, they'll take care of our guests."[39] Marriott understands that exceptional customer service starts with him. He measures four variables, all through employee surveys, which give a psychological state of affairs:[40]

1. *Quality of work life* — job satisfaction, job security, pay and benefits, opportunities for advancement, competent supervision, harmonious surrounding, and justice and fair play;

2. *Morale* — generally the link between morale and commitment is fairly clear;

3. *Energy level* — sense of wellness and psychological well-being; and

4. *Optimism* — a belief that there are new possibilities.

DEALING WITH CHALLENGING CUSTOMERS

When dealing with challenging customers, there are seven crucial steps you can take. It's important for leaders to become experts in conflict management so you can serve as role models for those who work with you.

1. *Stay calm yourself.* This isn't always easy, but it is critical that you set the pace for a calm, rational discussion with the customer and your team members.

2. *Let the customer vent.* From my experience, even the angriest of customers cannot keep yelling for more than 90 seconds. Sometimes

it's like an inflated balloon running out of the air. If you can move the customer into a private area, that is even better. Just know that at some point, the customer will run out of things to say and finally stop to take a breath.

3. *The customer has to let go of his or her initial anger.* Let the customer know that you respect him or her and are listening to what he or she has to say.

4. If the customer is upset in front of other customers, *encourage the customer to come to another area to speak with you more privately.* When an audience is involved, each party will spend time and energy trying to save face in front of others present.

5. *Avoid emotional trigger phrases* (Exhibit 5.2 is a list of these emotionally charged phrases and the opposite calming phrases).

6. *Gently set limits with abusive customers.* If a customer is cursing at you, gently say that you do not appreciate those comments.

7. *Consider delaying action or consulting a second opinion if it appears that your talks are stalled.*

8. *If appropriate, consider offering the customer something to compensate for his or her inconvenience.* Perhaps you can waive a copayment or offer the customer a voucher for a beverage in the cafeteria.

EXHIBIT 5.2   Emotional Trigger Phrases

When dealing with customers, there are several phrases that can trigger a negative reaction in your customer. It is important that all team members know which phrases trigger an angry emotion and how to use calming phrases instead.

Trigger Phrases	Calming Phrases
Policy	Here's what we can do
Can't	Can
Sorry	Thank you
No, I don't know	I can find out
But	And
You should have	I understand why you
Why didn't you	I can see why
Only thing we can do	The best option, I think

What Do Upset Customers Want?

Upset customers may want a variety of responses from you. By knowing what many upset customers usually want and need, you and your team will be better able to satisfy their needs and then be able to move onto problem solving. Your unhappy customer wants:

- ▲ *To be taken seriously* — The customer wants you to respond professionally, confidently, and seriously to his or her concern. Never use responses such as, "You've got to be kidding!" or "No way!"

- ▲ *To be treated with respect* — The customer does not want condescension or arrogance.

- ▲ *Immediate action* — The customer does not want you to look into it next month or even tomorrow; the customer wants you to do something now.

- ▲ *Compensation or restitution* — The customer wants someone to pay for the damage, and perhaps the customer's pain and inconvenience.

- ▲ *Someone to be reprimanded and/or punished* — Assure the customer that corrective action will be taken.

- ▲ *To clear up the problem so it never happens again* — Sometimes the customer just wants to know that some action has been put into motion so this problem will never happen again.

- ▲ *To be listened to* — This is the first thing that customers want. *They want to be listened to and heard.* Check with the customer to see that you have understood. Repeat what you understand the customer to be saying. Start your sentence with "Let's see if I understand…" or "I think I understand…" and then paraphrase.

CUSTOMER SERVICE VIOLATIONS

When approaching team members regarding customer service violations, it is important to take the following seven steps:

1. Go directly to the other team member in a private, respectful way.
2. Explain what you saw or heard and the effect it had on the customer.
3. Ask for the other team member's view of the situation.
4. Explore and discuss potential solutions in order to *recover* the customer.

5. If appropriate, personally find the customer if he or she has left the scene or telephone the customer to apologize. Use the service recovery procedure in the following section.

6. Maintain the self-esteem of both team members by saying something such as, "You're a valuable member of this team" and/or "Thank you for listening to me."

7. If this is a repeat violation or if the response you get from the other team member is inappropriate when you approach that individual, discuss the situation with your manager.

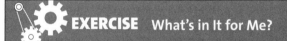

EXERCISE What's in It for Me?

- How can improved customer service help me?
- How can improved customer service help my medical practice?
- How can improved customer service help my patients?

Service Recovery

"It's not what you say, but what is heard. It's not what you show, but what is seen. It's not what you mean, but what is understood. Perception is reality." Although the author of this insightful philosophy is unknown, these precepts can be used to *recover* patients to your practice after an unsatisfactory ending to negotiating with an unhappy customer or after a customer service violation has resulted in a patient leaving the practice. One way to intercept an unhappy patient before that patient leaves your office is to implement the following system.

Procedure

Whenever a patient leaves your office, have at least one member of the staff ask the patient about the visit, such as, "How was your visit today?" "Did you have any questions or concerns I can help you with?" "Is there anything else we can do for you today?"

If the patient has had a satisfactory visit at your practice, these questions will reinforce your interest and caring for the patient's well-being. If the patient is upset or bothered about something, the previous three questions should encourage a response, when asked in a sincere, caring manner with eye contact. When the patient starts to answer your questions, follow the seven steps:

1. **Listen attentively.** Use body language that indicates interest and concern when the patient expresses dissatisfaction with some aspect of the service or care. Continue eye contact, nod to show understanding, and if appropriate, take notes.

2. **Ask open-ended questions.** After the patient has explained the problem, the team member should ask questions to clarify the patient's perspective of the problem and to obtain specific details about who, what, where, when, why, and how.

3. **Empathize.** This is not feeling sorry for someone. Empathy is about showing understanding and sensitivity to the situation, recognizing that the person is upset. An empathetic statement provides a sensitive touch that can calm an upset person and defuse his or her anger. For example, "I understand that you are frustrated by this" or "I'm glad you let me know how important this is to you."

4. **Find out what your patient wants.** Sometimes patients will tell a staff member what they want as a resolution. In other cases, the staff member must ask patients what they would like done to resolve the problem. Knowing what they want helps in two ways. First, it lets patients know they're important. Second, it provides a framework for staff members to resolve the problems. Many patients just want an apology. Others may want a team member fired for being rude. Knowing the patient's expectations will help your team respond appropriately. Sometimes it's appropriate to offer some options for the patient to choose.

5. **Apologize for the inconvenience or for not meeting the patient's expectations.** Apologizing is not an admission of guilt. It's validation of the patient's feelings. You can use such statements as, "I'm sorry this wasn't what you were expecting" or "I'm sorry the information was not clear to you." When offering solutions, it is important that protocols are established for responding to the most common patient concerns. "Under-promise and over-produce" is a great motto. If you tell a patient you will return his or her call by tomorrow at noon, call the patient before the deadline.

6. **Reach agreement with the patient on the next step.** Consultation may be needed with others on the team to find the best alternatives. The *problem* should be passed along, not the patient. Keep the patient apprised of the next steps that are being taken.

7. **Follow up and bring the problem to closure.** Thank the patient for bringing the complaint forward. Let the patient know that

voicing his or her complaint was the right thing to do. It may be appropriate to send a personal note reiterating your appreciation that the patient brought the complaint to your attention.[41]

Airlines are often skilled in their handling of complaints. Airlines routinely offer free tickets to passengers who are bumped from flights. Once a flight attendant uncorked a champagne bottle right next to me and sprayed me with champagne from head to toe. After drying me off and giving me a dry cleaning voucher for my expensive suit, the flight attendant handed me an unopened bottle of champagne with a clever note that read "Next time, the drinks are on *us!*"

HOW TO BUILD A CUSTOMER-DRIVEN MEDICAL PRACTICE

To build a customer-driven medical practice, it is important for the organization to provide leadership. Physicians and administrators together need to create a vision, a mission, and values and norms that include and emphasize patient service quality and patient satisfaction. Leaders "walk the talk" as champions and role models.

Skills training should be offered to all team members. Training in the importance of service quality and how to identify the practice's internal and external customers is paramount. Offer an introduction to the *moments of truth* theory. Give team members ways to enhance their skills in communication, conflict resolution, and dealing with challenging customers. Emphasize that being a team member in your practice requires empathy and courtesy. Finally, make sure to train all team members in customer service recovery.

Every new employee must be screened for customer focus. The idea is to build a customer-oriented team. For new employees, the orientation process must include training in customer service. Customer service behaviors can become part of every position description and can be coordinated with your performance appraisal system.

Institute periodic assessment for continuous service quality improvement. Measure and track customer satisfaction. One of the main reasons practices do not provide quality customer satisfaction is that they do not have adequate information about when they are and are not satisfying customers. One way to do this is to create a patient satisfaction survey. The following section offers a strategy for doing this.

Tips for Creating a Patient Satisfaction Survey

There are several ways to measure patient satisfaction in your practice. Once you determine who your patients are and what are their moments of truth, you can use written questionnaires, in-person one-on-one interviews, telephone interviews, follow-up phone calls, focus groups, a suggestion box, *mystery shoppers*, employee input, and video cameras.

Satisfied patients can improve your bottom line by staying loyal to your practice and referring new patients. Patient satisfaction surveys are an easy way to gauge the needs of your patients and whether you're meeting them. Responses from patient satisfaction surveys, especially if patients describe a specific visit, can offer a snapshot of a larger issue in your practice (Exhibit 5.3). Use these tips for your patient satisfaction survey:[42]

▲ *Determine your timeline for distributing the survey.* Do you want to collect satisfaction data once a year or on an ongoing basis? Do you want an overall rating or a rating for an individual appointment?

▲ *Include questions about patient flow, parking, wait times, appointment availability, and physician communication style.* Retail clinics are appealing to patients who need a short-notice appointment or have a problem outside of normal practice hours. Is it possible for your practice to offer those services?

▲ *Ask patients to give details on their perception of their care.* Are their questions answered during each visit? If they have a chronic condition, do the physician and staff give them adequate education and resources? This can provide insight into improving patient compliance and quality measures.

▲ *Consider using an online platform for your patient satisfaction surveys.* Sites such as SurveyMonkey and Zoomerang offer basic services for free, and you can view your results online. Send your patients a link to take the survey via e-mail or post a link on your practice Website, if you have one.

▲ *Ask questions about improvements to patient communication,* such as, "Would you be interested in an online patient portal to view your lab test results and schedule appointments?"

▲ *Give patients the option of submitting their surveys anonymously.*

▲ *Ask who each patient's favorite staff member is and why.* Share that information with that staff member to boost morale.

▲ *Encourage clinic and front office staff to ask patients to participate in the survey.*

EXHIBIT 5.3 | **Patient Satisfaction Survey**

Your Logo Here
Harry B. Campbell, M.D.

Dear Patient: Our goal is to provide comfort, convenience, and satisfaction as well as the very best medical care to all our patients. We'd like to know how you feel about our medical services, our patient-handling systems, our physicians and staff members. Your comments will help us evaluate our operations to ensure that we are truly responsive to your needs. Thank you for your help.

PLEASE RATE THE FOLLOWING:

	Excellent	Very Good	Good	Fair	Poor	Does Not Apply
A. YOUR APPOINTMENT:						
1. Ease of making appointments by phone	5	4	3	2	1	N/A
2. Appointment available within a reasonable amount of time	5	4	3	2	1	N/A
3. Getting care for illness/injury as soon as you needed it	5	4	3	2	1	N/A
4. Getting after-hours care when you needed it	5	4	3	2	1	N/A
5. The efficiency of the check-in process	5	4	3	2	1	N/A
6. Waiting time in the reception area	5	4	3	2	1	N/A
7. Waiting time in the exam room	5	4	3	2	1	N/A
8. Ease of getting a referral when you needed one	5	4	3	2	1	N/A
B. OUR STAFF:						
1. The courtesy of the person who took your call	5	4	3	2	1	N/A
2. The friendliness and courtesy of the receptionist/office staff	5	4	3	2	1	N/A
3. The helpfulness of the receptionist/office staff	5	4	3	2	1	N/A
4. Keeping you informed if your appointment time was delayed	5	4	3	2	1	N/A
5. The caring concern of our nurses/medical assistants	5	4	3	2	1	N/A
6. The professionalism of our lab or x-ray staff	5	4	3	2	1	N/A
C. OUR COMMUNICATION WITH YOU:						
1. Your phone calls answered promptly	5	4	3	2	1	N/A
2. Clear and concise phone communications	5	4	3	2	1	N/A
3. Getting advice or help when needed during office hours	5	4	3	2	1	N/A
4. Answering your questions in a way that was easy to understand	5	4	3	2	1	N/A
5. Your test results reported in a reasonable amount of time	5	4	3	2	1	N/A
6. Effectiveness of our patient education materials	5	4	3	2	1	N/A
7. Our ability to return your calls in a timely manner	5	4	3	2	1	N/A
8. Your ability to contact us after hours	5	4	3	2	1	N/A
9. Your ability to obtain prescription refills	5	4	3	2	1	N/A

PLEASE COMPLETE THE OTHER SIDE   Form: 1761B   Provider: 30   Site: 10   Specialty: S 11

→

(Exhibit continues)

EXHIBIT 5.3 *(continued)* **Patient Satisfaction Survey**

D. YOUR VISIT WITH THE PROVIDER:
(Doctor, Physician Assistant, Nurse Practitioner)

	Excellent	Very Good	Good	Fair	Poor	Does Not Apply
1. Willingness to listen carefully to you	5	4	3	2	1	N/A
2. Taking time to answer your questions	5	4	3	2	1	N/A
3. Amount of time spent with you	5	4	3	2	1	N/A
4. Explaining things in a way you could understand	5	4	3	2	1	N/A
5. Instructions regarding medication/follow-up care	5	4	3	2	1	N/A
6. Thoroughness of the examination	5	4	3	2	1	N/A
7. Advice given to you on ways to stay healthy	5	4	3	2	1	N/A
8. Knowledge of important information about your medical history	5	4	3	2	1	N/A
9. Showing respect for what you had to say	5	4	3	2	1	N/A
10. Including you in decision making about your treatment plan	5	4	3	2	1	N/A

E. BILLING:

	Excellent	Very Good	Good	Fair	Poor	Does Not Apply
1. Helpfulness of people who assisted you with billing/insurance	5	4	3	2	1	N/A
2. Clarity of the billing statement	5	4	3	2	1	N/A
3. Accuracy of the billing statement	5	4	3	2	1	N/A
4. Promptness in resolving billing/insurance questions or problems	5	4	3	2	1	N/A

F. OUR FACILITY:

	Excellent	Very Good	Good	Fair	Poor	Does Not Apply
1. Hours of operation convenient for you	5	4	3	2	1	N/A
2. Overall comfort	5	4	3	2	1	N/A
3. Adequate parking	5	4	3	2	1	N/A
4. Signage and directions easy to follow	5	4	3	2	1	N/A

G. YOUR OVERALL SATISFACTION WITH:

	Excellent	Very Good	Good	Fair	Poor	Does Not Apply
1. Our practice	5	4	3	2	1	N/A
2. The quality of your medical care	5	4	3	2	1	N/A
3. Overall rating of care from your provider	5	4	3	2	1	N/A

	Definitely Yes	Probably Yes	Don't Know	Probably Not	Definitely Not
4. Would you recommend the provider to others?	5	4	3	2	1

(Please circle)

IF NOT, PLEASE TELL US WHY: _____

_____

IF THERE IS ANY WAY WE CAN IMPROVE OUR SERVICES TO YOU, PLEASE TELL US ABOUT IT:

_____

_____

SOME INFORMATION ABOUT YOU:

GENDER		PATIENT'S AGE		ARE YOU:	
Male	1	Under 18	1	A new patient	1
Female	2	18-30	2	A returning patient	2
		31-40	3		
		41-50	4		
		51-64	5		
		65+	6	*Thank you very much for your help!*	

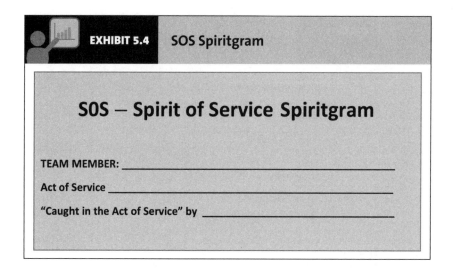

- ▲ *Use the survey feedback to help make decisions in your practice workflow and hiring.* Patient feedback can serve as a job assessment tool.
- ▲ Ask patients if they have ever referred someone to your practice; if not, would they consider doing so.

Spirit of Service

When I held a position of vice president of service management, we developed a process whereby anyone at any time could catch physicians, team members, volunteers, or vendors in the act of service and give them an "SOS Spiritgram." At the monthly all-hands team meeting, our CEO used a "spirit of service (SOS)" megaphone and presented the SOS Spiritgram to the deserving team member in front of the entire team. This ceremony was fun, celebratory, and educational, as it reinforced to everyone the moments of truth that were needed for excellent service. There were times when I received a SOS Spiritgram (Exhibit 5.4), and I enjoyed it as much as everyone else!

CHAPTER PRESCRIPTIONS

- Find *moments of truth* in your medical practice: "Anytime a patient comes into contact with any aspect of your medical practice, however remote, is an opportunity to form an impression." Teach every team member to recognize the moments of truth for your patients.

- To encourage empathy, have your team members put petroleum jelly on a pair of glasses to imagine how cataracts affect vision or wear heavy gloves to imagine what it's like to have arthritis of the hands. Sit in the waiting room for 10 minutes to see what your patients feel as they sit in your chairs, read your magazines, and listen to your TV stations.

- Welcome complaints. For every person who complains there are 24 who have a similar complaint but have not told you about it.

- Obtain patient feedback in written surveys, telephone surveys, and focus groups.

- Hold contests for the best quality service ideas and celebrate the winners.

- Teach all team members to deal with challenging customers in a successful way.

- Teach your physicians, physician assistants, and nurse practitioners to communicate effectively with patients.

- With your team members, develop house rules for customer service that include behaviors that make coworkers feel valued, supportive, and productive in their work.

ENDNOTES

1   R.L. Kennedy, *The Orders of Change: Building Value-Driven Organizations* (New York: McGraw-Hill, 1995).

2   Noel Tichy and Ram Charan, "Speed, Simplicity, Self-Confidence: An Interview with Jack Welch," *Harvard Business Review* (September-October 1989), https://hbr.org/1989/09/speed-simplicity-self-confidence-an-interview-with-jack-welch.

3   P. Senge, *The Fifth Discipline* (New York: Doubleday/Currency, 1990).

4   "Mission Statement," Vanderbilt University Medical Center, accessed Nov. 16, 2015, www.volunteermatch.org/search/org62214.jsp#more_info_tab.

5   "About Kaiser Permanente," Kaiser Permanente, accessed Nov. 16, 2015, http://share.kaiserpermanente.org/about-kaiser-permanente/.

6   Allergy & Asthmas Center of Inland Empire home page, accessed Nov. 16, 2015, www.allergyasthmactr.com/.

7   J.M. Kouzes and B.Z. Posner, *The Leadership Challenge*, 3rd ed. (San Francisco: Jossey-Bass, 2003), 87.

8   C.A. O'Reilly, "Corporations, Culture, and Commitment: Motivation and Social Control in Organizations," *California Management Review* 23 (1989), 9–17.

9   "Credo," Vanderbilt University Medical Center, accessed Nov. 16, 2015, www.mc.vanderbilt.edu/root/vumc.php?site=Elevatesite&doc=19079.

10 "MGMA, ACMPE, and MGMA Center for Research Consolidated Mission, Vision, and Value Statements," About MGMA, accessed Nov. 16, 2015, www.mgma.com/about/about-mgma-medical-group-management/mgma-and-acmpe-mission-vision-amp;-values.

11 Q. Studer, *Hardwiring Excellence* (Gulf Breeze, FL: Fire Starter, 2003), 51.

12 F.J. Barrett, "Creating Appreciative Learning Cultures," *Organization Dynamics* 24 (1995), 36–49.

13 Dewitt Jones, *Celebrate! Change Your Lens, Change Your Life* (St. Paul, MN: Star Thrower Distribution Corp., 2012), DVD, www.starthrower.com.

14 L.A. Rouillard, *Goals and Goal Setting* (Menlo Park, CA: Crisp Publications, 2003).

15 P.F. Drucker, *The Essential Drucker: The Best of Sixty Years of Peter Drucker's Essential Writings on Management* (New York: HarperCollins, 2003), 112.

16 W.A. Schiemann, "Aligning People Achieve Top Performance," *Leadership Excellence* (August 2007), 20.

17 "Attitude Quotes," AndrewsQuotations.com: A Collection of Famous Quotes and Life Lessons, accessed Nov. 16, 2015, www.andrewsquotations.com/quotes/attitude/attitude-quotes-2/.

18 Christian D. Larson, "Chapter VII: How Man Becomes What He Thinks," in *Your Forces and How to Use Them* (1912), www.sacred-texts.com/nth/yfhu/yfhu09.htm.

19 R.W. Emerson, "Essay IV: Spiritual Laws," in *Essays: First Series* (1841), www.emersoncentral.com/spirituallaws.htm.

20 Erika Andersen, "21 Quotes from Henry Ford on Business, Leadership, and Life," *Forbes* (May 31, 2013), www.forbes.com/sites/erikaandersen/2013/05/31/21-quotes-from-henry-ford-on-business-leadership-and-life/.

21 Tom Peters, *Reinventing Work: The Project 50* (New York: Knopf, 2001), 17.

22 "Consumer Assessment of Healthcare Providers & Systems (CAHPS)," Research, Statistics, Data and Systems, Centers for Medicare & Medicaid, accessed Nov. 16, 2015, www.cms.gov/Research-Statistics-Data-and-Systems/Research/CAHPS/index.html?redirect=/cahps.

23 *Merriam-Webster's Learner's Dictionary*, s.v., "customer," accessed July 5, 2015, www.learnersdictionary.com/definition/customer.

24 Karl Albrecht and Ron Zemke, *Service America!* (Homewood, IL: Dow Jones-Irwin, 1985), 96.

25 Albrecht and Zemke, *Service America!*, 96.

26 Albrecht and Zemke, *Service America!*, 21, 27, 43.

27 Albrecht and Zemke, *Service America!*, 27.

28 "SAS Group," Wikipedia, accessed Nov. 16, 2015, https://en.wikipedia.org/wiki/SAS_Group.

29 Albrecht and Zemke, *Service America!*, 21.

30 Albrecht and Zemke, *Service America!*, 43.

31 Valarie Zeithaml, Leonard Berry, and A. Parasuraman, *Delivering Quality Service* (New York: Free Press, 2009).

32 "Case Study: Increasing Sales by Service: Technical Assistance Research Programs [TARP]: Customer Service Is a Profit Center," *Executive Blueprints* (2006), 3, www.executiveblueprints.com/_cases/service_tarp.pdf.

33 "Case Study: Increasing Sales by Service," 3.

34 "Case Study: Increasing Sales by Service," 4.

35 Karl Albrecht, *At America's Service: How Corporations Can Revolutionize the Way They Treat Their Customers* (Homewood, IL: Business One Irwin, 1988).

36 Anne-Maire Nelson, Steven D. Wood, Stephen W. Brown, Sheryl Bronkesh, and Zachary Gerbarg, *Improving Patient Satisfaction Now: How to Earn Patient and Payer Loyalty* (Gaithersburg, MD: Aspen, 1997), 95.

37 Nelson et al., *Improving Patient Satisfaction Now*, 96.

38 John C. Maxwell, *Winning with People* (Nashville, TN: Thomas Nelson, 2007).

39 Albrecht and Zemke, *Service America!*, 108.

40 Chip Bell, *Customers as Partners: Building Relationships That Last* (San Francisco: Berrett-Koehler), 173.

41 Liz Osborne, *Resolving Patient Complaints: A Step-by-Step Guide to Effective Service Recovery* (Gaithersburg, MD: Aspen, 1995).

42 Madeline Hyden, "Tips for Creating a Patient Satisfaction Survey," MGMA *In Practice* blog (Aug. 15, 2011), www.mgma.com/blog/tips-for-creating-a-patient-satisfaction-survey.

PART 2

Leading, Coaching, and Mentoring the Team

CHAPTER 6

The Role of Leaders

Only three things happen naturally in organizations: friction, confusion, and underperformance. Everything else requires leadership. Leadership is "the lifting of people's vision to a higher sight, the raising of their performance to a higher standard, the building of their personality beyond its normal limitations," says Peter Drucker.[1]

Great leaders are made, not born. This is one of the greatest discoveries of the 20th century. This is not to imply that being a leader is easy. Every year, more than 10,000 books on leadership are published, and yet great leaders are difficult to find.

Lucky for me, I learned about leadership from the late Dr. Warren Bennis a few years before I was involved in the hospital-of-the-future project. I met Bennis at American Medical International's Corporate College in 1984, when he had just finished his research for his coauthored book, *Leaders: The Strategies for Taking Charge*.[2] He was searching for competencies that leaders have in common and interviewed 90 recognized leaders from a variety of professions. I believe his findings are as relevant today as they were 25 years ago, and many leadership books today reiterate what Bennis found long ago.

After interviewing generals, corporate executives, university presidents, even Arthur Fiedler, the famous orchestra conductor, Bennis found that leaders have four similar strategies. The first strategy is attention to a clear vision for the organization. The second strategy enables the leader to communicate that vision so everyone knows where the leader is trying to take the organization. The third leadership strategy he found is that leaders trust those who work for them and behave so they can be trusted in return. The fourth strategy is deployment of self through positive self-regard. Successful leaders know themselves well — what they like to do and don't like to do. They have the ability to recognize strengths, compensate for weaknesses, and keep learning. They also become interpersonally competent — they listen, nurture, and empathize.

Bennis considers this fourth strategy to be "emotional wisdom," what we now call emotional intelligence. Among my lessons learned is the importance of deleting the word *fail* from my vocabulary. Bennis's leaders described what others might consider a failure as a *glitch, mistake, setback,* or some similar word. But they didn't use *failure.* Failure is final and implies total lack of success. For the successful leader, failure is a beginning, the springboard of hope. And these leaders were headed toward such a compelling vision that failure was not an option, so they deleted it from their vocabularies.

For the past 25-plus years, I've been sharing these leadership lessons that Dr. Bennis taught me. And they've been proven to work in every organization, every industry, and even in families. Although there have been hundreds of leadership theories and thousands of leadership books since *Leaders* was published, I believe most of them can be distilled into these four characteristics. So, let's look at these four strategies more closely.

LEADERSHIP STRATEGY 1: THE LEADER'S VISION

The Bible warns, "Where there is no vision, the people perish."[3] Leadership starts with the vision. I include mission, values, and goals in this category too. For more information about developing your vision, please refer to Chapter 2. A leader must first develop a mental image about the desirable future state. This image, a vision, may be as vague as a dream or as precise as a goal or mission statement, according to Bennis. The critical point is that it articulates a view of a realistic, credible, attractive future, a condition that is better than what now exists. It provides the leader with the all-important bridge from the present to the future of the organization.

It's imperative that the vision of the leader for the organization is congruent with the vision of the leader for himself or herself. What would you say are your personal vision, mission, and values? I wonder what your team would say about your personal vision, mission, and values. You might be surprised about what others might say about you and your vision. Alfred Nobel was. Nobel was the founder of the Nobel Peace Prize. Nobel, a 19th-century scientist and the inventor of dynamite, was one of the wealthiest men in Europe. He held 355 patents. The story I've heard is that he somehow found the eulogy that was to be published at his death. For famous persons, a life chronology and eulogy are prepared ahead of time so that they will be ready to publish immediately when the person dies. When he read the description of his life, Nobel was shocked and disappointed because he wanted to be known for helping humankind more than for his inventions. To rectify this, he founded the Nobel Peace Prize that has been given for more than 100 years and has caused Nobel's memory to stay alive and be strengthened each year. He is remembered not as the inventor of dynamite, but as a great benefactor to humankind.

Most of us dread the thought of dying, but having a vision of how we want to be remembered can inspire greatness in us. I believe people become leaders when they become passionate about their personal vision, mission, and values — and are inspired to do great things that have long-lasting impacts for their family and society. The very essence of leadership is that you have to have vision. You can't blow an uncertain trumpet.

Identical Personal and Professional Visions

Many leaders apply the same vision, mission, and values to all facets of their lives. As I've already mentioned, mine is "to serve as a catalyst in the optimum development and performance of people and their organizations." I even have it printed on the back of my business card so that my name and my vision are physically linked. Each day when I present my business card to someone, I am reminded about my vision and it becomes reinforced.

LEADERSHIP STRATEGY 2: LEADERS COMMUNICATE THE VISION

"Leaders are the most results-oriented individuals in the world. They get results because their visions are compelling and pull people toward them. Leadership is the capacity to translate vision into reality," writes Bennis.[4]

Leaders communicate their visions through words and actions. Being in a leadership position, you can never stop communicating. Team members want to be a part of something bigger than themselves, so it's important that you continually describe your lofty, compelling vision.

The Leader's Words Communicate the Vision

As Jim Collins writes in *Built to Last,*

> Vivid description ... is a vibrant, engaging, and specific description of what it will be like to achieve the BHAG [big, hairy, audacious goal].

Think of it as translating the vision from words into pictures, of creating an image that people can carry around in their heads. We call this "painting a picture with your words."[5]

Henry Ford vividly described his vision:

> I will build a motor car for the great multitude. It will be so low in price that no man making a good salary will be unable to own one — and enjoy with his family the blessing of hours of pleasure in God's great open spaces ... When I'm through everybody will be able to afford one, and everyone will have one. The horse will have disappeared from our highways, the automobile will be taken for granted ... [and we will] give a large number of men employment at good wages.[6]

"Passion, emotion, and conviction are essential parts of the vivid description," writes Collins. "Some managers are uncomfortable with expressing emotion about their dreams, but it's the passion and emotion that will attract and motivate others."[7]

Winston Churchill understood this when he described the BHAG facing Great Britain in 1940. He didn't just say "Beat Hitler." He said:

> Hitler knows he will have to break us on this island or lose the war. If we can stand up to him all Europe may be free and the life of the world may move forward into broad, sunlit uplands. But if we fail, the whole world including the United States, including all we have known and cared for, will sink into the abyss of a new Dark Age, made more sinister, and perhaps more protracted, by the lights of perverted science. Let us therefore brace ourselves to our duties, and so bear ourselves that if the British Empire and its Commonwealth last for a thousand years, men will still say, "This was their finest hour."[8]

The Leader's Actions Communicate the Vision

I've found that many people in leadership positions don't realize the power they have and how the people who report to them watch everything they do for clues of what is important and how they are to behave.

Actions by leaders speak much louder than words. Are your words aligned with your behavior? For example, are you saying that patient satisfaction is important, yet you keep patients waiting for an hour or more in the lobby? Are you saying that the health and life balance for your staff is important, yet you skip lunch, drink coffee all day, and stay late every night? Do you talk about trusting those on your team, yet micromanage them as they try to complete their work? Albert Schweitzer said, "Example is not the main thing in influencing others. It is the only thing."[9]

I believe that the most significant factor affecting the behavior of people on the job is the behavior of their boss. Most people recognize the impact of their boss's behavior on their own behavior. However, they fail to recognize that their behavior has a similar powerful effect on the behavior of their team members.

Recently I was interviewing for a consulting assignment with the CEO at a major medical facility. It was a Tuesday and the CEO was wearing a bow tie. After an hour-long discussion, the CEO offered me the position and invited me on a tour of the facility. During the tour he introduced me to his management team, and to my surprise and delight, every guy on his team was wearing a bow tie. Yes, the CEO's behavior "spoke loudly" and had a powerful effect on the behavior of his employees!

As the administrator-on-call during a stormy, windy weekend, I made rounds in a healthcare facility where I worked and discovered leaves, twigs, and water throughout the lobby. Because it was the weekend and the staffing was stretched thin, I decided to sweep the lobby myself. The mantra we had been preaching was "we do windows," and I was "walking the talk." The 30 minutes that I spent that Sunday sweeping the lobby became the talk of the staff and volunteers for weeks. There is great power in communicating your vision by example.

Contrasting Good and Poor Communication

When Bennis wrote that successful leaders communicate the vision, he often spoke of the contrast between the communication styles of Ronald Reagan and Jimmy Carter during their terms as president. Reagan was known as the "Great Communicator" and used picture images to explain what could have been abstract messages. For example, when describing the enormity of $1 trillion, he compared it to the Empire State Building.

Conversely, Jimmy Carter was described as someone "unimpressive in his ability to communicate, which greatly hampered his rallying power ... One of the women in his cabinet remarked 'how difficult it had been to work for him because she never knew what he stood for' ... 'Working for him was like looking at the wrong side of a tapestry — blurry and indistinct.'"[10] Please know that this story about Jimmy Carter is not meant to be a negative reflection on Jimmy Carter who won the Nobel Peace Prize in 2002, but merely to contrast communication styles.

Communication Aligns Behavior with Organization Goals

Communication as a best practice aligns team members with the organization's vision and goals and is essential in driving results. Wirthlin Worldwide is a strategic research organization that has done research for more than 25 years, resulting in excess of 350 studies. Their research indicates that "alignment depends on effective internal communications that, when combined with consistent and effective leadership behavior, empowers employees to improve their performance, satisfy the customer, and enhance organizational success and reap the many personal benefits thereof."[11]

In addition, "Employees who are very satisfied with communication are much more aligned with the company business plan ... in fact, employees who are satisfied with their company's communications are dramatically more satisfied with nearly every aspect of their work, significantly more positive in their attitudes, and much more committed to the company for which they work."[12]

So how can companies improve communications? Wirthlin Worldwide found that there are six core attributes that best explain communication satisfaction. The important drivers for managers to consider when building action plans for improving employee alignment via effective communication are to:[13]

1. Listen and respond to employee feedback (this attribute has the most strength in driving satisfaction with communication);
2. Work with employees toward the same objectives;
3. Provide employees with the information they need to fully contribute;
4. Recognize employees for their accomplishments;
5. Prove opportunities for involvement in solving problems; and
6. Be honest.

Employee alignment with company goals and values is highly dependent on leadership behavior and on internal communications that educate, engage, engender commitment, and motivate employees to pursue a common purpose. Today's most effective leaders articulate the vision and values that provide the glue — the basic philosophy and sense of direction, and value set — that draws everyone together. These shared values can be a primary vehicle for more effective employee communications.[14]

Alignment can be a difficult task. According to the Conference Board, CEOs today are quite worried about how to get employees to buy in to company goals and value, and for good reason. While an aligned organization can reap many benefits, decision making in an organization that lacks alignment can lead to chaos and poor results, as individuals make decisions that are not connected with achieving higher-level objectives.[15]

According to Wirthlin's 2004 alignment survey, satisfaction with communication at work declined significantly over the previous year, and one-fourth of those surveyed were dissatisfied with communications.[16] For several years, Wirthlin Worldwide employee research has demonstrated a direct relationship between employee alignment and communication in the workplace.

At a Marriott hotel in Northern California, the department managers meet every Friday afternoon to discuss any situations that have occurred with customers, employees, and vendors during the previous week that they could learn from.

During these weekly meetings, the managers talk about their vision, mission, values, and goals. Together they discover ways to continually improve.

The management team at a large international bank that is going through a lot of change uses some of their weekly meeting time brainstorming about some of the tough questions that they will be asked by team members and customers. Their goal is to have consistent answers to these questions so that not only can they present a united front but also be able to communicate the bank's position more clearly.

I encourage my clients to use a portion of their weekly management meetings to discuss issues that have occurred recently as well as to prepare for the future.

Communicating Department Goals as well as Big-Picture Goals
"What does it mean to me?" is the plea of more than half of employees surveyed. Aligning employees with the business plan is essential to driving results. The good news is that among employees surveyed, two-thirds say they understand the company's business plan and their personal role in achieving it, yet the bad news is that fewer than half say their manager

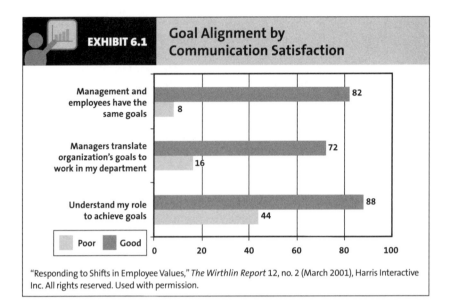

EXHIBIT 6.1 | **Goal Alignment by Communication Satisfaction**

Management and employees have the same goals — Good: 82, Poor: 8
Managers translate organization's goals to work in my department — Good: 72, Poor: 16
Understand my role to achieve goals — Good: 88, Poor: 44

Legend: Poor, Good. Scale: 0, 20, 40, 60, 80, 100

"Responding to Shifts in Employee Values," *The Wirthlin Report* 12, no. 2 (March 2001), Harris Interactive Inc. All rights reserved. Used with permission.

translates the plan for the work unit. This is not unusual. Although employees can understand the big picture through consistent and repetitive communication, they often struggle with the local translation of their department or business unit goals. Exhibit 6.1 from Wirthlin Worldwide shows goal alignment by communication satisfaction. (See Chapter 17 for further discussion of how to break down larger goals into departmental goals and then to individual performance goals with criteria.)

Ways to Communicate the Vision, Mission, Values, and Goals

Communicating your vision can take many forms, and your audience will need frequent reminders of where they're going, what's important, and, for your team members, what they are being paid to do. Your team will be made up of those whose dominant communication sense comes from seeing, others who prefer hearing, and yet others who prefer kinesthetic communication.

Most men are visually oriented, which means they respond to pictures, signs, banners, and colors. They also respond to descriptions of the vision, mission, values, and goals that use words that are visual. Some facilities demonstrate their vision and mission through brochures that show smiling, attractive staff members helping patients. Many organizations have the vision, mission, and values framed and displayed in the lobby and conference rooms, as well as printed on all the newsletters and correspondence. I've been involved with one facility that created two brochures with pictures. One of the brochures was to demonstrate the vision and mission as they applied to each constituency — patients, physicians, employees, and community. The other brochure contained pictures that depicted the values. For example, compassion was depicted by a nurse wiping the tear from a young boy's cheek.

Teamwork was demonstrated by several team members painting a room together — steadying the ladder, holding the paint can. Listening was a frame of a man's and woman's faces where the man was speaking and the woman was intensely focused on his lips. Visually oriented people respond to words such as *picture, clear, perspective, reveal, show, distinguish,* and *shortsighted.*

Most women prefer a kinesthetic communication style as their dominant style. Therefore, when communicating the vision, mission, and values, try to appeal to this kinesthetic style. Give examples of what the values mean from a feeling standpoint — get them in touch with what it feels like when there is teamwork, when a patient receives quality care, how the people in the organization benefit when the budget is met. The pictures in the brochures and on the Website that give clear examples to visual communicators can communicate to the kinesthetic as well by eliciting feelings. Kinesthetically oriented people respond to words such as *impact, stir, touch, shock, irritate, sharpen,* and *move.*

The third type of communication style is auditory; those who prefer to pay more attention to the sounds of the world have an auditory communication style. This is how most people try to communicate — by talking. Our traditional school system is designed for the auditory-oriented individual. Teachers usually stand in front of the class and talk. Unfortunately, most men are visually oriented and most women are kinesthetically oriented. About 20 percent of people prefer auditory as their primary system for communicating. For those who are auditory, sounds and words are a good way to communicate the vision, mission, values, and goals. Talk about the mission, vision, values, and goals all the time. Auditory-oriented people respond to words such as *sound, hear, ask, amplify, say,* and *tone.*

What does this mean to you as a leader who understands that communication about the vision, mission, values, and goals is critical to success? It means it's important to communicate to all the styles. Use pictures, sounds, and touch. Although we have primary communication systems, we also use the backup systems. For example, I prefer visual-oriented communication with my kinesthetic orientation as a close second.

A client provided me with a great example of how important these communication systems can be. Pat was complaining to me that her husband was a spendthrift and that despite a substantial income, her family had no savings. I asked her if her husband was aware of her concerns. "Yes," she said. "I tell him and tell him and tell him about it." I asked what he does when she tells him. Pat said, "He says, 'show me!' so I go into more detail time after time." Knowing about these representative communication systems, I smiled and said, "Why don't you draw him a picture showing the household income and expenses? I'll call you next week to see what happens." Two days later, Pat called me and joyfully announced, "He *got it*!" Her husband is visually oriented and needed a picture to understand what his wife was communicating.

Communicating Clearly Through Actions

Many of the Marriott hotels understand the importance of communicating their messages. In a Houston Marriott, the hotel distributes a one-page weekly newsletter that contains the vision, mission, values, and goals. One of the 10 behaviors desired by the leaders is highlighted, and there are exercises that accompany it. For example, one recent newsletter highlighted Principle 9: "I Anticipate Needs of Guests and Coworkers." The newsletter presented several situations for each department to practice: A guest is asking a question in English and the responding associate speaks limited English; an associate is pushing a cart loaded with heavy boxes for a guest and the wheel gets stuck; the supply of clean glasses in the restaurant is running low. "To recap: Anticipating associate needs helps us meet the needs of our guests. Watch for clues, listen, act before being asked." Throughout the newsletter, Marriott demonstrates what Marriott believes is important and its expectations of its workforce.

Actions Speak Louder Than Words

As a leader, you are always *on stage*. Your actions must be congruent with your words. What Schweitzer said bears repeating, "Example is not the main thing influencing others. It is the only thing."[17] It's critically important for leaders to be attuned to both their verbal and nonverbal communication. When nonverbal behavior is congruent with verbal messages, the meaning of words is reinforced.

In a verbal message, the words themselves make up 7 percent of the message. The other 93 percent is delivered through nonverbal behavior — the tone of voice is 38 percent (voice quality, pitch, rate of speech, volume, intonation, pauses, even yawning), and the facial expressions and body posture is 55 percent (body movements, use of space, eye movements, gestures, and dress).

Even without saying words, a manager is sending nonverbal messages about the depth of his or her understanding and the degree of empathy.[18] For example, strong words of confidence such as, "I'm absolutely certain that this change is for the better," stated with a downcast look and with a flat tone of voice, would be difficult to interpret. Chances are that the receiver of the communication wouldn't believe that the speaker thinks the change really is for the better.

At the hospital of the future, we had a process called "Walk in My Shoes" where employees switched jobs for three hours in order to develop empathy for each other. Our CEO took on the role of the lobby receptionist, who also answered phones for the facility. By doing this, John demonstrated that he believed every position is important. Additionally, he provided exceptional customer service during his three hours on the plank, so he modeled that behavior too.

Another example of *walking the talk* of our values, vision, and mission happened the evening that the senior management team took over the kitchen at the facility. We often celebrated and recognized team members and departments, but because the celebrations usually involved food, the food service department always worked during celebrations. We put on food service uniforms, made a huge spaghetti dinner, served a seated dinner to all the food service team members, and cleaned up our mess at the end. The employees loved it!

Beware of Vertical Communication

Remember the childhood games "Pass the Secret" and "Telephone"? One person whispers a secret to another who repeats the secret to another for several iterations. At the end, the last recipient states loudly what he or she heard. Everyone laughs because it is such a far cry from the original secret.

The same is true of communication in organizations. If the chair of the board calls the president and tells him or her something, on average, only

EXHIBIT 6.2	Vertical Communication in Organizations and Percentage of Accuracy

			% Original Message Received
1st layer	→	2nd layer	63%
2nd	→	3rd layer	56%
3rd	→	4th layer	40%
4th	→	5th layer	30%
5th	→	6th layer	20%

E. Bormann, et al., *Interpersonal Communication in the Modern Organization*, 2nd ed. (Englewood Cliffs, NJ: Prentice Hall, 1982), 183.

63 percent of the message is assimilated by the president. If the president relays the same message to a vice president, 56 percent of the message arrives.

When the vice president relays it to the next in line, 40 percent arrives. The next person in line receives 30 percent, while the next person receives only 20 percent of the original message (see Exhibit 6.2).[19]

This concept is extremely important for leaders to understand. Choosing the appropriate vehicle for your communication is as important as what you're trying to communicate. Every day there are staff meetings where those involved in the meeting are to communicate important information to others who are not in the meeting. No wonder people in organizations are often confused about what is important and what they are expected to do!

Inaccurate and incomplete reception of information is also a problem in upward communication. Senders often filter information so that it reflects their orientation (for example, information thought to be nonessential is eliminated). Additionally, senders have a tendency to screen out information that could potentially be viewed as negative and to overemphasize information thought to be positive. I believe this is one of the main reasons that many of the top leaders in an organization think that the morale in their workplace is better than it really is. Often, the leaders are not given accurate information about the problems and unrest among their staff members.

A process called *mirroring* works extraordinarily well to gain rapport if mutual trust in competence is already established. Mirroring is the matching of certain behaviors of the other person. The four mirroring techniques are:

⚙ EXERCISE   The Goal Journey

At your next staff meeting, choose five of your team members to participate in this exercise and have four wait outside the room.

To the one in the room (person A), say this:

> There are new goals for this year that I want to make sure are clear to you. Then I want you to share them with your staff members and have them pass these goals to everyone on our team. The first area is patients and their families. *I want our patient satisfaction score to go up at least 5 percent from last year.*

> The next area is teamwork among staff members. *Let's increase teamwork by 10 percent* over last year when we conduct our in-house survey again this year. Yesterday, one patient told me Jennifer was complaining to her about Tim!

> Another goal is to recruit *a few more physicians* during next year to round out our staff and *at least two more nurse practitioners.*

> The next area is revenue — we've just got to make more money. Our insurance companies are squeezing us and Medicare is too. We need *to increase our net revenue by 6 percent next year* so we can give salary increases and buy that new MRI [magnetic resonance imaging] machine.

Next, invite one of those from outside the room to return to the front of the room with you and have the person who was the first recipient of your goals tell this individual (person B) what the goals are. Then invite another to return to the room and have person B recite the goals to person C. Repeat the process wherein person C recites the goals to person D, and then person D recites the goals to person E. Finally, ask person E to repeat what he or she has been told about the goals. Then discuss what happened during this exercise.

Note: This exercise is available as an electronic file.*

---

matching voice tone or tempo or both; matching breathing; matching rhythms of movements with a different movement; and matching body postures. When rapport is not present, it becomes top priority in communication.[20]

Sometimes Words Hinder Communication

Messages given through the spoken word may be misleading. Here's a sample dialogue between a department manager and the supervisor:

DEPARTMENT MANAGER: "I want you to do everything possible to get this project done on time."

SUPERVISOR: "Does that mean I can hire more people?"

---

*Instructions to access the electronic files are available in Appendix A.

DEPARTMENT MANAGER: "Well, no. We would have the problem of letting people go after the project is done, which would make for bad public relations, or we'd have the problem of finding other projects for them."

SUPERVISOR: "Then can I work my people overtime to any extent that seems necessary?"

DEPARTMENT MANAGER: "Well, we've got to watch the budget. ..."

In this example, the phrase "everything possible" is too general and, therefore, confusing.

The Fundamental Purpose of Communication

In summary, Bennis found that having the ability to communicate the vision is a characteristic of successful leaders. The fundamental purpose of communication in an organization is to enable and energize employees to carry out its strategic intent — its vision, mission, values, and goals.

What makes communication management in some organizations better than in others? Experts have found that successful communicators think about communication in three ways:

1. *They value people.* They trust them, share huge amounts of information with them, and consider team members as partners, not mere job holders.

2. *They manage communication to improve organization performance.* They use communication to focus people on what is important — vision, mission, values, and goals. They make sure that information is available to make the best decisions at the right time. They ensure that people understand how the organization works and how each individual contributes to success.

3. *They view communication as a core critical process.* They always focus on communication systems and how they can improve the systems.

I concur with Jim Shaffer, principal and senior consultant of Towers Perrin, that "the single most common finding from every communication best practice study we've ever seen, whether conducted by an individual, company or professional organization, is that the CEO actively and visibly leads the effort."[21]

Companies that use communication as a best practice know that the communication process is always working, continuously bombarding the organization with formal and informal information, cues, signals, and codes

EXERCISE A Visual Way to Show How Even Seemingly Simple Communications Need to Be Clearly Structured

In a meeting with several of your team members, distribute large colored squares of construction paper (approximately 8½ inches square). Tell them that you'd like them to work for you and their job is to manufacture a product using this square. The firm has received the largest order ever from a customer, and being the generous boss that you are, you are going to share the profits with them. Tell them there are only two requirements of them: (1) they must keep their eyes closed during the exercise; and (2) they cannot ask you any questions. Then proceed to give the following instructions:

"Now close your eyes and hold the square out in front of you."

"Fold the square in half ... Now tear off the upper right-hand corner." "Fold the square in half ... Now tear off the upper left-hand corner." "Fold the square in half ... Now tear off the lower right-hand corner." "Fold the square in half ... Now tear off the lower left-hand corner."

"Okay, that's it! Open your eyes and open up your product and hold it up for all of us to see!"

There will be different shapes of squares, and as your team members look around, there will be lots of laughter. The different construction paper colors promote the reality that the squares are different from each other.

PROCESS QUESTIONS AND COMMENTS
Now ask, "What happened?" Then add, "We've got to start all over, and it looks like we're not going to make very much profit! What caused all these squares to become different? I used small words in my directions ... fold and tear. What would have made our communications more effective?"

Typical ways to improve communication include:
- ▲ Allow them to ask questions;
- ▲ Give them feedback as they go along;
- ▲ Show them a prototype of what they are supposed to be making — they may have ideas and better ways to create the product; and
- ▲ Carry the conversation to the workplace. What can you take back to your organization that you learned from this exercise?

Team members *need to know* the big picture and vision of where they are headed.

Note: This exercise is available as an electronic file.*

*Instructions to access the electronic files are available in Appendix A.

that come from leadership actions, reward systems, body language, office layouts, working conditions, decision-making processes, human resource policies, the way people dress, and so on.[22]

LEADERSHIP STRATEGY 3: TRUST THROUGH POSITIONING

Trust is the lubrication that makes it possible for organizations to work. According to Bennis, trust implies accountability, predictability, and reliability.[23] Trust is the glue that maintains organizational integrity.

Without trust, it is impossible to create a high-performing team. Although trust can be hard to describe or define, we know when it's present and when it's not. We trust people who are predictable, make themselves known, and make their positions clear.

When working with management teams, I often have them discuss which behaviors create trust and which do not. The goal is for people in leadership positions to translate trust into behaviors they can exhibit on the job, and then to behave in a trusting manner at all times. I divide the leaders into groups and have them respond to the following two questions:

1. What behaviors by leaders decrease your trust in them?
2. What behaviors by leaders increase your trust in them?

Elements of Trust

Over the years, I've found that there are four main elements of trust. These are:

1. Honesty — no lies, no exaggeration;
2. Openness — willingness to share information and ideas;
3. Consistency — predictable behavior and results; and
4. Respect — dignity and fairness.

Behaving in a trustworthy manner and your degree of trusting others are important components for leader awareness. Trusting behaviors involve being open and sharing, whereas trustworthy behaviors involve acceptance and support. Trust must be earned. It is hard to build and easy to destroy. In Exhibit 6.3, you can see how trust is broken with disappointments over time and does not return to its initial level.

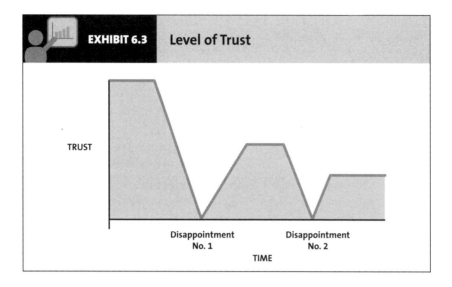

EXHIBIT 6.3 Level of Trust

TRUST

Disappointment No. 1

Disappointment No. 2

TIME

Trust exists in relationships, not in someone's personality. Although some people are more naturally trusting than others, and it is easier for some people to be trustworthy, trust occurs between people. And the level of trust is constantly changing as two people interact. To some extent, everything you do affects the trust level between you and the other person.

The key to building and maintaining trust is in being trustworthy. The more accepting and supportive you are of others, the more likely they will disclose their thoughts, ideas, theories, conclusions, feelings, and reactions to you.

The more trustworthy you are in response to such disclosures, the deeper and more personal the thoughts a person will share with you. I've found that if you want to increase trust, you should increase your trustworthiness.

As a leader building a team, it's important to understand that cooperation increases trust and competition decreases trust. Because trust is higher among collaborators than among competitors, you can reward your team for collaborative efforts. Additionally, initial trusting and trustworthy actions within a group can create a self-fulfilling prophecy. The expectations you project about trust often influence the actions of other group members toward you.

According to Graham Lowe, a partner at Great Places to Work Institute®
Canada, there are several principles that can help leaders develop trust-
based cultures:[24]

▲ Determine where your organization is on the trust continuum. Is it
relatively easy to have open conversations about how business
decisions affect employee trust, or is trust simply not talked about
at the executive table?

▲ Managers need to understand that every interaction is an opportunity to build trust, and that missteps can quickly break trust.

▲ Focus on a few key trust-building changes and pursue these consistently and relentlessly, recognizing that transforming a culture is
evolutionary, not revolutionary.

▲ Understand that how you actually carry out changes to improve
the work environment — especially by involving team members in
the process — is more important than what the changes are.

▲ Leverage what's already special, encouraging team members to
communicate and celebrate the unique strengths of the culture
that energize them to contribute their best.

▲ Focus on active communication with team members through multiple channels: town-hall meetings, focus groups, surveys, and, perhaps most important, face-to-face interactions between senior
managers and workers on the front lines.

LEADERSHIP STRATEGY 4: DEPLOYMENT OF SELF THROUGH POSITIVE SELF-REGARD

The fourth strategy is deployment of self through positive self-regard.
Successful leaders know themselves well — what they like to do and don't
like to do, their ability to recognize strengths and compensate for weaknesses, and their willingness to take risks. They are also perpetual learners
and listen, nurture, and empathize with others. Leaders steadfastly work to
develop their own talents.

Bennis considers this fourth strategy to be "emotional wisdom,"[25] and I
believe it is what we call *emotional intelligence* today. In 1990, Peter Salovey
and John Mayer coined the term "emotional intelligence,"[26] and emotional
intelligence quotient (EQ) was made popular by Daniel Goleman several
years after Bennis wrote about these four leadership characteristics.[27]

EXERCISE

HOW GOOD ARE YOU AT CREATING TRUST?

Credibility
- How visible are you with your team members? Do you manage by walking around?
- Do managers *walk the talk*? Do behaviors match their words? Do they keep their promises?
- How effective is the two-way communication? Do you ask questions and involve your team vs. give directives?

Respect
- Do you view someone as an *employee* or as a whole person?
- How collaborative is decision making?
- Have you put the right people in the right jobs and given them the resources to be highly effective?

Fairness
- How consistent is the distribution of benefits and perks?
- Are promotion processes widely understood and consistently followed?
- What can employees do when they need to appeal a decision?

Camaraderie
- How do teams and supervisors welcome new team members to the company?
- How much fun is it to work here?
- Are you better at task accomplishment than relationship building?
- How are team members involved in the community?

Pride
- Have you defined what you want your team member experience to be?
- Would you recommend your company as an employer to your close friends?
- How have you connected a team member's job to a tangible outcome?

Adapted from G. Lowe, "Best Workplaces 2006: Trust is Tops — Building a Better Workplace Culture," *Canadian Business* (Apr. 10–23, 2006), glowe@greatplacetowork.ca.

Goleman describes emotional intelligence as the ability to manage ourselves and our relationships effectively. Emotional intelligence consists of four fundamental capabilities: self-awareness, self-management, social awareness, and social skill. The skills of emotional intelligence are central to leadership. Research around this topic supports Goleman's work: "Interpersonal ineptitude in leaders lowers everyone's performance: It wastes time, creates acrimony, corrodes motivation and commitment, builds hostility and apathy."[28]

EXHIBIT 6.4   Emotional Intelligence Quotient Behaviors

THE SMART APPROACH TO EQ

Emotional intelligence is the ability to understand and manage your thinking, emotions, and behaviors, as well as understand and influence the emotions and behaviors of others, in ways that promote outstanding performance.

Attribute	Definition	Characterized by
Self-Awareness	The ability to truly understand one's thinking, feelings, and the impact these have on every behavior and decision we make.	• Catching emotions in the moment. • Ability to recognize and name the emotion. • Recognizing that emotions impact on decisions, choices, and behavior.
Managing Emotions and Impulses	The ability to catch unhelpful emotions and master these emotions to control impulses and delay gratification.	• Managing impulses and negative emotions. • Staying focused on goal-oriented, core activities. • Staying calm, channeling emotions in a constructive way.
Attitude of Optimism	The ability to think in ways that promote resilience and the capacity to bounce back from adversity and stay focused on goals.	• Having a mindset that promotes resilient thinking. • Seeing obstacles as temporary and staying "in the game." • Able to anti-"catastrophize" and corral a problem, isolating its impact on other areas.
Reading the Emotions of Others	The ability to display empathy and tune into the emotions of others.	• Seeking first to understand before being understood. • Recognizing others' situation by using questions and "really listening" to the message. • Understanding the underlying emotions of the message.
Teaming up with Others	The ability to work with others in a constructive way to engage them in a way that motivates them to want to work with you and assisting them to stay focused and deliver results.	• Demonstrating positive expectations of others. • Supporting and collaborating with others. • Giving people recognition or credit for a job well done.

"The SMART approach to EQ," *AttitudeWorks e-zine.* (Dec. 13, 2004).
www.attitudeworks.com.au/AW_pages/resources/articles/003/A003_041213_SMART-EQ.html

This leadership strategy of emotional intelligence — managing and expressing emotions effectively — is regarded as a key factor in organizational performance. More than 500 studies have shown that managers high in EQ exceed targets by 20 percent, whereas low-EQ managers underperform by 20 percent. Exceptional leaders attribute 90 percent of their success to emotional intelligence. The primary cause of executive failure is deficit in emotional intelligence.

How evolved is your emotional intelligence? Exhibit 6.4 describes some EQ behaviors.

Leadership Traits

Having highly developed emotional intelligence supports the findings of Collins in *Good to Great*.[29] Collins and his researchers report that one of their most surprising results of the research of good-to-great companies was what he calls "Level 5 Leadership." To turn a good company into a great one, one might think that the leaders would be high-profile principals with big personalities who make headlines and become celebrities. On the contrary, Level 5 leaders combine extreme personal humility with intense professional will. They channel their ambition toward the goal of building a great organization. These leaders set up successors for success when it's time for them to leave the helm, are compellingly modest, and have unwavering resolve.

EXERCISE How Are You Communicating the Practice's Mission, Values, and Goals?

Earlier you identified the mission, values, and goals of your practice.

How Are You Communicating Them?
If we walked into team members' offices and asked them about the goals, values, and mission of the medical practice, what would they say? Is every team member in the practice clear on their view of the goals, values, and mission? What values and goals are the leaders rewarding? Are there mixed messages? Starting today, what can the leaders do differently to communicate the mission, values, and goals of the practice?

Note: This exercise is available as an electronic file.*

---

*Instructions to access the electronic files are available in Appendix A.

MAKING COMMUNICATION A BEST PRACTICE

Some questions to ask in order to make communication a best practice are as follows:[30]

- ▲ What is our current philosophy of information sharing? What are we willing to share? What are we unwilling to share? Is there a business reason for not wanting to share certain information? What prevents us from adopting "always tell the truth" as a simple guideline? Why is that guideline realistic or unrealistic in our environment?

- ▲ Do we have a business strategy? Is it clear? Is it shared? Among whom? Who doesn't know that strategy? Is there a business reason for sharing it more widely, or for not sharing the strategy more widely? Do we need to build greater ownership in the business strategy through more involvement in its creation?

- ▲ Are there critical process drivers or organization capabilities that represent high-impact opportunities for improvement? To what extent could better communication management contribute to improving these areas?

- ▲ What communication barriers exist to implementing the business strategy or achieving specific performance requirements?

- ▲ What are the best opportunities for improving performance through improved communication management?

- ▲ What specific course or courses of action should be taken to improve communication?

- ▲ How have other parts of the organization addressed similar communication problems? What can be learned from them?

- ▲ How have other organizations addressed similar communication problems? What can be learned from them?

- ▲ What's the best way to study what others have done and apply it to our organization?

CHAPTER PRESCRIPTIONS

- Remember that strong leaders have a clear, realistic, and exciting sense of what the organization's future will be. This vision helps to move employer and team member along on the same plane, toward the same meaningful goals.

- Strong communication is another necessary trait that good leaders need. Communicate with your team members verbally, in writing, and by actions. Team members who feel as if they're working toward the same goals with you are much more apt to find purpose in their jobs.

- Promote an environment based on trust as you foster honesty, openness, consistency, and respect within your organization — know that this is a vital element to a strong organization and well worth the time that you put into it.

- Constantly strive to have positive self-regard. Know yourself well and strive to be the person with whom you can be most proud. In short, be the type of person or boss you would want to be around.

CHAPTER 7

Leading Through Change

"The only person who likes change is a baby with a wet diaper."[31] Mark Twain said this long before the 21st century, yet it applies today more than ever. Another great Twainism that applies to change is, "If it's your job to eat a frog, it's best to do it first thing in the morning. And if it's your job to eat two frogs, it's best to eat the biggest one first."[32]

Being a leader during times of change is very challenging and, at times, an exhausting assignment. It is often hard enough to keep ourselves motivated and moving forward toward the goals during times of chaos and change. The added responsibility of moving a team forward can be a formidable task that many of us find daunting. Yet, one thing we know for sure about change is that the rate of change is going to accelerate.

MIND SHIFT FOR LEADERS: CHANGE IS INEVITABLE, GROWTH IS OPTIONAL

Change energizes some organizations and paralyzes others. (See Exhibit 7.1 for a quiz to see how well your organization manages change.) How can this be? What is the discerning factor? Research shows that the behavior of managers is the single most important factor in how people in the organization will accept change. The good news is that there has been an abundance of research about change — how to lead people through change and what to do with ourselves when we get stuck. We know that there are predictable stages that everyone passes through when exposed to change, no matter how large or small the change is. We also know that people have certain predictable behaviors at each one of these stages of change. Because of this, we are able to appropriately respond as leaders to get our teams back on track toward the goals.

Self-management is the toughest chore for leaders during times of change. It is no longer survival of the fittest, but survival of the most flexible. In

EXHIBIT 7.1   **Quiz: How Well Does Your Organization Manage Change?**

Managing change is one of the critical factors in the success of an organization. Take this quiz to see how well your organization manages change. Circle one response for each question that most closely reflects your answer.

A. Are team members involved in deciding what should be changed?
1. They learn about change through the "grapevine."
2. They are told about change by management.
3. They are told about the change and asked for feedback.
4. They have significant input on what the change should be.

B. Are team members clear about the goals of the change?
1. Goals? What goals?
2. Team members think the goals are confusing and vague.
3. Some of the team members are clear about the goals of the change.
4. The goals of the change are clear to all team members.

C. How good is the information flow to team members during the change?
1. They aren't usually told what's happening.
2. Communication is limited to senior management.
3. Attempts are made to communicate to team members about the change.
4. Most team members are clearly informed and understand the change and its purpose.

D. How defined is the implementation plan for the change?
1. Implementation plan? What implementation plan?
2. Implementation plans are sketchy with poorly defined steps, roles, and responsibilities.
3. Some of the plans are thoroughly thought out and developed, but most are not.
4. Most plans have concrete steps with roles, resources, and responsibilities clearly defined.

E. Are good support systems—rewards, structure, training—in place?
1. Changes in support systems are not even discussed.
2. Changes in support systems are discussed, but little action is taken.
3. Some changes in reward systems, training, and resources occur.
4. Support systems are continuously adjusted to support changes as they occur.

F. Are measures of success agreed upon before the change is implemented?
1. Measures of success are not even discussed.
2. The measure of success is that we survive the change.
3. Some measures of success are used, but some are vague.
4. We systematically decided what measures the success of change.

(Exhibit continues)

EXHIBIT 7.1
(continued)

Quiz: How Well Does Your Organization Manage Change?

G. Is the success of the change evaluated?

1. No one even thinks of evaluating whether the change was successful.
2. Someone suggested that the managers evaluate the success of the change.
3. Some aspects of the change are examined and evaluated.
4. Significant aspects of the change are reviewed, evaluated, and altered if appropriate.

SCORING:

Give yourself points by adding the numbers for the answers you chose.

7–14 points: Your organization has major barriers to implementing change. It is time to take a systematic approach and design procedures for implementing change.

15–21 points: Your organization has made some efforts toward a systematic process for implementing change, and it is time to significantly improve it.

22–28 points: Your organization has many aspects of a well-designed implementation process. Congratulations, and continue the good communication and planning.

© 2016 Susan A. Murphy, MBA, PhD

Note: This exhibit is available as an electronic file.*

times past, the mighty oak tree was an image leaders visualized; now the image needs to be a willow tree, capable of swaying and bending.

One of the most effective leadership tools during times of change is a mirror. Look at yourself and your reflection. What do you see? Would you want to be led by you? Do you see a credible, balanced, professional leader who is going in a direction you think is a good one? Would you put your faith in you? Would you be inspired by someone like you to go the extra mile toward the goals? Some people in leadership positions today are so confused and off-balance that no one wants to follow them. The staff sees little commitment or passion about the goals in these unfocused leaders. Leaders set the climate. If the leader seems confused or doesn't seem to care, the passion wanes in the staff. Not many people will follow someone who doesn't know where he or she is going, so they stop following. And you can't be a leader without followers!

---

*Instructions to access the electronic files are available in Appendix A.

When changes are occurring in your organization, what are the steps the leaders must take to prepare? What about your team? Each person may react differently to the changes. How do you as a leader keep them focused on the organization goals during this time of distraction? How do you take care of yourself and lead at the same time? Some changes are even more difficult on the leaders than on the staff members.

First, I shall address ways to prepare your organization for change. Then I'll introduce the four stages of change and what leaders can do for their employees during each of the stages. Finally, I shall give a prescription for self-management that will keep you balanced and focused physically, emotionally, spiritually, and mentally.

Changes in the workplace appear in all sizes and shapes. In healthcare, a change can include everything from a new piece of equipment to a new team member to entirely new ownership. There are certain dynamics underlying every change. Even what would appear to be positive change has some loss or letting go of the old. When I was involved with the hospital-of-the-future project, we worked for three years toward the goal of opening the facility. The day finally came for us to move from our temporary headquarters into the new facility, and I recall my unexpected feelings of loss and sadness as I left my familiar office, parking place, and phone system. Even if the change is your idea, it can cause a number of behaviors and feelings that, if not understood, can impede the progress of your organization.

PREPARING FOR CHANGE

To prepare for change, you must find out as much as possible about the change, assess the readiness of your team, create a communication plan for the change, prepare your team, implement the change, and reward and celebrate. The following sections discuss these tasks in more detail.

Find Out as Much as Possible About the Change

A leader is the linking pin that connects his or her department to the organization. The leader must stay alert and aware of changes that affect the team. What are the reasons for the change? How do you see the change affecting individual employees and the work group as a whole? When is the change occurring? What do you anticipate to be the positive and negative impacts of the change?

Assess the Readiness of Your Team

Is your team ready to undertake another change? Does your team have a positive history of accepting change or was the last change traumatic? What did you learn from how your team accepted the last change? Learning from your past experiences can be an important step toward understanding what leadership actions to take.

The 20-50-30 rule states that during a change, generally 20 percent of the people are "change friendly," 50 percent are "fence sitters," and 30 percent are "resistors." Experts believe that leaders should give generous attention to the 20 percent who are change friendly and spend the remainder of their energy wooing the 50 percent who are sitting on the fence. It is tempting to give the noisy 30 percent most of the attention, but this is not the best use of your time and energy. Never presume that you must acquire buy-in from everyone before moving on. How long will it take to obtain buy-in from everyone? As a leader, your role is about achieving results, not getting everyone to feel happy about what is going on.

Create a Communication Plan for the Change

You wouldn't start out on a journey without checking a map and planning which route might be best. That same logic applies here. You will need a communication plan.

Identify your key audiences and how and when you will communicate with them. Your staff members should hear the information first before you start telling others. You want them to feel valued and to hear about the change firsthand, from you. I know of a bank whose employees learned of the plan to downsize from a newspaper article. The shock, embarrassment, anger, and hurt that the employees experienced inflamed an already difficult situation. Even the employees who were not directly affected by the layoff said they would never again be able to trust the organization.

Don't be afraid that you will be over-communicating. This is virtually impossible during times of change. Repeat key information over and over again. Listening is at an all-time low during times of change. In fact, just when you think you cannot repeat the information one more time may be the instance that many members of your team may be hearing you for the very first occasion.

Practice answering tough questions. Imagine the types of questions you will be asked, and rehearse the answers. Make your answers clear and easy to understand. If you don't know an answer, don't make one up. Admit that you don't know, then find out the answer and respond when the answers become available.

Above all, tell the truth. If you have privileged information that you have been told in confidence, let your team know. Professional adults understand when you say, "I do have additional information, and as soon as I am given permission to share it, I will immediately do so." Your team has been studying your responses for some time now, and they know when you are not telling the truth. Maintaining their trust is especially critical during times of change.

Plan to keep your key audiences up to date with information and answers. During times of change, silence will be filled with rumors and speculation, and the grapevine becomes a vineyard. Days without any updated information can seem like an eternity to your team. Even if you have no new information, let your team know that there are no more developments and that you'll keep them informed.

Communication styles differ among all of us. As described in Chapter 6, we are predominately visual, auditory, or kinesthetic learners. When communicating about the change, take advantage of all three styles. Have printed material or demonstrations for the visual team members. One of my clients printed a weekly *Transition Newsletter* for all to see. For the auditory members, keep talking and listening. For the kinesthetic members, give them something to touch, such as memos, symbols, and samples. Provide handouts that provide them a place to physically write down the information.

Prepare Your Team

Make contingency plans. If things go one way, what will you do? What will you do if things go the other way? Anticipate the unforeseen, the unexpected. The old adage about "the harder I work and the more I plan, the luckier I get" is certainly true with change management.

Encourage input and suggestions from your team. Describe the change as clearly as possible and then provide an atmosphere that allows for questions, clarifications, and recommendations. They may have some valuable ideas to help with the implementation. They may also give you insight into areas of resistance. One astute manager I know poses a creative question at the beginning of her weekly staff meeting: "What is the most outrageous rumor that you've heard this week?" Thus, she makes everything safe for discussion and is aware of her team's real concerns.

Anticipate the skills and knowledge that your team members will need to thrive on after the change is implemented. How will the change affect their work? Will they need to learn to use new equipment? To master new job responsibilities? Have you prepared training plans for them with objectives and timetables? One overzealous organization offered computer training two months before the new computers arrived. By the time the new computers were installed, everyone had forgotten how to use them. This was time-consuming and expensive. A leader's job is to help the team be successful, so plan carefully.

"Me" is the first part of "merger." How interesting, because during change, our most important concern is "me"! Your team wants to know "What's going to happen to me?" Self-preservation is instinctive. Resolve these "me" issues as soon as possible. "What will I be doing?" "Whom will I report to?" "Will my pay and benefits be affected?" "Will I still have a job?" As soon as you answer these questions for your team members, the sooner they will be able to support the organizational change.

Implement the Change

Allow for resistance. In fact, get resistance out in the open. Even the change-friendly group is going to have some initial resistance — it's just part of being human. Accept all feelings — good and bad — as real, honest expressions.

Telling your team members how they *should* feel isn't going to help matters. Try to make it easy for people to open up to you, and be patient when reaching beyond the superficial conversation to get to the true issues; otherwise, you may be solving the wrong problems. Although you may be tempted to disallow all resistance, doing so drives it underground, which makes it more dangerous than ever.

Beware of sabotage of the change effort. Saboteurs can poison your team. There have been incidents where employees have let important things slip through the cracks or even perpetrated more malicious acts. I know of an engineering company that laid off part of its workforce in order to stay in business. When the company started outsourcing some services, several of the employees gave false calculations to the other company to sabotage the outsourcing effort. In this situation, ordinary citizens could have been hurt from faulty bridges and roads.

Make your team accountable for day-to-day results. When team members are filled with anxiety and fear, it is difficult to get them to focus on the daily assignments. This is exactly what they need to do. The patients and families need your team to focus on what needs to be done for them. As a leader, it is imperative that your team's job performance remains of high quality.

Reward and Celebrate

Organizational change can be difficult and challenging work. It is grueling to simultaneously balance day-to-day activities with actions needed to move the organizational change forward. Once the change has been successfully implemented, hold a celebration to honor and recognize the extra effort put in by the staff and leaders. One characteristic of a high-performing team is that the team members celebrate success. Celebrating success increases confidence that enhances risk-taking so future changes have a better chance. Plus, it makes everyone feel appreciated and recognized.

WHAT ABOUT THE PEOPLE ON YOUR TEAM?

Every person who experiences change goes through four predictable stages. By understanding this phenomenon, I have found it much easier to deal with all the change in my world. By anticipating the stages and the behaviors that your team members will exhibit during the stages of change, you can ensure that your team will attain high performance during these chaotic times. These four stages are resistance, confusion, exploration, and commitment.

Stage 1: Resistance

Resistance is the first stage that we experience during change. All change involves resistance, even positive change. Change means a shift from the known to the unknown, and we need to adjust before we can become fully productive again. The behaviors during the resistance stage include sadness, resentment, anxiety, cautiousness, sarcasm, apathy, anger, withdrawal, rumors, stubbornness, and complaining. These are expensive emotions and can cost your organization through low productivity, no creativity or risk-taking, high absenteeism, sabotage, and rumors.

A leader's goal for team members who are in the resistance stage is to help move the team members through this stage as quickly as possible. Leadership actions necessary during this stage include listening carefully to your team, making the change safe for discussion, holding meetings for information and questions, being visible, offering support and reassurance, keeping team members accountable for day-to-day results, setting short-term goals, and telling the truth. It is important that the leader embrace the change and act as a role model and cheerleader for the change.

The anger and criticism that your team feels needs to be aimed at someone, and it will usually be pointed at you and the other managers. Although this can be extremely difficult at times, you must not take these reactions personally but recognize them to be part of the change process. Your presence, support, and reassurance are essential ingredients to successfully move your team through resistance.

Stage 2: Confusion

Confusion is the second stage of the change process. The shock is over, but your team members are realizing that what was familiar and known is gone. There is confusion about where to focus their attention and energy. The greater the change and the confusion are, the greater the frustration and fear.

The behaviors exhibited during the confusion stage include grumbling and complaining, questions and more questions, poor listening, escalated political behavior, erratic performance, and frustration. This is a very costly stage as well, and the leader needs to focus on moving the team through it as soon as possible. Some of the costs include decline in quality, duplication of effort, poor quality, good team members leave, and competitors move in and take customers with them.

This confusion stage is the most critical stage for the leader to help the team adjust to the change. Leaders must have clear goals and communicate them to the team. You'll need to provide answers and more answers, repeat key information often, and set short-term goals. It is critical that leaders stay approachable during this time. Priorities and expectations will need to be made clear, and individual roles and responsibilities may need to be spelled out in detail. If training is required for the change to occur, you'll need to start it during this stage. A key element of this phase is that the customers should not be allowed to suffer during this time of change or you'll lose them.

Stage 3: Exploration

The exploration stage involves an atmosphere of positive energy and optimism. Your team will start to regain a sense of self-worth and focus on possibilities that are inherent in the change. You will be able to feel the transition to this stage because the whole climate starts to feel upbeat. Your team will talk less about the past and more about the future. When I consult with clients who have just lost their jobs, I tell them that my goal is to get them to this stage of exploration. During this phase, they will see themselves as competent and productive, and they'll see the world as full of new possibilities.

Behaviors exhibited during the exploration stage include renewed energy, willingness to take small risks, optimism, reduced anxiety, and acceptance of the change. This stage begins to produce euphoria, in contrast to the energy-draining stages of resistance and confusion. Your team will regain a sense of control, and productivity will increase. As a leader, it's important for you to realize that there can be some costs to the organization at this stage as well. The enthusiasm can backfire with targets and goals set beyond possibilities. Attention to details is crucial.

Strong leaders are needed at this stage also. Your team needs you to keep communication alive, clarify goals and priorities, keep the team focused, encourage creative thinking, establish policies and procedures, and give the change a chance. Sometimes a leader is fooled into thinking that once the team has reached Stage 3, the change process is over. You need to stay alert to the task and the change process involved.

Stage 4: Commitment

Team members who reach the commitment stage feel secure, productive, and like an integral part of a successful organization. Your team members in Stage 4 will have high energy levels, high productivity, and be willing to take risks and take action. Additionally, they will openly discuss their views and accept differences where previously fear might have prevented this.

From the leadership standpoint, you must stay alert to other changes on the way. Because this stage can seem so positive and productive, it's easy to develop a false sense of security and complacency. The groupthink phenomenon occurs in the commitment stage because cohesion and the desire to avoid conflict are high.

Alert leaders at the commitment stage pay attention to the needs of their customers, stimulate new ideas and creativity, reward high performance, continue to be involved with their team members, and celebrate successes.

Simultaneous Changes and the Stages of Change

Because of the permanent white water of today's world, leaders and teams barely finish one change when another occurs. Many changes are happening at the same time. You might have one team member going through many changes and be at a different stage for each change. For example, your team member may be in Stage 4 with a new piece of equipment and Stage 1 with a new charting system. Simultaneously, he or she may be in Stage 2 following a change in his or her personal life with a move to a new house.

The rate of traveling through the stages of change varies with each team member. One team member may be stuck in the resistance stage with regard to the new computer system, while another may be in the commitment stage helping others learn the computer. Some get stuck in Stage 1 or Stage 2. For example, I know of some physicians who have never accepted the fact that managed healthcare is inevitable. These physicians are stuck in the first stage of change, resistance, where they are still in denial, still angry, and waiting for the day when all patients will pay a fee for service.

You may need to take diverse leadership actions with different team members depending on the stage of change they are in. A grid to demonstrate how different leadership actions are appropriate for team members passing through the stages of change is shown in Exhibit 7.2.

EXHIBIT 7.2	What Change Is Occurring?	
Team Member	**Stage 1, 2, 3, or 4**	**Leadership Action Needed Now**

© 2016 Susan A. Murphy, MBA, PhD
Note: This exhibit is available as an electronic file.*

*Instructions to access the electronic files are available in Appendix A.

HOW ARE YOU DOING DURING ALL THIS CHANGE?

"Mirror, mirror on the wall,..." A mirror is a key leadership tool during times of change. Take a good, hard look at yourself. Are you balanced? Positive? Approachable? A role model for your team?

One of my favorite announcements on an airline is when the flight attendant says, "In case of turbulence, put the oxygen mask on yourself first and then those around you." I've found that healthcare professionals usually put the oxygen on others first and then travel hypoxic through life. As a leader during times of change, apply the oxygen mask to yourself first. Without your leadership, the team will suffer.

How Our Bodies Respond to Change

Within seconds after we hear of a change, our body responds. This is the same response that prehistoric people found effective in their dealings with saber-toothed tigers, allowing them to fight or take flight. Although the saber-toothed tigers are extinct, today we can similarly respond to sudden announcements about budget cutbacks, mergers, and new government regulations.

Within seconds after you perceive the stressor situation, the hypothalamus in your brain triggers your pituitary gland to release adrenocorticotropic hormone (ACTH) into the bloodstream. ACTH goes directly to the adrenal gland to release adrenaline into your bloodstream, catapulting your body into an aroused state. Within the initial eight seconds, every cell of your body is alerted and becomes organized to respond to the change. Your blood pressure increases, your liver is alerted to produce more glucose, and breathing becomes more rapid to push more oxygen into the bloodstream to reach your heart and brain. Blood is diverted from nonessential areas such as the extremities, stomach, and intestines, and you might experience indigestion, diarrhea, and ulcers. Our bodies are geared to take physical action, but we usually don't take any. It is like driving a car with one foot on the accelerator and the other on the brake. Something has to give, and it is often our health.

SHARPEN YOUR SAW AND HELP YOUR TEAM DO THE SAME

People Can Become Exhausted

Stephen Covey was right: His habit 7 — Sharpen the Saw — is necessary for highly effective people.[33] What looks like laziness and resistance can be exhaustion. Self-control during change is an exhaustible resource.

An interesting research experiment around this issue involved college students.[34] For the study, the students were told to not eat for three hours ahead of time. They were hungry. On a table in the center of the room were two bowls. One held a sample of chocolates, along with the warm, fresh-baked chocolate-chip cookies. The other bowl held a bunch of radishes. Half the participants were asked to eat two or three cookies and some chocolates, but no radishes. The other half were asked to eat at least two or three radishes, but no cookies. Despite the temptation, all participants ate what they were asked to eat. None of the radish eaters snuck a cookie even with researchers out of the room — what willpower! At that point, the *taste study* was officially over, or so the college students thought.

Another group of researchers entered the room telling the students there was another unrelated study: "We're trying to find who is better at solving problems, college students or high school students." The college students were presented with a series of puzzles that required them to trace a complicated geometric shape; the puzzles were designed to be unsolvable. The researchers wanted to see how long the college students would persist in a difficult, frustrating task before they finally gave up. *The "untempted" students, who had not had to resist eating the chocolate-chip cookies, spent 19 minutes on the task, making 34 well-intentioned attempts to solve the problem. The radish-eaters were less persistent. They gave up after only 8 minutes, which was less than half the time spent by the cookies eaters and only managed 19 solution attempts.* Why did they quit so easily? The researchers believe they ran out of self-control.

In studies like this one, psychologists have discovered that self-control is an exhaustible resource. The radish-eaters had drained their self-control by resisting the cookies. Self-control is an exhaustible resource. When people try to change things, they're usually tinkering with behaviors that have become automatic. The bigger the change is, the more it will sap people's self-control. When people say that change is hard because people are lazy or resistant, that's incorrect. In fact, the opposite is true: Change is hard because people wear themselves out. The second surprise is that what looks like laziness is often exhaustion.

As a leader, it is critical to sharpen your saw as well as help your team sharpen their saws too. Covey's habit 7 is taking the time to sharpen the saw. By renewing the four dimensions of your nature — physical, spiritual, mental, and social and emotional — you can work more quickly and effortlessly.

CHANGE IS INEVITABLE, GROWTH IS OPTIONAL

What an exhilarating time to be in a leadership position where you can influence the future direction of your team. The rate of change in our organization will accelerate, and it has to. Leaders must plan for change, and this plan must include self-management (see Exhibit 7.1).

Even in the face of massive change, a plan for managing that change will greatly increase your chances for success. Planning for the impact of change clears your vision, builds your confidence, and increases your effectiveness. Your team and your organization are depending on you!

 CHAPTER PRESCRIPTIONS

- Change will never stop, but it will accelerate. Stay alert.
- Communicate goals frequently.
- Develop a communication plan for the change.
- Remember: Everyone sees each change differently.
- Learn the four predictable stages of change.
- Remember: No one skips a stage!
- Beware of the costs to the organization of not paying attention to each stage.
- Be patient, listen, and encourage each other.
- Be proactive and positive; create an empowered workplace.
- Find your sense of humor.
- Look at the BIG PICTURE.
- Stay informed and get involved.
- Plan for the impact of change; don't let it bowl you over — you can all face it head-on as a team.

CHAPTER 8

Situational Leadership Model: From Directing to Delegating

Many managers ask what kind of leader they should be; should they be involved or aloof? Should they be more of a coach or be more hands-off? Should they behave differently with new hires than with more senior employees who have worked in the organization for years? What if employees are learning new skills; should you leave them alone and let them learn from their mistakes, or be right there to catch them? These are excellent questions when aligning team performance with organizational goals.

The Situational Leadership® model created by management experts Paul Hersey and Kenneth Blanchard answer these important questions.[35] In the Situational Leadership model, the leader leads each employee by the level of experience of the employee — not the preference of the leader. The model was created in the early 1970s and has proven to be a very effective way to align employee behavior with organizational goals.

According to Hersey and Blanchard, the principal components of leadership are task focus (how, what, when, and where to get things done) and the cultivation of relationships (the two-way communication between the boss and the employee). These exist on continuums. In the case of task focus, some employees need little direction and would be insulted if constantly told what to do and how to do it (those are the ones who would rightly protest that you micromanage them), whereas others require more guidance — for example, in the case of a new hire just learning the job. At the extreme, task focus means the hierarchical command-and-control approach.

Similarly, the relationship component speaks to the fact that some employees need constant reassurance and feedback, whereas others are competent and confident and require only an occasional pat on the back. At its extreme, the cultivation of relationships means that no decisions are reached without negotiation — a flatter approach — but one that can impede progress.

Leadership may seem like an impossible balancing act. If you're too controlling, your team members may dig in their heels and move at a snail's pace to counteract your direction. Conversely, if you're too warm and open, your department may be filled with love, but achievement may suffer when team members spend too much time dealing with personal issues instead of working. Besides, you may end up taking too much of the responsibility for work production upon yourself.

Your team members will respond better to leaders who have adjusted their approach to suit the individuals they supervise and situations in which they find themselves. To treat a dependable, knowledgeable, experienced team member as you would a new trainee would be a disservice to your team and your organization. You manage a team member based on his or her competence and commitment level, not the style that is most comfortable for you. In fact, you may have to override your preferred management style because it simply is not the style the team member deserves.

Hersey and Blanchard's Situational Leadership model will help you tailor your management approach to your team members' needs. The model shows you how and when to focus on relationships, when to concentrate on the job, how and when to delegate tasks, and what to do when a team member backslides and requires discipline.[36]

LEADERSHIP STYLES

According to Hersey and Blanchard, there is no one single style of leadership but rather a sequence of four styles: directing, coaching, supporting, and delegating. These styles are progressive, meaning that an effective leader will progress from one to the next as the skills and needs of his or her team members evolve.

Directing is the most controlling style, while delegating is the least. Your team member's competence and commitment to do a task — also known as "job maturity" — dictate which leadership style you choose. Your team member's competence increases as his or her levels of relevant knowledge and experience, problem-solving ability, and performance grow. Your team member's commitment increases as his or her persistence, positive work attitude, drive for success, and desire to accept responsibility grow.

The more competent and committed your team member, the less directive you're likely to be and the more you will move toward delegating. Many healthcare leaders are often most comfortable with the middle two styles — coaching and supporting. These styles emphasize a leader's relationship with a team member and are the most collaborative. But good managers must also be directive or delegating when the situation calls for these approaches. Let's look at which styles are best in which situations.

Directing

Directing, as demonstrated by the statement "Let me explain to you exactly what I need," is appropriate when a team member has low competence (is new to a job), low commitment (doesn't feel like doing it), or both. Directing involves one-way communication: A manager explains to the team member how to go about achieving the task, and the team member does it. This style is useful when the team member needs instruction in order to be successful. Directing is especially valuable when:

- A team member is new or is just beginning to learn a new skill;
- You have a problem with a team member who is not committed to doing a good job, and you need to take charge of the situation;
- Time is limited;
- No alternatives are possible (as when a new policy or procedure is handed down from the government); or
- You must win this goal, project, or negotiation or your job or the organization will go under.

Recently, when a client of mine learned about the directive style, he remarked, "I just hired an experienced senior marketing vice president with a salary of $200,000. Are you saying that I still have to use a directive style with him?" My answer was, "Yes, I am. All new hires deserve a directive style." But you can adjust this style slightly with someone who is very experienced. It would be unwise to lecture the new hire on how to do his or her job — if the new hire is a pro, he or she should know that already — but you should communicate your goals and expectations for his or her position. You should also warn the new hire about political potholes — if, for example, there's bad blood between two physicians. In this case, your directing would be about expectations rather than methodology. Every team member, no matter how experienced or expensive, needs to know your organizational goals, philosophy, expectations, and job requirements.

The directing style is best thought of as temporary. In the long run, competent workers learn their jobs and don't need to be told what to do.

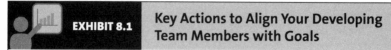

EXHIBIT 8.1 | **Key Actions to Align Your Developing Team Members with Goals**

1. Discuss the goal and why it is important.
2. Describe the performance area for development and why it is important.
3. Seek team member's opinion and, if appropriate, ask him or her to identify specific ways to enhance performance.
4. Give feedback on team member's ideas and add your own.
5. Summarize action items and set a follow-up date.
6. Express confidence and support.

Note: This exhibit is available as an electronic file.*

Conversely, if a team member can't or won't learn under your guidance, he or she may be ill equipped to handle the job, and you'd best find a better fit or be rid of such a team member. The agenda of the directing style is, "handle the position or leave it."

Coaching

"Tell me what you think about this" is an example of dialogue used in coaching style. During coaching interactions, a manager is somewhat directive, because the team member is still learning, but two-way communication exists between them. A coaching manager will solicit the team member's ideas and opinions in problem solving, but retains control over the ultimate decision making. Coaching falls within the parameters of a flat, collaborative approach. As your team member is learning a new skill, there are some key actions that a leader can take to encourage the team member to align optimal performance with goals (Exhibit 8.1).

Supporting

As demonstrated by the question, "What do you suggest?" the supporting style of management works well with a team member who has gained greater competence and commitment to a task and has demonstrated that he or she knows how to do it. Using this style, a manager would begin to allow the team member to take the lead in determining a plan of action or in solving problems. Dialogue moves the action forward, and a manager will often take the team member's opinions or suggestions unless serious flaws are seen in them. Transitioning from coaching style to supporting style can be difficult because some managers find it easier to simply supply answers to their team members' questions rather than soliciting their team members' input. The team members themselves may find the coaching style

---

*Instructions to access the electronic files are available in Appendix A.

safer, as it can be frightening to fly on your own for the first time. The supporting style is a useful one to adopt, particularly among healthcare professionals, because it allows for give and take in working relationships.

Delegating

The delegating style is appropriate when a team member is fully competent and committed to his or her tasks. "Let me know if you need help" is an example of delegating dialogue. When delegating, a manager will give team members responsibility without input or direct supervision. As Blanchard once said about managing in a delegating style, "Don't just do something, sit there!"[37] Delegating, like directing, involves more one-way communication, but this time, rather than the communication coming primarily from the manager, it's the team member who reports back to the boss about his or her progress or ideas.

Be sure to delegate when circumstances are right; that is, when your employees demonstrate high competence and commitment to their tasks. As their leader, it may be up to you to increase their competency with training programs and other skill-building activities.

CHOOSING THE RIGHT LEADERSHIP STYLE

You may find that you're most comfortable coaching or supporting all of your team members when, in fact, some weaker members of your team might benefit from directing while others are quite ready for you to delegate tasks to them. Your ability to match the most appropriate leadership style to a team member and then allow him or her to grow into the next phase — say, from supporting to delegating — will benefit the team member as well as your entire department. Your appropriate guidance increases productivity, performance, and morale all around.

The quiz in Exhibit 8.2 will help you test your understanding of the Situational Leadership model; that is, when you should use which leadership style. There are right and wrong answers, based on the model.

REAL-LIFE APPLICATION OF SITUATIONAL LEADERSHIP MODEL

Over the years, I've explained the Situational Leadership model to thousands of leaders because I believe it's such a powerful way to skillfully move

EXHIBIT 8.2 **What's Your Situational Leadership Acumen?**

We all have a preference for a particular leadership style or styles, but team members deserve the styles they need, not the one we are most comfortable with. The following quiz will help you choose among directing, coaching, supporting, and delegating styles based on the competence and commitment of the team member. Pick the appropriate management style in the following situations.

1. You've hired a new team member who is anxious to excel, but he hasn't done this kind of work before. Do you:
   a. Give him an assignment and check in a week later to see if he has done it?
   b. Ask him about his ideas and then let him run with the ball?
   c. Tell him exactly what you expect, then monitor him to see if he's performing?
   d. Discuss different ways to approach the work, and then suggest to him what would be best?

2. Your team member has been on the job and knows how to do her work quite well. Today she comes to you with a problem that you know she can solve on her own. Do you:
   a. Tell her to figure it out herself?
   b. Discuss options with her, but tell her which option to take?
   c. Tell her what to do and monitor her closely?
   d. Ask her what she would do?

3. You've been away from work for the past 10 days with a sick family member. A significant assignment came up and one of your team members started working on it without you. Although you have never assigned him this kind of work before, he is making great progress. Do you:
   a. Discuss his approach and give him ideas about how to proceed?
   b. Leave him alone and check in with him periodically?
   c. Take the assignment back and do it yourself?
   d. Talk it over with him but tell him how you'd like it done?

4. Your team member can do her work but often needs guidance from you. Lately her assignments have been coming in with mistakes. Do you:
   a. Ask her how she plans to resolve this problem?
   b. Review with her what the problems are and write a plan of action, then meet the following week to discuss it?
   c. Sit down and clearly explain what you want and when you want it?
   d. Leave her alone because she has been dependable and will probably get better with time?

(Exhibit continues)

EXHIBIT 8.2
(continued)

What's Your Situational Leadership Acumen?

Applying Hersey and Blanchard's theory to these questions, the correct answers would be:

1. *C.* A directing style is recommended because the team member is a novice.
2. *D.* A supporting style would be best, given the team member's competence and commitment.
3. *B.* A delegating style is appropriate for a team member who can handle work independently.
4. *B.* A coaching style is needed, because the team member requires more guidance to improve her performance.

P. Heim and S. Murphy, *In Company of Women* (New York: Tarcher/Putnam, 2003), 263. Used with permission.

EXHIBIT 8.3

People Model Using Situational Leadership

Team Member	Knowledge Base 1	Original/Creative Thinking 2	Operational Execution 3	DNA Maturity M1–M4 4
Matthew	Supporting	Directing	Coaching	M2
Hillary	Delegating	Delegating	Delegating	M4
David	Directing	Supporting	Directing	M1

© Dr. Raj Nathan. Used with permission.

employees from orientation, to a new skill, through to delegation. One of my clients, Dr. Raj Nathan, developed his "people model" using Situational Leadership (Exhibit 8.3).

First, Nathan defined four desired characteristics that he wanted his team to develop. These characteristics are (1) knowledge base of position; (2) original and creative thinking; (3) operational execution; and (4) DNA, acquired during the job, which develops as the employee matures in the role and becomes competent and committed (employee delivers results, market share, and revenue).

Per Nathan, DNA refers to what the company describes to be inherent characteristics consistent with the business objectives at the time. This measures how the person is progressing toward developing those desired characteristics. During start-up, a manager may need to be internally focused to set up systems. Later as practice develops, the manager may need to be coached to network externally to build business. Some team members have the DNA blueprint that can be developed fully to match what the manager's job requires, others may not.

In the example provided in Exhibit 8.3, Nathan uses the delegating style of leadership with Hillary because she is *mature*, meaning competent and committed in her job. (Levels of maturity go from M1, the lowest, to M4, the highest.) David is the least mature in his position, so Nathan would use a directing style with him in areas 1 and 3, and supporting style in area 2. The goal is to have all employees move toward delegating. When the employee achieves the delegating style M4, the manager and employee set new goals for the employee.

DEVELOPING DELEGATING SKILLS

Because the ability to delegate is one of the key skills of an effective leader, I'm going to discuss why it's important and how to delegate in more detail. Delegating responsibility is one of the best ways to help people prepare for future leadership roles and free up more of your time to handle other leadership duties and accomplish additional goals. Sharing responsibilities can keep your team members engaged, interested, and enthusiastic, and it creates a feeling of involvement. You might be reluctant to delegate because you want to make sure the job is done perfectly (your way). However, if you don't share the responsibility for having a successful department and reaching goals, you can make your team members feel unimportant, apathetic, and unengaged.

How does the leader and the organization benefit by delegating?

- The leader gains satisfaction watching others grow and develop;
- Delegation helps decrease the risk of the leader's burnout from being spread too thin;
- The organization saves money by completing the job with a lower-paid team member; and
- The leader is able to spend time on executive activities once freed from the tasks that can be delegated.

How do the team members benefit?

⏶ Team members become more involved and committed;

⏶ They increase opportunities to develop leadership skills and to be promoted within the organization; and

⏶ Their jobs become enriched because of new challenges, more authority, and more goals and projects are undertaken and completed.

Whom do you choose? There are several ways of delegating to team members. You can ask for volunteers with a sign-up sheet or show of hands, appoint someone who might lack self-confidence and won't volunteer, delegate to a group to get more people involved, or choose the best-fit candidate who has the skills or who could easily develop them.

How to Delegate

Use the following 10 steps when delegating projects.

1. *Analyze your tasks and identify one that gives you freedom and benefits your team member.*

2. *Describe the framework of the assigned project.* We all do better when we know why the task was initiated, so explain the background and share why the team member has been selected for this task.

3. *Describe the desired end results.* Just as with a jigsaw puzzle, a picture helps you construct the puzzle more rapidly. Don't tell the team member step by step how to accomplish the goal; let him or her think of his or her own ideas. General George Patton said, "Don't tell people how to do things, tell them what to do, and let them surprise you with their results."[38]

4. *Define the limitations of time, money, and other resources.* Research shows that managers and staff may be in agreement about important elements of the job but often don't understand about the boundaries and guidelines in which they operate, whether it's the urgency or seriousness of a project or how much money or labor is dedicated to it. Provide clear boundaries.

5. *Ask the team member to restate the assignment and deliverables, and ask for his or her willingness to accept the assignment.* This provides a good review of the project where you can answer questions and assess the person's enthusiasm, competence, and commitment. Don't ask, "Do you understand?" Many team members will say "yes," even when they don't understand for fear of looking stupid.

6. *Discuss initial ideas the team member has for completing the assignment.* This can give you a sense of how well the person grasps the project. It also provides you an opportunity to make suggestions that could help avoid errors and cover areas that might otherwise be missed.

7. *Decide how and when feedback will be given.* Specify the frequency and the reporting — written or verbal — that you want. Also, let the team member know that you are going to provide him or her with feedback when appropriate.

8. *Let go as much as is necessary.* You need to let the person do the job! Delegate the responsibility and the authority when appropriate. Don't micromanage — most responsible people do not appreciate someone looking over their shoulder or retrieving parts of the assignment before they have a chance to complete it.

9. *Keep a delegation diary.* Once you realize how effective and uplifting delegation can be for you and your team, you'll want to delegate more often. Keep a written record of which projects you've delegated to which team member.

10. *Ask team members to fill out an evaluation,* such as the one shown in Exhibit 8.4, so that you can strengthen your delegation skills too.

Barriers to Delegation

If you want to be a successful manager, you'll have to give up the notion that you can do everything yourself. As obvious as that may seem, learning to properly delegate responsibility may be the toughest part of your job. Here are some of the most common barriers to delegation:[39]

▲ *Lack of confidence in your team.* This syndrome is best described as "What happens if something goes wrong?" If a team member isn't ready to tackle a job, the problem is frequently because of a lack of training or coaching that the manager should be providing.

▲ *Lack of self-confidence.* Many managers, especially those recently promoted or hired, feel insecure. They may feel overwhelmed by their new responsibilities and fear their boss, peers, or their team members. As a result, they regress to the familiar security and routine of the work they did before they became managers.

▲ *Aversion to risk taking.* Delegation requires taking a calculated risk. Even with clear communication, good instruction, proper controls, and trained team members, some projects will not be successful.

EXHIBIT 8.4 **Checking Your Delegating Skills**

How well do you delegate? Circle the number for each question that best describes you—the higher the number, the more it describes you.

1. Delegation to me means handing over responsibility for results, together with the requisite authority and decision-making power.

   5   4   3   2   1

2. I make sure that controls are built into all the tasks and projects I delegate.

   5   4   3   2   1

3. I'm willing to admit that some of my team members are able to do the jobs as well, or better, than I can.

   5   4   3   2   1

4. I find that when I am out of the office, the office continues to function properly and productively and provides excellent service.

   5   4   3   2   1

5. When a problem occurs on a project I've delegated, I give the team member a reasonable chance to work it out by him- or herself.

   5   4   3   2   1

6. I involve my team in goal setting and problem solving.

   5   4   3   2   1

7. When I delegate work, I provide all the details that I know.

   5   4   3   2   1

8. When I delegate projects, I ensure that everyone concerned is aware of who's in charge.

   5   4   3   2   1

9. I seldom ask a team member to do something I would not be willing to do.

   5   4   3   2   1

10. I make sure to acknowledge when performance is good as well as when it is off-target.

    5   4   3   2   1

Please add up your total points.

A score between 42 and 50 suggests you are on target; 35 to 41 suggests that you are doing okay; any score less than 35 suggests you need to strengthen your delegation skills.

Now, ask your team to complete this questionnaire about you!

© 2016 Susan A. Murphy, MBA, PhD

Note: This exhibit is available as an electronic file.*

*Instructions to access the electronic files are available in Appendix A.

▲ *Fear of creating a rival.* This is a "What if the team member does too well?" syndrome. Rather than make an opportunity for a talented individual, some managers go out of their way to discourage new projects and play down existing accomplishments. Morale in the department will reflect the manager's insecurity.

▲ *Fear of appearing lazy.* Delegation might be construed by both superiors and staff as the manager trying to avoid work. This can be a sensitive point. These managers often feel that it's a sign of weakness to need help keeping up with workloads.

▲ *Lack of role models.* This is a "monkey see, monkey do" syndrome. If a superior doesn't delegate, the staff member will conclude, "My boss got to where he is with that style of leadership. Why shouldn't I do the same?"

▲ *Reluctance to yield territory.* Insecure managers guard their space and will often fight to protect it, believing that it represents power and security. They mistake delegation for giving up responsibility and authority. By sharing territory, team members will approach tasks with much more interest and enthusiasm than they would if they were assigned a job in which they held no stake.

OPERANT CONDITIONING IN EMPLOYEE DEVELOPMENT

Praise, when given in the form of goal-focused, FAST (frequent, accurate, specific, timely) feedback, can keep your team progressing — from needing constant direction to working independently toward the goals you've established. When you praise behavior of which you approve, your team member is apt to repeat the task to your liking and to learn and grow on the job. This is the simple principle of operant conditioning, which means praising the baby steps along the way toward reaching a final goal.[40]

Ken Blanchard frequently describes how trainers at SeaWorld used operant conditioning to teach Shamu the whale to leap into the air.[41] At first, Shamu swam randomly in her tank. But every time she passed over a submerged rope, her trainers rewarded her with a fish. Soon, Shamu understood that swimming over the rope provided her with delicious feedback, so she limited her swimming to the area in the tank directly above it. As she caught on, her trainers slowly raised the rope to the surface of the water. Eventually they held the rope above the surface, and Shamu, ever eager for her reward, began to leap out of the tank. Finally, the trainers removed the prop altogether, and Shamu jumped over an imaginary rope. What a great example — although somewhat Pavlovian in nature.

Children learn through operant conditioning too. Think about that first "mama" or "dada." Once the tot utters any sort of familiar sounds, we adults start celebrating; we call the relatives, discuss college plans, and plot out our child's potential career. We don't wait for our baby to utter complete sentences before we reward his or her efforts. Yet, often we wait for our team members to achieve all their goals before responding.

As a team member moves in a direction you'd like him or her to take, the individual will warm to your positive feedback. If you wait until the person has actually accomplished the goal before you say anything positive, you may be waiting a long time. You'll be creating a "no news is good news" culture, which can actually be negative. Praise the well-thought-out effort and the steps along the way toward achieving goals, not just the achievement itself.

Be sure, however, that you don't overpraise, or your team will become used to positive feedback, and it will lose much of its punch. In fact, I recommend that you use praise irregularly. When employees expect the praise, it doesn't have the same impact as when you give it sporadically and candidly.

You may also want to vary how you deliver praise. You can write a note, bring in doughnuts, or congratulate your team member in a meeting. One of my clients started putting positive stickers on good reports turned in by her team members. Once she had depleted her sticker supply, her staff requested that she buy more. They liked their little rewards. Another manager intermittently wrote personal notes on the payroll stubs of team members who showed superb performance.

DISCIPLINING THE BACKSLIDING TEAM MEMBER USING SITUATIONAL LEADERSHIP

Up to this point, we've explained how to develop *green* team members through each of the four progressive leadership styles to the point where you can delegate to them. Let's switch gears for a moment to explore how to handle a performance problem by using the Situational Leadership model. If an employee fails to meet commitments and isn't achieving his or her goals, you must step in with some sort of disciplinary action. Discipline is an integral part of effective leadership; without it, the message you convey to all your team is that performance doesn't matter. However, if the disciplinary action is not managed strategically and is not handled carefully, the team member may feel personally attacked and become defensive.

Admittedly, correcting unproductive behavior can be difficult. Discipline is a sensitive issue for many leaders and team members because you are asserting your authority over someone else. New managers may feel reluctant to discipline a team member, especially if he or she tends toward avoiding conflict. Alternatively, being unfamiliar with appropriate techniques or feeling insecure in his or her position, the manager may overcompensate and come across as too cold, strident, or punitive.

Unfortunately, neither extreme is constructive. Your ability to lead may be seriously impaired if you are unable to set appropriate limits with team members and then follow through consistently. Your practice's output and morale can suffer because the reluctance to discipline can make you appear to be a weak manager and can hamper productivity. If, conversely, you become overbearing, your staff will resent you and feel as if you've treated them unfairly.

Disciplining a backsliding team member is not impossible. There are effective ways to handle it. First, bear in mind that your response to poor performance should be based on the significance of the infraction — quick and intense if the problem is critical or patient and moderate if it's less serious. Verifying your decision, going into a regressive mode, keeping it professional, keeping your cool, and firing the team member if you must are five steps that will help you pull an errant team member back in line.

Step 1: Verify Your Decision

Make every attempt to observe the problem yourself before you say anything to your team member. Be sure you are talking to the right person about the right problem. Then discuss the problem with your boss or your human resource manager. To protect yourself and your practice from lawsuits, familiarize yourself with your organization's disciplinary procedures and be sure to follow them carefully. (Chapter 9 includes a formal disciplinary procedure that you may incorporate into your organization.)

Step 2: Go into a Regressive Mode

Your next step is to determine the Situational Leadership style you've been using (directing, coaching, supporting, or delegating) and then back up one style. For example, if you've been delegating, step back to a supporting style.

Set up a private meeting with your team member. Raise your concerns with him or her by asking questions such as, "I was surprised to see that your accuracy rate is way down. What's happening?" By discussing the problem in a non-accusatory tone and private setting, you might discover that your team member is bored with this assignment or angry with you or someone else in the department. Then come up with a list of specific, measurable, attainable, results-oriented, and time-bound (SMART) goals you'd like your team member to improve: Increase attention to detail by proofreading all the person's work and increase his or her skill on the computer by having the person take workshops. SMART goals are discussed in detail in Chapters 2 and 4.

From my experience, a manager's supportive attention helps wayward team members get back on track more than 90 percent of the time. But if supporting makes no difference, you may need to backtrack into coaching. This is where your previously established SMART goals will keep the discussion on a professional rather than personal level. Your strategy here is to divert the conversation from you and the individual and then focus it on the individual and the individual's agreement. The issue is the person's choice rather than your attitude. You might say, "We've agreed on these goals, but you're not achieving them." Then establish a schedule of regular meetings and written goals to be accomplished between the meetings. If after several weeks of this regimen you're still not getting the performance you expect, tighten the leash further to more frequent meetings during which you take notes (the team member gets a copy of these). These written work plans and your formalized evaluations can serve as documentation if you must terminate the team member in the future.

Finally, if all else fails, you must back into the directive style. You might say, "Let me tell you exactly what I need you to do today. If you have a problem with this, come to me, and I'll give you additional directions." Give your team member the choice of changing his or her performance or accepting punishment, which might be a written warning in the individual's personnel file.

You might even ask the individual to define his or her own negative consequences should there be continued underperformance. The idea is to avoid taking on the role of executioner but to make the disciplining process self-reprimanding. The problem is the team member's, and the team member needs to fix it. We guarantee that the individual will chafe at this and will probably be rather cold toward you, especially if he or she knows how to accomplish the task in question. The person may even quit. Nevertheless, in cases of incompetence or lack of commitment, it's important to stick with the directing style. As the leader, you're ultimately responsible for the quality of work that your team delivers. This team member has had several chances to improve performance and has chosen not to. The team member needs to change or get out of your organization.

Step 3: Keep It Professional

If, during your discussions, your team member reveals a personal problem (the individual explains, for example, that an alcoholic spouse is acting out again), do not advise about what to do at home; this crosses the line between manager and counselor. Never forget that you are a leader, not a psychiatrist. You can be supportive by recommending that the person contact the employee assistance program or another support group, but your focus must remain on the team member's workplace behavior; that's the area of your professional expertise.

Beware of your inclination to feel sorry for a team member in such a situation. When managers start to feel sorry for their employees, they often provide those individuals with an excuse for delivering low-quality work. You must keep standards high for all team members. That's the leadership role.

If a team member needs a leave of absence, grant one. If the individual is ill and can't produce the same quality of work he or she has consistently generated, it may be time for the rest of the team (including you) to pitch in and help for a limited time. However, don't lower the standards of excellence for the rest of your team because one person is having difficulty on the home front. This is not fair to your organization, the other team members, or yourself. And by all means, never share disciplinary issues or team members' personal problems with other staff members. They'll get the message that you gossip, thereby destroying their trust in you. Keep the issues confidential.

Step 4: Keep Your Cool

Be sure that all of your conversations are carried out in an even tone. Asserting your authority with a recalcitrant employee does not mean yelling. Yelling instantly pushes your employee into defensiveness. Besides, telling off a staff member makes you look as if you're out of control and a poor leader — an emotional dictator, perhaps — and will weaken your power, damage your relationships, and undermine your credibility. The goal is to maintain your composure.

If your team member yells at you, respond calmly; it's difficult to continue shouting at someone who speaks slowly and evenly. It helps to maintain eye contact. If you're in a public area and the altercation occurs in front of other team members, invite the irate individual into your office to vent in private.

Step 5: Fire the Team Member, If You Must

What happens to a team member who can't or won't perform? This doesn't mean the individual is a bad person. It just means the person is in the wrong job. There has to be another place for this individual. Your conversation might resemble the following: "Because of your many computer errors, you leave me no choice. I am now giving you a written reprimand. A record of this event will be placed in your personnel file. Starting immediately, you need to produce accurate computer reports. The next time your computer reports are incomplete or inaccurate, you will receive a suspension. Continued errors can lead to termination. You are a valuable team member here, and I believe you can be accurate. I want you to succeed in this." If the problem persists, be consistent in following through with the steps you've laid out.

It would be unwise to undermine your team's productivity by allowing a poor performer to continue without feedback. Besides, the team member may become a great asset at another organization in a different role. Rather than continuing to send your underperforming team member to still another training class, be direct, counsel him or her, and explore the individual's areas of strength with him or her. And if you must, send the team member on his or her way. This demonstrates respect for the individual as well as your other team members and the organization as a whole.

CHAPTER PRESCRIPTIONS

- Have clear SMART goals and communicate them.
- Empower your team members by giving them clear roles and responsibilities. In short, don't micromanage.
- Lead each of your team members based on his or her competence and commitment in the job.
- Adapt your leadership style to the team member; this isn't a one-size-fits-all situation — remember that you're dealing with individuals.
- Although many of us usually prefer to *coach* our team, discern when to *delegate*. As a leader, it's your responsibility to provide guidance and direction.

CHAPTER 9

Tough, Positive Leadership

Did you know that an airplane traveling from Denver to Atlanta is off course 99 percent of the time? Because of external and internal factors, such as wind turbulence, air traffic controllers' directions, or a faulty compass reading, the airplane must continually adjust its flight path to reach Atlanta. This also happens in the workplace with team member behavior. Their behavior must continually be realigned with the organizational goals.

Something is always getting in the way and adjustments are required. For example, physicians whose goals are to keep patient appointments running on schedule can be thwarted when a patient arrives late, which throws the schedule off track. Or when three patients present with emergencies on the same day and must be fit into the schedule. Or when one patient mentions a life-threatening symptom and must be handled immediately. When thrown off course, it's imperative to readjust and become aligned with the goals as quickly as possible.

Effective leaders talk about the organizational goals all the time. In Chapters 2 and 4, I discuss the importance of specific, measurable, achievable, results-oriented, and time-bound (SMART) goals. All team members must have SMART goals that are clear enough so they know when they are reaching them. And as soon as they get off target in relation to the goals, their behavior needs to be addressed before it becomes a habit. Experts agree that if behavior continues for 21 days, it can become a habit.

In this chapter, I will cover a powerful way to deliver feedback that will decrease defensiveness in your team members, allow them to accept praise and work toward continuous improvement, and get them back on track when they're off target. For many years I led a three-day seminar called "Tough Positive Management" that is based on principles that will be included in this chapter. Dr. Willard Zangwill writes about them in the book *Success with People*.[42] I've found that when leaders use Zangwill's

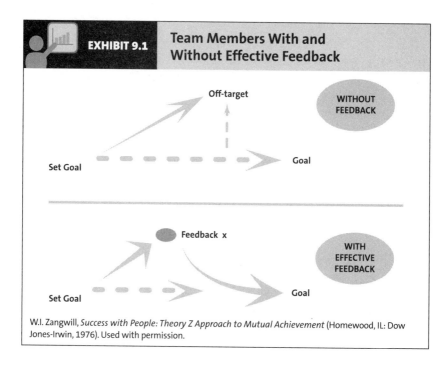

EXHIBIT 9.1 Team Members With and Without Effective Feedback

W.I. Zangwill, *Success with People: Theory Z Approach to Mutual Achievement* (Homewood, IL: Dow Jones-Irwin, 1976). Used with permission.

principles, team members excel, organizational cultures become healthy and goal oriented, and even personal relationships transform.

The illustration in Exhibit 9.1 shows what happens when team members are not aligned with the goal — once they get too far off target, it takes leadership actions to get them aligned once again with the goal. The sooner they receive feedback about their behavior, the quicker they can get back on course.

EFFECTIVE FEEDBACK KEEPS FOCUS ON GOALS

How does a leader keep team members focused on attaining SMART goals? One of the best ways is to understand and practice giving effective feedback. To feed can mean "to nourish" and "provide for." I've found that some managers use feedback as a chance to do just the opposite — to crush the spirits of their team. In this chapter I'll show you that effective feedback can be the breakfast of champions!

All of your team members need clear input from their leader as they move toward their goals. According to management guru, Ken Blanchard, working without getting feedback about one's performance is akin to playing night golf; you swing at the ball but don't have a clue where it goes.[43] Another example of not getting feedback is bowling with a curtain hiding the bowling pins. You throw the ball down the alley but can't see how many pins you've knocked down. You've taken an action, performed a behavior, but don't know how you're doing toward achieving your goal. I believe one reason video games are popular is that you know very quickly where you are at achieving your goal. The flashing lights, noises, and numerical score provide immediate feedback.

An impressive statistic is that performance effort by employees increases by more than 230 percent when employees receive information about both the goals and feedback as compared to only the goals or only feedback.[44]

Team members are hungry for input. Frequently, clients proudly proclaim, "I just leave my 'stars' alone. I don't want to get in their way!" In my experience, those stars, if queried, would be eager for feedback from their managers about their performance. Even stars can get distracted and veer from their objective; they need feedback to stay motivated and to learn how they can get even better at what they do. Tiger Woods, known for being the best golfer in the world, is continually working on his swing in an effort to stay on top of and improve his game through his personal coach's feedback plus computer swing analysis and videotape feedback.

FAST FEEDBACK

Drawing on a concept developed by business writer Bruce Tulgan, I suggest adopting the following guidelines for providing feedback to your team members. Tulgan created the acronym FAST when referring to feedback, meaning input that is frequent, accurate, specific, and timely:[45]

▲ *Frequent:* Giving a team member feedback once a year and expecting the individual's behavior to change is like dieting only on your birthday and expecting to lose weight. Provide regular feedback about assignments and other professional behaviors.

▲ *Accurate:* Whether positive or negative, you are on shaky ground if you take hearsay as truth. Be sure you have firsthand knowledge of any behavior that you're mentioning to your employee.

▲ *Specific:* Detail what made the behavior so good or so bad. "Your charting on the patient was thorough, legible, and consistent with Medicare reimbursement guidelines," you might say to a new physician. "Your presentation was succinct and logical. The comparisons with our competitors painted a clear picture for us about future positioning for our practice." Team members are likely to repeat behavior you have reinforced in this positive way, and they'll have a better chance of stopping negative behavior when you've been clear and specific about it.

▲ *Timely:* Generally, the longer a pattern persists, the more it becomes ingrained. Behavioral researchers say that it takes 21 days for behaviors to become habitual. This can be good news and bad news. If a team member has been performing well in a certain area, after three weeks the person will probably continue to perform well. If the individual has been performing poorly, unfortunately, those actions will also become ingrained. It's important to give feedback to your team as soon as you observe noteworthy positive or negative behaviors. The closer in time that an act is either praised or corrected, the better the chance of reinforcing or stopping that behavior. Behavioral experts call the time immediately after a behavior the "educable moment." Effective leaders take advantage of the educable moment and provide feedback often.

Don't wait to give important feedback. This applies to positive comments too. A manager attending a performance appraisal workshop I was conducting smugly stated that he would put letters in an employee's human resource file when the employee did a good job. After congratulating the manager, we asked him how frequently he did this. He looked bewildered, and then with a sheepish grin said, "My gosh, I haven't done it in over three years!"

Tulgan's FAST feedback model demonstrates what effective feedback looks like. But how do you know how and when to give it? If you give feedback too critically, your team member may become defensive. If you praise too frequently, the individual may become habituated and stop listening. If you dwell on the negative, you may perpetuate the problem. In the following sections, I will give proven leadership practices for giving FAST feedback in ways that will align team member behavior with your medical practice goals.

POSITIVE REINFORCEMENT INCREASES GOAL-FOCUSED BEHAVIOR

Positive feedback increases the chance of a team member repeating a behavior. Leaders can foster a goal-focused culture in their organizations by using positive reinforcement whenever possible. The use of positive reinforcement increases the chance that team members will move toward behavior that leaders want, instead of away from behaviors they don't want. Negative feedback can have the opposite effect. Although negative feedback will decrease the likelihood that the team member will repeat the behavior you don't want, negative feedback can cause anger, defensiveness, and resentment. A workplace that is filled with negative reinforcement veers everyone away from the goals and can have devastating effects on the team members.

Some recent research indicates that when positive reinforcement is given, levels of the brain chemicals dopamine and serotonin increase. These chemicals cause us to have a better feeling of well-being. Serotonin is a chemical that helps maintain a happy feeling and seems to help keep our moods under control by helping with sleep, calming anxiety, and relieving depression. Dopamine affects brain processes that control movement, emotional response, and the ability to experience pleasure and pain. In studies with Vervet monkeys, serotonin levels were dependent on positive reinforcement. Without encouragement and praise, serotonin levels decreased and the monkeys demonstrated marked decreases in energy, reduced dominance, and a marked tendency to behave more impulsively — and what researchers describe as depression set in.[46]

NEGATIVE FALLOUT FROM NEGATIVE REINFORCEMENT

Isn't negative reinforcement effective in stopping behaviors you don't want in your medical practice? The answer is "yes" — in the short run. You will stop the poor behavior in its tracks, and there are times when it's appropriate to use it. I will explain appropriate use of negative reinforcement later in this chapter.

A manager who consistently criticizes the staff can cause higher absenteeism rates, reduced energy level, tension, demoralization, petty thievery, conflict, sabotage, and dissent. If not careful, you could be creating an entire culture of negative reinforcement. I've witnessed cultures that are so negative that they seem to contain carbon monoxide, resulting in an atmosphere that is odorless, tasteless, colorless, yet damaging and deadly. The manager is the main *carrier*. I call this the "carbon monoxide effect." When working with clients, I often give them an oxygen mask as a constant reminder that their role as a leader includes pumping oxygen into the culture!

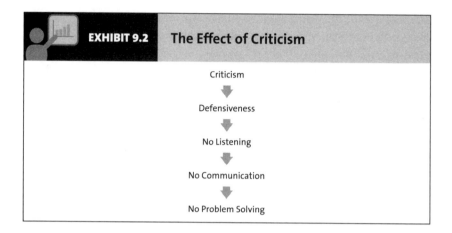

Effective leaders learn that there are adverse side effects to frequent use of negative reinforcement. There are negative consequences for managers who use criticism as a management style (Exhibit 9.2). Their team members will:

▲ Avoid the person who criticizes them;

▲ Withhold information;

▲ Get angry;

▲ Feel more stress;

▲ Make more mistakes;

▲ Become more cautious and risk-averse;

▲ Withhold creative ideas;

▲ Avoid bringing bad news; and

▲ Succumb to the "carbon monoxide effect" in their culture.

POSITIVE REINFORCEMENT VS. NEGATIVE REINFORCEMENT

Several years ago I heard the story of a college sorority treasurer who posted the names of the members who were up to date on their sorority dues and then read the names at the meeting, giving these members attention and appreciation for their support. Previously, the practice had been to read the names aloud of those who were late, and these members gave reasons why they were late and made their payments even later. With the new tactic of posting names of compliant members, a fascinating thing happened to those who were late — they paid their delinquent dues so their names would be added to the list of those who were current.

I put this into practice when working with a group of physicians and their patient medical records. Because insurance payers require that charts be completed and signed by physicians, this is always a tug-of-war between physicians and administrators. Instead of posting a list of physicians with delinquent charts, I posted the names of the physicians who were current with their patient charts. Magically, my experience matched that of the sorority treasurer; the physicians became more compliant and completed their patient records. Positive reinforcement can change negative behavior.

Positive Feedback as a Powerful Tool

Positive feedback can be a powerful management tool. When given in the form of FAST feedback, praise can dramatically improve performance by moving team members from needing constant direction to working independently toward the goals you've established. When you praise behavior of which you approve, your team member is apt to repeat the task to your liking and to learn and grow on the job. This is the simple principle of operant conditioning. When a team member is learning a new skill, you can give the person positive feedback about the progress toward the goal. It isn't necessary for the team member to behave perfectly before giving positive feedback. You can praise the team member for improvement in learning a new skill.

There are literally thousands of ways to deliver positive reinforcement. In fact, Bob Nelson's book *1001 Ways to Reward Employees*[47] presents formal and informal ideas from a myriad of companies and industries. You can surprise your team members with a widely distributed memo extolling their recent achievements — be sure to explain specifically what behaviors you are commending. Some managers give tickets to local events. Some bring in doughnuts. Others offer dinners for two as positive feedback so team members can spend an evening with their significant other. From my experience, money is not always the best incentive. Many people prefer verbal or written validation and appreciation. Dr. Warren Bennis said, "So many otherwise able managers act as if compliments come out of their bank accounts."[48]

Recently, on a cross-country flight, I mentioned to the passenger next to me how much joy I receive from giving positive recognition to flight attendants when they give exceptional service. I explained to him that I often write a compliment on the back of my business card and hand it to a flight attendant at the end of the flight — the flight attendant can then give a copy to her supervisor for extra credit. The passenger said he could top that — he immediately took out a business card, wrote a complimentary note on it, and gave it to our flight attendant right then. Smiling at me, the passenger said, "Why wait until the end of the flight? Let's give the positive reinforcement now with four hours left on the flight, and get some great service now!" Well, the passenger certainly was a quick learner, although I found his motives to be self-centered and manipulative; however, as predicted, the service we got during the next four hours was fantastic.

How to Give Praise

Praise can be an effective way to give FAST, positive feedback. However, many studies indicate that praise can make team members uncomfortable and untrusting of management. This is often because the praise given is very general and nonspecific, and team members report that they feel the comments are insincere and even manipulative.

When giving praise, talk about the specifics that you noted. For example, a manager might say, "You were terrific with that patient who called." A more specific comment would be more effective, "You did an excellent job when Mrs. Jones called. By speaking slowly, clearly, and calling her by name, you were able to calm her. I heard you problem solving with her and arranging for her to come in to the office this afternoon. Thank you."

By giving positive, specific feedback immediately after an event, the behavior is reinforced. Discuss the act, not the person. Be specific and state your personal reaction to it. Be totally sincere, because your team have been observing you ever since you became their manager, and they can immediately detect when you're being less than sincere. Another suggestion is to let the team member know that you appreciate that behavior. In the previous case, the team member knows that her manager likes when she uses the patient's name, speaks slowly and clearly with empathy, and problem solves with the patient. The manager concludes the feedback with a "thank you." These actions will align team performance with organizational goals (Exhibit 9.3).

EXHIBIT 9.3	**How to Give Praise**

1. Provide feedback immediately after action has taken place — "educable moment."
2. Provide specific details about what you observed that team member did well.
3. Show how behavior relates to organizational goals.
4. Let employee know that you appreciate effort and good results.
5. Remember not to use "yes, but"; don't assign more work.
6. Praise "approximately right" behavior with learners.

Note: This exhibit is available as an electronic file.*

Catch Team Members Doing Something Right

During the past 25 years, Tom Peters and Ken Blanchard have been encouraging leaders by asking them to MBWA, "manage by walking around" as Peters recommends, and to "catch people doing something right," as Blanchard pleads in *The One Minute Manager*.[49] These actions tie in well to giving positive reinforcement for goal-focused activities in all aspects of your organization.

An interesting study done by Ohio State University Fisher College of Business suggests that, in the absence of feedback, pay becomes more important. "When employees aren't given a lot of feedback about how they are doing, they have to use pay as their measure of worth. This magnifies the importance of salary as a way to feel appreciated and for employees to gauge their importance."[50]

Effects of Negative Reinforcement

Negative reinforcement can lead to defensiveness from team members, and this can eventually lead to a culture of carbon monoxide. Work cultures with carbon monoxide are destructive and filled with defensiveness, blaming, sabotage, paranoia, factions, and can not only hurt morale and productivity, but can actually make team members ill.

When team members receive reprimands, most of them feel defensive. I've asked thousands of people how they feel when they are reprimanded or scolded at work for making mistakes. Ninety-nine percent have confessed to having adverse reactions. They say that, physically, they feel their pulse increase, their face blush, breathing becomes more rapid, and they can feel their blood pressure mount. They stop listening. Additionally, they turn to

---

*Instructions to access the electronic files are available in Appendix A.

self-talk with comments about their boss such as "You think you're so smart," "I can't wait till this day's over," "If you had to put up with what I have to put up with ..." Adrenalin levels increase, leading many of us to want to either fight or flee. At the time when managers are thinking that their team members are listening exclusively to their input, most team members are not. What the manager is saying is not even on the team member's radar screen. If the heart rate exceeds 100 beats per minute, it is very difficult to hear what others are saying no matter how hard we try. Once they become defensive, team members are too physically, mentally, and emotionally distracted to hear what the manager is saying.

HOW CAN LEADERS STOP NEGATIVE BEHAVIOR WITHOUT NEGATIVE REINFORCEMENT?

From my experience, at least 95 percent of non-goal-oriented behavior can be converted to goal-oriented behavior through the use of positive reinforcement. To decrease or stop a behavior, positively reinforce the opposite behavior. As the opposite behavior increases, the initial undesirable behavioral will decrease. If physicians are delinquent in completing patient charts, positively reinforce those who complete charts in a timely manner. If patients are not greeted in a welcoming, professional manner, positively reinforce those who greet patients in a welcoming, professional manner. If new team members are not oriented and accepted by the current healthcare team, positively reinforce those who orient and accept new team members. More serious mistakes may require a more direct remedy, which will be covered later in this chapter (that is, unsafe practices, falsifying records, use of drugs, sexual harassment, insubordination, theft, and lies).

Focus on the Goal, Not the Mistake

When a team member strays from a stated goal, managers often focus on what that person did wrong rather than on what the individual was supposed to do right. For example, if Laurie should start work at 8:00 a.m. but arrives at 8:20, most managers would say, "Laurie, you're 20 minutes late! Go to your desk and don't let it happen again!"

Greeting a team member like this can cause her to become defensive. She might stop listening to you, start justifying her position with a million excuses, or even cite times that you haven't been punctual. It would therefore be more effective to say, "Laurie, I need you to be at your desk by

8:00 a.m. to take incoming calls. You are the only patient representative on duty between 8:00 and 9:00, and our clients have to be able to reach you to make appointments and schedule tests." With such a goal-oriented approach, Laurie will be better able to concentrate on the solution. She will be reminded of why she needs to reach the goal of arriving on time at 8:00 a.m.

This method of focusing on the goal instead of pointing out the mistake can serve to create a goal-oriented culture instead of creating a defensive, blaming culture filled with carbon monoxide. Following are several examples where I'll show a typical non-goal-oriented response and then the preferred positive, goal-oriented response to behavior that is not aligned with organizational goals.

For Minor Mistakes

Example 1: Team member is 10 minutes late and is the only person scheduled to work at the reception desk from 8:00 a.m. to 8:30 a.m.

- ▲ *Non-goal-oriented response* — "You are 10 minutes late. Patients are waiting outside in the hallway, and the phones are ringing off the hook."

- ▲ *Goal-oriented response* — "It's important to be here at 8 o'clock. You are the only one scheduled at that time and customer service is our number one goal."

Which response would encourage the team member to focus on the patients?

Example 2: Team member has written a well-researched memo that will be important for negotiating a complicated contract with a vendor.

- ▲ *Non-goal-oriented response* — "Hi, Henry. I just read your memo. You forgot to put in the contract requirements, and a lot of your points are unclear. I think it had better be redone."

- ▲ *Goal-oriented response* — "Hi, Henry. I just read your memo. Our goal is to justify our position and you've obviously done some good research on this. I think it would be better to reorganize it so your points will be clearer. Also, add in the contract requirements, since that might come up in negotiations. Then everything will be taken care of, and we will present a strong case for our position."

Which manager would inspire Henry and show appreciation of Henry's work?

Example 3: Several complaints have been received about the billing department. The medical group manager calls in the billing supervisor, who has been under extreme pressure for a number of weeks, to discuss the situation.

    ▲ *Non-goal-oriented response* — "I have received several complaints about your operations. Here they are. What are you going to do about them?"

    BILLING SUPERVISOR (angrily): "Are those same stupid patients griping again?"

    (Note: Pointing out the mistake produces a defensive reaction.)

    ▲ *Goal-oriented response* — "We received some feedback about our services that you might be interested in seeing. Let's go over it and see if it gives us some new ideas that will speed our service or improve our efficiency."

Example 4: Recently, Karen, a nurse practitioner in the practice, spent a lot of money for temporary employees through an expensive registry. The medical group manager approaches her while she's charting on her last patient.

    ▲ *Non-goal-oriented response* — "Why do you need so much expensive temporary help? You have already received approval to hire two permanent employees! What's wrong with you?"

Most people, upon hearing this, would justify themselves with excuses by saying: "It's not *my* fault. Jerry, our human resource manager, has been overloaded in processing new people and hasn't even advertised yet."

Compare the preceding response with the following:

    ▲ *Positive goal-oriented response* — "How can we cut down on the number of temporary employees so we can ensure that our patients receive care from our own high-quality team and also meet budget goals?"

Given this opener, most people would immediately start thinking of ways to decrease the temporary help and might come up with some good ideas.

    EMPLOYEE: "Well, Jerry in human resources has been busy, but I think it's about time I went over there and spoke to him myself. Maybe something can be done."

In this last example, the non-goal-oriented manager asked about a mistake, but the positive goal-oriented manager asked about a solution and a goal.

EXHIBIT 9.4 **How to Correct a Minor Mistake Using the Goal Focus Exercise: Practice Dealing with Minor Errors**

1. Do NOT point out the mistake.

INSTEAD

2. Point out the goal and stress the value of accomplishing the goal.
3. If appropriate:
   a. Seek team member's suggestions and opinion.
   b. Indicate your willingness to help.

W.I. Zangwill, *Success with People: Theory Z Approach to Mutual Achievement* (Homewood, IL: Dow Jones-Irwin, 1976). Used with permission.

Examples summary: To decrease most behaviors, one does not need to apply negative feedback but instead should positively reinforce the opposite, the goal that you want to achieve. Stressing the mistake is a negative-feedback approach. The opposite of pointing out that someone is doing the job wrong is behaving in a way that achieves the goal (Exhibit 9.4).

More serious mistakes — unsafe practices, falsifying records, use of drugs, sexual harassment, insubordination, theft, lies — may require a more direct remedy. These issues will be discussed later in this chapter.

WHEN MANAGERS BECOME EMOTIONAL

Yes, managers have feelings too, and sometimes staff members cause managers to become frustrated, concerned, upset, and angry. Leaders worry that sharing their feelings with their team will make them vulnerable, but it's important that you identify these feelings and get them out of the way before switching to problem solving. It is almost magical how you can become less emotional and more rational once you've identified your emotions and then expressed them out loud. By starting a conversation with "I'm disappointed, upset, and frustrated ...," you grab the team member's attention and effect a more incisive discussion.

I've found that once we name the emotion, the emotional response is defused. When you wait until the end of the discussion to mention the emotion, the tone of your voice, facial expression, and body language can appear out of control. It's important that leaders do not appear out of control because some employees lose respect when they see their boss losing

EXERCISE Practice Dealing with Minor Errors

1. You notice that one of your nurses has started leaving the door to the patient exam rooms open so that patients are sitting in their patient gowns without privacy.

2. You overhear one of your staff members on the telephone saying, "You've got to wait until next Thursday, and that's all there is to it! We already have plenty of patients, so if you need to switch to another doctor, go for it."

3. One of the physicians in the practice does not always complete her charting in patients' charts. This can negatively affect your billing and leaves your medical practice more vulnerable to lawsuits because "if you didn't chart it, you didn't do it."

4. You overhear two of your staff members arguing loudly in the break room and everyone hears them, including patients, families, and physicians. One said, "You always take the last of the coffee and never make another pot. I'm sick and tired of your laziness and selfishness." The other one counters, "I do not. And your attitude is the one that needs adjusting!"

Sample Responses

1. "Our goal is for patients to feel comfortable and respected. Please make sure to close the doors to the exam rooms, especially when patients are dressed in skimpy patient gowns."

2. "Our goal is to have 100 percent patient satisfaction. Please ask the patient for his name and phone number, and whether we can call him back within 10 minutes, after we talk about the schedule and options."

3. "Our goal is to be as professional and cost-effective as possible. I'd appreciate it if you'd complete your patient charting every day. This will protect us legally as well as allow us to bill for services immediately. Let's talk about this. Is there something I can do to help?"

4. "Please lower your voices. Our goals are teamwork and 100 percent patient satisfaction and that means a professional, respectful atmosphere. Let's talk about what's going on here."

Other example errors to respond to could involve situations when:

▲ A new physician doesn't take a complete history on a new patient.

▲ The technician who schedules tests doesn't explain to a patient that she needs to fast before her test next Tuesday.

Note: This exercise is available as an electronic file.*

composure. However, when the emotion is stated in advance, the leader can more professionally discuss the behavior and consequences the behavior caused. This technique of identifying the emotion, stating it up front, and then proceeding into a problem-solving discussion is useful in both professional and personal relationships.

---

*Instructions to access the electronic files are available in Appendix A.

It can also be effective to state the harm that the team member's mistake has caused you and the medical practice. In the previous examples in this chapter about how to handle minor mistakes, I recommended that the leader state the goal and not focus on the mistake in order to decrease the team member's defensiveness and keep the team member focused on the goal. In this case, the leader is becoming emotional, and it is the team member's behavior that cannot continue because it is negatively affecting the medical practice.

You might say, "Dana, I'm upset and frustrated. Because of your continued tardiness, we got backlogged with our patients' appointments yesterday, and they're complaining about their long waits. Two of your coworkers worked overtime to make up for your missed time. You need to come in on time and carry your share of the workload."

In the preceding example, the manager stated the emotions he felt at the beginning of his comments. When you can feel that you are becoming emotional over a performance issue with a team member, there are some steps you can take to remain in control of your emotions. First, identify what emotion you are feeling. Are you angry? Frustrated? Upset? Disappointed? (Exhibit 9.5).

Next, determine what the goal is that your team member did not reach and identify the consequences of the behavior. For example, because of not behaving in a goal-focused manner (for example, the team member was tardy), the consequences of her behavior are that patients are complaining and coworkers worked overtime.

Step 5 in Exhibit 9.5 is to end the discussion on a positive note. I believe it's important to *finish every team member discussion in a positive manner* because this is one of the most effective ways to ensure that team members will return to the work setting and be productive again. If they leave meetings feeling angry with you or the medical practice or their coworkers, that anger will adversely affect their interactions with patients, coworkers, and others. The leader's behavior during these discussions will determine whether the team member will be more goal focused or less goal focused.

BEWARE OF THE SANDWICH APPROACH

By the *sandwich approach* to feedback, I mean delivering praise first, then bringing up the goal-focused behavior that you want to see, and then

EXHIBIT 9.5

How Leaders Should Deal with Their Emotional Reactions to a Team Member's Mistake

When a team member's mistake is grave enough that it arouses an emotional reaction in the leader:

1. Act, don't react. Take a deep breath and collect your thoughts.
2. Identify the emotion that you're feeling ... anger, frustration, upset, concern, disappointment ...
3. Identify the goal that was not met and the negative consequences that occurred.
4. Meet with the team member. State your emotion first, then the consequences of the non-goal-focused behavior.
5. End the discussion on a positive note, letting the team member know that you want him or her to be successful and believe he or she can be.

W.I. Zangwill, *Success with People: Theory Z Approach to Mutual Achievement* (Homewood, IL: Dow Jones-Irwin, 1976). Used with permission.

ending on a positive note. The sandwich is good news, then bad news, and then good news again. Some management books recommend this approach as a way to soften the constructive criticism by tossing out a bit of praise first and ending on a positive note. I find that it leads to confusion.

An example of this sandwich approach is as follows: "Good morning, Jack. Your charting is thorough, legible, and easy to read. It's important that you arrive on time and are ready to care for patients so patients have minimal waiting time. It's a pleasure to have you on the team."

Although you might believe this preserves your relationship with your team member, I think it's confusing. Your team member may remember the praise at the beginning and the end, but may also miss the meat in the middle.

Consequently, his feelings may be spared, but he neither hears nor deals with the behavior that is not goal focused — that of not being ready to work when his shift starts. Give the FAST feedback and then end with a statement such as "I believe in you and am happy to be working with you."

Ask Your Team Member to Repeat What You've Said

The truth about communication is that most of us are more interested in what we're saying than in what's being said to us. We're better at talking than listening. Feedback, especially negative, will be better absorbed by team members if you ask the team to tell you what they think they need to do based on your comments about their performance. Having team members put the feedback into their own words will reinforce it. You might ask, "What is it that you've gotten out of this meeting that you can get started on right away?"

Feedback Quiz

Most managers are uncomfortable providing feedback because many of them have never had a good role model. Giving feedback that is goal focused and doesn't put your team on the defensive is important. Take the quiz in Exhibit 9.6 to see if you are feedback-savvy.

MANAGEMENT ERRORS TO AVOID WHEN GIVING FEEDBACK

I've seen managers make key errors when they are providing feedback for their team. Following are four key errors to avoid:

▲ *Perception error.* Some managers assume that the same rewards have identical value for everyone on their team. Raises may not reinforce sustained performance for some employees because they may believe they're entitled to them or believe the reward is too little or too late. Get to know your team well and identify specific experiences that are reinforcers for each person who works for you.

▲ *Contingency error.* Rewards don't seem like incentives if staff members can get a reward regardless of behavior. For example, fringe benefits won't increase performance because they are given across the board. Make direct connections between reinforcers and rewards: "You can get _____ if and only if you do _____."

▲ *Immediacy error.* It's worth mentioning again because it's so important. Provide FAST feedback to reinforce desirable behavior immediately — the longer the delay, the less value your reinforcement has. Spend more time with your team members and reinforce desirable behavior the moment it happens.

▲ *Frequency error.* To create high performers and a goal-focused culture, reinforce positive behavior frequently, not sporadically. Intermittent or infrequent positive feedback that occurs only during annual performance appraisals or during employee-of-the-month ceremonies does not have a meaningful effect on team members' performance.

EXHIBIT 9.6   Feedback Quiz

MY FEEDBACK ...

1. **Is private.** (I choose a place where the person can hear my comments without being distracted or embarrassed.)   _____ True _____ False

2. **Receives the time it deserves.** (I plan the time and use it just for the purpose of giving feedback to someone.)   _____ True _____ False

3. **Is goal focused.** (I always include the goal that we are targeting. "Because we want our patients to have a great experience with us, I want you to always ask them if they have any additional questions before they leave the office.")   _____ True _____ False

4. **Keeps the self-esteem of the person intact.** ("You are a valuable member of this team.")   _____ True _____ False

5. **Is frequent.** (I give feedback often, and give it immediately after actions that need to be changed or rewarded.)   _____ True _____ False

6. **Is specific, with clear examples.** ("I need you to delegate more. You spent all your time on scheduling and we need the supplies to be ordered in a timely manner.")   _____ True _____ False

7. **Focuses more on the future than the past.** (I talk most about what can be done to improve, rather than what went wrong.)   _____ True _____ False

8. **Gives information that helps the person make decisions.** ("Your team wants you to involve them more in planning.")   _____ True _____ False

9. **Gives suggestions for growth and development.** ("I think you could work more on negotiating and conflict management skills, especially if you want that new role.")   _____ True _____ False

10. **Allows for discussion.** ("Tell me what you are thinking. What do you want to do about this?")   _____ True _____ False

11. **Creates next steps.** ("Let's meet again next week to create a coaching plan for you. Please think about what you'd like to include in the plan.")   _____ True _____ False

12. **Gives a team member the opportunity to repeat what he or she has taken from the discussion.** (People remember what they say more than what other people say, so have them use their own words and voice.)   _____ True _____ False

13. **Is consistent.** (I do not play favorites. I give similar amounts of feedback without singling out certain employees.)   _____ True _____ False

How did you do? If most of these statements are true for you, congratulations! Now, go ask your team members if they agree—ask them to tell you the truth.

Adapted from B. Kaye and S. Jordan-Evans, *Love 'Em or Lose 'Em* (San Francisco: Berrett-Koehler, 2005), 188.

EXERCISE   Types of Feedback

Which type of feedback do you use most often? Least often?

Silence — No response is provided.

Impact: Decreases confidence and performance in the long term, creates surprises during performance reviews, can create paranoia.

Criticism — Identifies behaviors or results that are not up to standard.

Impact: Generates excuses and blaming of others, tends to eliminate related behaviors, decreases confidence, leads to escape and avoidance, hurts relationship.

Advice — Identifies behavior or results that are highly regarded.

Impact: Improves confidence, can improve relationship, increases performance.

Positive reinforcement — Identifies behavior or results that are desired.

Impact: Increases confidence, increases performance, increases motivation.

Note: This exercise is available as an electronic file.*

WHEN TO USE POSITIVE AND NEGATIVE REINFORCEMENT

The behavior modification flowchart in Exhibit 9.7 illustrates that when behavior can be tolerated, use positive reinforcement. When it cannot be tolerated, it is appropriate to give negative reinforcement.

When Negative Feedback Is Appropriate

More than 95 percent of the time, you can guide team members back on track toward the goal by stating the goal and the reason for the goal. The other 5 percent of the time, the most effective approach is to give negative feedback to the poor-performing employee. Starting the disciplinary process is never easy, but it may be necessary to keep the medical practice team operating at optimum level. When starting this process, you would be best served to keep your team member's self-esteem in mind as well as the performance goals.

As an example, let's use the case of David in the patient billing department whose job it is to accurately and promptly bill patients, insurance companies, and the government for patient office visits, procedures, and tests. As his manager, you have used positive feedback to emphasize the medical practice goal for accuracy, timeliness, and customer service in dealing with these payers. You can no longer tolerate his errors, rude behavior, or

*Instructions to access the electronic files are available in Appendix A.

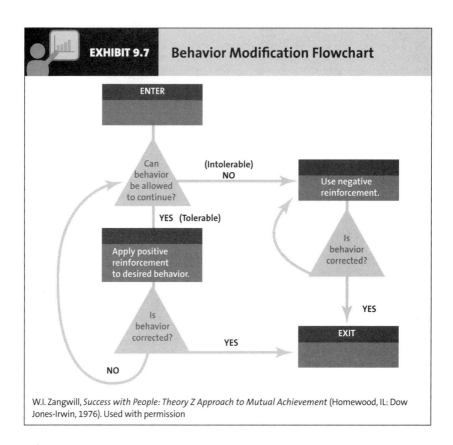

EXHIBIT 9.7   **Behavior Modification Flowchart**

W.I. Zangwill, *Success with People: Theory Z Approach to Mutual Achievement* (Homewood, IL: Dow Jones-Irwin, 1976). Used with permission

computer glitches. As the manager, you are certain that this is not a training issue. Rather, you believe that David could change his behavior, but chooses not to.

Could One Perform If One's Life Depended on It?

One way to determine whether this is a training issue or performance issue is to ask the question: "Could a team member perform his or her job *if his or her life depended on it?*"

Sometimes people simply cannot perform the job. For some physical jobs, they may not be strong enough. For some other positions, they may not have the mental capability to calculate math problems. Or sometimes, in the case of David, they are behaving carelessly and not focused on helping the team, and as a result they are hurting the service level and quality of the practice.

CRITERIA FOR STARTING THE DISCIPLINARY PROCESS

As the manager, you've decided that you can no longer tolerate David's behavior and decide to begin the disciplinary process. To begin the disciplinary process that could lead to termination for a team member such as David, you should be able to document that the team member's performance doesn't meet a reasonable, objective standard and that the individual was given a fair chance to succeed. This means that:

- ▲ The standard of performance is reasonable, measurable, and reachable;
- ▲ There is documentation demonstrating that the team member failed to meet the standard required; and
- ▲ The team member had a fair chance to succeed and received progressive discipline. Typical steps are oral warning, written warning, next-to-last step discipline, and finally termination.

As the employer, you must ensure that you have done everything reasonably possible to help the employee succeed. You must also objectively document the team member's behavior and document the actions you have taken.

Verify That Your Decision Is Solid

Your first step is to verify your decision. You may discuss a team member's poor performance with another manager, your human resource department, or an external consultant. However, never share disciplinary issues with your other team members. These matters are confidential.

Meet with Team Member in Private

After you've verified that your decision to begin the formal disciplinary process is correct, decide exactly what you are going to say. Conduct the discussion with the team member in private. As in the case with David, say that you can no longer tolerate his errors, rude behavior, or computer glitches.

Give him the choice of either changing his performance or accepting punishment, which in this case would be a written warning. Leave the choice up to him. The idea is to avoid taking on the role of executioner yourself but to make the process self-reprimanding. You might say, "I want you to be successful, and I believe you can be, but it's up to you." This will serve to direct his attention toward himself. The problem is his, and he needs to fix it.

EXHIBIT 9.8   Disciplinary Action Steps

1. Verify that discipline is appropriate.
2. State the problem, how it is counter to the goals of the practice, and refer to previous discussions.
3. Ask for any reasons for lack of change in behavior toward goals.
4. Describe disciplinary actions you are taking and the disciplinary process.
5. Outline specific steps to solve the problem.
6. Assure team member of your support.

Note: This exhibit is available as an electronic file.*

If the mistakes continue unabated, your conversation with David might go as follows: "Because of your many intolerable computer and billing errors, you leave me no choice. I am now giving you a written reprimand. A record of this event will be placed in your personnel file. Starting immediately, I want you to produce accurate billings and reports. The next time your patient billings are incomplete or inaccurate, you will receive a suspension. Continued errors can lead to termination. You are a valuable team member here, and I believe you can be accurate. I want you to succeed in this." Then be consistent in following through. (Exhibit 9.8 shows the steps for disciplinary action.)

Move On

After you have given negative feedback to your team member, let it go. Don't continue to emit cues that you're still dissatisfied with the person's performance. Return to business as usual and act as if the team member will work in a stellar fashion from this point on. If you believe that the team member will screw up again, then sure enough, the individual will — it can be a self-fulfilling prophecy.

When Disciplined Team Members Act Out

If the disciplined team member has a hard time letting go of anger, the individual may continue to sulk for a while. Depending on the significance of the negative feedback and the level of acting out, I recommend that you give the team member some time to digest the news.

If, however, the team member's anger is affecting your practice's service level, quality, or productivity, you'll need to chat with the individual in private. Help rebuild the team member's self-esteem by recognizing areas of excellence. You might say,

---

*Instructions to access the electronic files are available in Appendix A.

"David, I want to make sure you heard what I was saying about your performance. You're a valuable asset to us; your work is good in many ways. But I've noticed since our discussion that your body language and tone of voice have changed. It appears to me that you've gotten defensive. I just want to reassure you that you have lots of promise here. Still, I would appreciate it if you could focus back on your work and focus on being the good team member that I know you can be."

TERMINATING A TEAM MEMBER

No manager likes to terminate a team member, but sometimes it's necessary. A poor performer can hurt the overall performance of the practice so that goals are not met. A manager who doesn't consistently hold all team members accountable for high standards will lose the respect of the entire team. There are both legal and psychological implications in terminating a team member.

Four steps should be followed when terminating a team member, which help protect yourself and your organization from possible lawsuits:

1. Make sure you've first discussed with your team member those areas of his or her performance that you consider to be deficient.

2. Ensure that you have followed each of the discussions with a written memo that outlines the specific areas of deficiency discussed, the levels of performance expected, and the time limits you've set with the team member to achieve those expected levels of performance. Send one copy of this memo to the team member and put a second copy in the individual's personnel file. Make sure you've documented the deficiencies clearly enough and that they are sufficiently serious to be considered grounds for termination by an outside examiner.

3. Know your company's termination procedures.

4. Make sure you have the concurrence of your company's human resource department and that you coordinate with this department the preparation of final paychecks and severance arrangements.

Leadership Actions During the Termination Meeting

It's time to let David go. He is continuing to damage the performance of your team. Some of the steps to take are described in the following paragraphs.

Step 1: Explain that you are terminating the team member because deficiency areas you discussed in the past have not been corrected. "David, I'm sorry, but I'm going to terminate you because you haven't met the levels of performance we agreed were necessary to keep your job when we met January 4, February 2, February 20, and March 10." Be firm but fair — the time for counseling has passed. Because you and David jointly set performance goals that he has failed to achieve, plus you have offered your support on many occasions, there is no need to justify your position.

Step 2: Focus on the issues, not the team member's personality. This may be difficult because a team member may express disbelief and shock. Make certain the team member recognizes that your decision to terminate him or her is irrevocable, and that it's impossible for the individual to continue in the job. The best way to achieve this goal is to take full responsibility for the decision. Don't blame it on someone else, or the team member may believe the decision can be reversed.

Inform the team member of the termination date and of your plans for making the transition easy. "David, I'm terminating you as of today. I haven't mentioned this to any of your coworkers."

There are four customary phases that terminated employees often experience over several days after the termination, and knowledge of these phases can help to prepare you to handle the situation.

- ▲ *Phase I — Shock and disbelief.* Even though you've warned them and documented those warnings in writing, some team members cannot believe you're actually terminating them. Symptoms include quiet, withdrawn behavior.

- ▲ *Phase II — Self-pity.* The team member believes he or she has been singled out and treated unfairly. Symptoms include sad expressions and complaints.

- ▲ *Phase III — Hostility.* The team member transfers the blame to you and the organization. The individual may try to get the job back, receive more favorable compensation, or ask for favors.

- ▲ *Phase IV — Acceptance.* As a team member begins to accept the finality of the termination, he or she starts to look toward the task of finding a new job.

Step 3: Describe the termination policy for pay and benefits. A way to minimize a team member's anger and hostility is to carefully describe the separation provisions. This also makes it easier for you to stay firm when the

EXHIBIT 9.9 Steps for Terminating a Team Member

1. Explain that you are terminating the team member because the deficiency areas you discussed in the past have not been corrected.
2. Inform the team member of the termination date and of your plans for making the transition easy.
   Phases: Shock and Disbelief, Self-pity, Hostility, Acceptance
3. Describe the separation provisions.
4. End the termination interview on a positive note by expressing confidence in the team member.

Note: This exhibit is available as an electronic file.*

person tries to obtain additional pay and benefits. "Our policy is to provide one week of separation pay and here's your final paycheck that includes accrued paid time off. I have made arrangements for our human resource representative, Nicole, to discuss your health insurance options."

Step 4: End the termination interview on a positive note by expressing confidence in the team member. A team member who has been terminated usually feels insecure and a bit lost. You're terminating the team member because the individual failed to meet the performance standards of a specific job, not because the individual is a failure as a person. Often, a person who performs poorly in one organization succeeds in another. "David, I believe the root of the problem is that there wasn't a good match between your skills and the requirements of the job. I believe in you and want you to find a job that is a good match for your talents." By expressing confidence in the employee, you can boost the person's lowered self-esteem and advance the individual to phase IV, the acceptance phase, more quickly.

Steps for terminating a team member are listed in Exhibit 9.9.

Acts of Gross Misconduct

Some acts of gross misconduct are so grievous that they may warrant summary dismissal. Some examples of gross misconduct include:

▲ Theft or fraud;

▲ Physical violence or bullying;

▲ Deliberate, serious damage to property;

▲ Serious misuse of the organization's property or name;

*Instructions to access the electronic files are available in Appendix A.

▲ Deliberate accessing of Internet sites containing pornographic, offensive, or obscene material;

▲ Serious insubordination;

▲ Unlawful discrimination or harassment;

▲ Bringing the organization into serious disrepute;

▲ Serious incapability at work brought on by alcohol or illegal drugs;

▲ Negligence causing loss, damage, or injury;

▲ Serious breach of health and safety rules; and

▲ Serious breach of confidence.

PRECALLING STRATEGY FOR PERFORMANCE PROBLEMS

Precalling is another helpful strategy in dealing with chronic performance problems. This entails asking your team member for the consequence he or she wants to undergo the next time he or she errs. For example, Ashley's weekly reports are due on Wednesday afternoons, but she usually doesn't turn them in until late on Thursday. This causes problems for you because you don't have enough time to study them before you must send them up to your boss. You've spoken with Ashley several times, and she assures you that "Next week I'll be better." But this hasn't brought about the necessary adjustment in her behavior.

The next time she turns in a late report you might say, "We've talked about how important it is for me to get this report on Wednesday, but you were late again this week. I'd like you to tell me what consequences you propose for yourself if this happens again next week."

Ashley will probably try to assure you, "I'll get it to you on time. Don't worry."

"That's fine," you might say. "But let's agree now on your consequence if it is late next week."

Ashley might be reluctant, and you may have to push, but don't let her leave without naming some penalty. She might decide that she has to stay late on Wednesday without overtime pay in order to finish it. Or she may agree to take the minutes for the weekly staff meetings (a universally hated task). Then if the report is late the following week, she knows what's going to happen to her because she chose the outcome. You must be consistent in making sure that the consequence is carried out, however, or you'll reinforce Ashley's bad habits.

What happens to the team member who just can't or won't perform? Indeed, it would be unwise to undermine your group's performance by allowing one team member to perform poorly. This hurts the team and makes you appear to be a weak manager. Rather than continuing to send your nonperforming team member to yet another training class, be direct with the individual. Counsel the person, and explore the individual's areas of strength. And if you must, send the team member on his or her way. This demonstrates respect for the individual, your other team members, and the organization.

Exhibit 9.10 is a sample of disciplinary policies and procedures.

COMPONENTS OF GOOD DISCIPLINARY PROCEDURES

Good disciplinary procedures should:
- Be put in writing;
- Say to whom they apply;
- Be nondiscriminatory;
- Allow for matters to be handled without undue delay;
- Allow for information to be kept confidential;
- Inform team members what disciplinary action might be taken;
- Indicate what levels of management have the authority to take disciplinary action;
- Require team members to be informed before any meeting of the complaints against them and supporting evidence;
- Give team members a chance to have their say before management reaches a decision;
- Provide team members with the right to be accompanied;
- Provide that no team member is dismissed for a first breach of discipline, except in cases of gross misconduct;
- Require management to investigate fully before any disciplinary action is taken;
- Ensure that team members are given an explanation for any sanction; and
- Allow team members to appeal a decision.

Exhibit 9.11 is a sample performance counseling memo for discipline.

EXHIBIT 9.10   **Sample Disciplinary Policies and Procedures**

XYZ Medical Practice maintains established Standards of Conduct and Performance and provides for disciplinary action when those standards are not met. Team members are required to conduct themselves in a professional, responsible manner on the job. Team members are expected to extend courtesy and cooperation to patients, visitors, vendors, and coworkers. Team members are required to perform their work in an efficient and professional manner within the times, levels of efficiency, and conditions established by management. Violations of Standards of Conduct and Performance may occur in varying degrees and may result in various forms of discipline, including verbal and written counseling, suspension with or without pay, demotion, or termination. Violations of Standards of Conduct and Performance are considered cumulatively.

VIOLATIONS OF STANDARDS OF CONDUCT AND PERFORMANCE

It is impossible to identify every type of possible misconduct, infraction, or performance problem that can result in discipline. The following is a partial list of actions considered in violation of the Standards of Conduct and Performance:

1. **Unsatisfactory Work Performance**—such as failure to perform work in an efficient, professional, and satisfactory manner; failure to meet established quantity/quality standards; carelessness; idleness: unsafe or unsatisfactory work habits.

2. **Absence Without Authorization**—such as absence without supervisory approval or advance approval when it would have been possible to obtain approval; failure to give notice of absence at the earliest possible time (leaving duty without authorization).

3. **Insubordination**—such as intentional failure to perform assigned work or follow instruction; failure to comply with organization policies, rules, and regulations; use of profanity by a team member toward his or her supervisor.

4. **Failure to Cooperate**—failure to cooperate with others in matters relating to work performance, such as giving false report; failure to submit current, legal registration/license/certificate as required for job; failure to complete annual physical and educational requirements within established time frames; failure to submit current proof of identity/ability to work in the United States in a timely manner; failure to maintain current "contact" information.

5. **Unsatisfactory Attendance**—such as a pattern of absenteeism or an excessive number of unscheduled days of absence; excessive use of sick time (whether or not paid extended sick benefit available); repeated failure to be at work on time. *Excessive* is determined relative to the "incidence of occurrence" for the unit as a whole, not strictly on the number of days or duration of absence.

6. **Breach of Confidence**—such as the release of confidential, proprietary, or harmful information concerning XYZ Medical Practice, its team members, its patients, its products and/or services to unauthorized persons; engaging in an activity that creates a conflict of interest.

(Exhibit continues)

EXHIBIT 9.10 *(continued)* — **Sample Disciplinary Policies and Procedures**

7. **Dishonesty**—such as failure to tell the truth or omission of information in matters pertaining to practice operations or the team member's absence from work; falsification of or omission on XYZ records, reports, or other statistics, including employment applications, time cards, personnel and/or employment records, theft, mishandling or misappropriation of XYZ money, supplies, material, or equipment, or the use of same for personal reasons or gain; unauthorized removal or use of any XYZ property or that of a patient or client, or another team member; engaging in illegal acts on work time or employer premises; violation of any federal, state, or local laws that adversely affect the organization; conviction in any court of law that may cause the individual to be regarded as an unsuitable team member.

8. **Insobriety**—such as having possession of, or reporting to work under the influence of, intoxicating liquors, drugs, or any other mood-altering agents, or otherwise being incapable of working as determined by management.

9. **Immorality**—such as engaging in immoral acts on XYZ premises or during working hours, or where such acts materially damage XYZ's image/reputation in the community or with its clients, prospective clients, patients, or guests.

10. **Engaging in a Criminal Act**—such as admission to or conviction of a felony; possession of unauthorized firearms or other weapons on XYZ property; sabotage; engaging in a conspiracy against XYZ or any of its team members, officers, or directors, or against any legally constituted authority or governing body.

11. **Other Violations**—such as disruptive or disorderly conduct on XYZ property, including fighting or attempting bodily injury, or the use of profane language toward others; interfering with the work of other team members; failure to observe security, traffic, parking, or health and safety regulations and/or practices; causing loss or destruction of materials, supplies, and/or equipment; threatening, intimidating, coercing, or abusing others; making public statements derogatory to XYZ, its management, or its directors.

DISCIPLINARY PROCEDURE

The practice manager, Human Resource Department, or designee must be consulted whenever possible prior to initiating formal disciplinary action. The type of disciplinary action taken depends on all the circumstances of the individual case. Disciplinary actions are based on several factors, including but not limited to the seriousness of the incident(s), review of the employment file, impact to the patient, department, or coworkers; actions are based on these factors and are issued on these factors.

Disciplinary actions include:

1. **VERBAL COUNSELING** is given for initial/minor offenses, such as isolated cases of tardiness. Supervisors and managers are responsible for maintaining a chronological record of verbal counseling.

(Exhibit continues)

EXHIBIT 9.10
(continued)

Sample Disciplinary Policies and Procedures

2. **WRITTEN COUNSELING** is given for more serious or repeated offenses that, if not corrected, will result in further disciplinary action. Depending on all of the circumstances, a second offense of the same or similar type may result in disciplinary actions ranging from a second written counseling up to and including termination.

3. **INVESTIGATORY SUSPENSIONS** with or without pay not to exceed 10 working days may be invoked for review of an occurrence, pending the decision to discipline or not.

4. Where indicated, **DISCIPLINARY SUSPENSIONS WITHOUT PAY** may be invoked for up to five working days, and must have the prior approval of the practice manager, human resource executive, or designee. In the cases of lapsed licensure/certification/registration or inability to provide proof of identity/ability to work, 30-day suspensions may be issued to facilitate team member compliance; failure to comply within proscribed timelines will result in termination of employment.

5. **FINAL WARNINGS** are the most serious form of counseling and, where appropriate, may be given when termination is imminent.

6. Some violations may warrant notifying the appropriate licensing/certification boards or agencies.

Written counseling and final warnings are to specify the nature of the offense, the actions necessary for correction, and the consequences of repeated offenses. Additional forms of disciplinary action requiring the practice manager or human resource authorization may include written warning with suspension, demotion, or probationary periods. A probationary period is a trial period whereby the team member demonstrates his or her ability to perform duties or maintain standards of conduct acceptable to XYZ Medical Practice. A probationary period is of sufficient duration to allow the team member to remove the cause for disciplinary action, but may not exceed 90 calendar days. When appropriate, a team member may be terminated prior to the completion of the probationary period. In all cases, probationary periods are established and documented by a written counseling completed by the department manager and the practice manager or human resource director or designee.

This policy does not in any way impede XYZ Medical Practice's right to discharge a team member without cause and without prior warning.

Note: This exhibit is available as an electronic file.*

*Instructions to access the electronic files are available in Appendix A.

EXHIBIT 9.11 — Performance Counseling Memo for Discipline

Name_____ Position_____ Department_____

This is a
☐ Correction ☐ Warning ☐ Suspension ☐ Discharge

_____ days, ending _____

Subject   ☐ Appearance   ☐ Attitude   ☐ Productivity

☐ Insubordination   ☐ Work Quality   ☐ Unauthorized Absence

☐ Other (Specify) _____

Format to Follow:
1. State the policy violated.
2. State what occurred.
3. State the action being taken.
4. State the disciplinary action to be taken at next violation.

Specify Supporting Details:

_____

_____

_____

Policy:

_____

_____

_____

Team Member Comments:

_____

_____

_____

(My signature below does not imply agreement with this counseling memo; it means only that I have discussed it with my supervisor and have received a copy.)

_____	_____	_____	_____
Team Member's Signature	Date	Supervisor's Signature	Date

_____	_____	_____	_____
Witness	Date	Witness	Date

Check if team member refuses to sign _____.

Copies to: Human Resources, Department, Team Member

Note: This exhibit is available as an electronic file.*

---

*Instructions to access the electronic files are available in Appendix A.

CHAPTER PRESCRIPTIONS

- Constantly keep the goals of your organization in mind as you evaluate the performance of your team members.

- Emphasize focused, FAST feedback that benefits your team members, your management style, and the goals/mission of your practice.

- Ask team members to repeat what you have said. We remember what we say better than what someone else says.

- When giving feedback, if your team member is off target, point out the goal, not the error.

- Remember that positive feedback increases the chance that a team member will repeat the positive behavior — never forget to compliment your team on a job well done. They'll inevitably work harder and want to be a part of a great team that appreciates them. Positive reinforce is a powerful management tool.

- Be specific when praising and/or criticizing team members. How do we know what to continue doing or improving unless we know exactly how those behaviors are expressed?

- If you're a constant criticizer, be prepared to deal with the carbon monoxide effect within your practice. Poisonous attitudes are all-consuming and deadly.

- Ultimately, your team members are a reflection of you. Actively communicate the goals of your practice with your staff and take the appropriate action (negative or positive) to ensure that your mission is carried out.

CHAPTER 10

Running Effective Meetings

"A meeting is an event where minutes are taken and hours are wasted." This popular phrase is often attributed to William Shatner's *Star Trek* character, Captain James T. Kirk. But there's nothing funny about unproductive meetings.

What exactly is a meeting? One of the definitions of *meeting* as noted by *Merriam-Webster's Learner's Dictionary* is "a gathering of people for a particular purpose (such as to talk about business)."[51]

When is a meeting effective? A meeting is effective when it achieves its objectives in a minimum amount of time to the satisfaction of the participants. An unnecessary or poorly run meeting can negatively affect participants because they feel like their time is not valued.

IMPROVE YOUR MEETINGS — IMPROVE YOUR ORGANIZATION'S CULTURE

One of the fastest ways to improve the culture of your organization is to change the way meetings are conducted. The cost of ineffective meetings is so high that when Andy Grove was CEO of Intel, he personally taught every new employee a course about how to run effective meetings. In addition, every conference room at Intel had a poster with four questions:

1. Do you know the purpose of this meeting?
2. Do you have an agenda?
3. Do you know your role?
4. Do you follow the rules of good minutes? (See Exhibit 10.1 for meeting minute guidelines.)

Effective meetings can improve teamwork, communication, morale, self-esteem, commitment, interactions with customers, and productivity. By starting and ending on time, the leaders demonstrate discipline. In addition,

EXHIBIT 10.1   Meeting Minute Guidelines

▲ Meeting minutes are an essential tool in creating group memory and necessary for effective meeting follow-up.

▲ Assign someone to take minutes during the meeting.

▲ Instruct the minute taker to include the following information in the minutes: meeting title, date, facilitator, and attendees.

▲ Good meeting minutes include key issues discussed, decisions made, and the dates and purposes of next meetings (and other details as needed).

▲ Publish meeting minutes **within 24 hours** of the meeting's conclusion and share with meeting participants; organization links, sponsors, stakeholders, customers, and so forth; and anyone else with a need to know.

leaders communicate trust, respect, and support to others by how they share information and listen to participants' questions and ideas. Leaders encourage collaboration and creativity in meetings through creating an atmosphere of openness in problem solving and decision making, as well as taking the time to celebrate and acknowledge success.

My research into behaviors in high-performing teams indicate that these characteristics are essential for high performance and they can be reinforced in organizing and running effective meetings. There is no reason to wait any longer — you can start running more effective meetings today!

WORKERS REPORT 25 PERCENT OF TIME IN MEETINGS IS WASTED

A study asked 400 U.S. workers employed in office environments, "In general, what percentage of the time you spend in meetings is wasted?" The mean answer was 25 percent. In addition, the researchers asked, "Which of the following mistakes do meeting leaders commonly make?"[52] They received the following answers:

▲ Not having a clear purpose or agenda for the meeting — 30 percent;

▲ Not sticking to an agenda — 30 percent;

▲ Not ending on time — 20 percent;

▲ Not starting on time — 15 percent; and

▲ Inviting people who don't need to attend — 14 percent.

My research about effective meetings indicates that several characteristics of ineffective meetings cause participants to "be bothered a lot." These include drifting off the subject, poor preparation, questionable effectiveness, lack of listening, verbosity of participants, length of the meetings, and lack of participation. Most participants in frequent, ineffective meetings admit to bringing other work to meetings and daydreaming, and almost 50 percent admit to dozing off during meetings.

As the leader, it is in your control to change your meetings by having yourself, other meeting leaders, and participants change how they prepare for and what happens during meetings.

CALCULATE THE COST OF A MEETING

You can use the following formula to calculate the cost of a meeting:

Number of Participants × Hourly Salary of Each Participant
× Length of Meeting = Cost of Meeting

For example, the cost of a two-hour in-house meeting for five people whose salaries plus fringe benefits average $100 per hour would be:

5 people × $100 × 2 hours = $1,000

If the meeting is held off-site, costs would include indirect costs (such as travel, room rental charge, refreshments, equipment charge, and planning charge) as well as opportunity costs of how that time, money, and resources could have been spent productively elsewhere.

Ineffective meetings also have hidden costs. One of those hidden costs often incurred is called the *meeting recovery syndrome*. This is the amount of time it takes for people to calm down after an upsetting, ineffective meeting. The amount of time varies. It can be anywhere from one day to one week. Occasionally an organization never recovers from meetings. Many employees can easily recall a meeting that triggered the meeting recovery syndrome in them. This syndrome not only affects the people who attended, but also others in the organization through a ripple effect. This is the meeting-after-the-meeting that occurs in the hallways, restrooms, and break rooms around the organization. Often, attendees of upsetting meetings also take the emotion home with them.

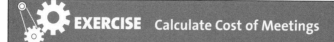

EXERCISE   Calculate Cost of Meetings

During the next seven days, calculate the cost of each meeting you attend and each meeting that you hold.

IS YOUR MEETING NECESSARY?

Meetings in business are necessary to share information, coordinate individual efforts, solve problems and make decisions collectively, garner support for ideas, sell ideas, and celebrate successes. Are all meetings necessary? No! Questions to ask when making the decisions about whether to schedule or attend a meeting include:

- ▲ "Why am I scheduling or attending this meeting?"
- ▲ "What do I want to accomplish or gain?"
- ▲ "What information will be exchanged or decisions made?"
- ▲ "Who will be attending that I need to meet or gain their support?"
- ▲ If you are the one deciding whether to hold the meeting, then ask "Do I need to hold the meeting? What are other ways to meet my objectives without holding a meeting?" (Alternatives to meeting include telephone calls, conference calls, e-mails, and teleconferencing.)

WHAT MEETINGS CAN ACCOMPLISH

Meetings are essential in business, and it's up to *you* to take charge of the meetings in your life in order to make them productive and effective.

Better Decisions Can Be Made

When meetings are effective, better decisions are made because the issues have been clearly delineated and understood by people with different perspectives. And when differences arise in meetings, they can be explored in a professional and productive way.

Broader Buy-In and Consensus

It's important that employees at all levels buy in to the major decisions of their organization. Everyone needs to support decisions, ideas, and

EXHIBIT 10.2   **Decisions by Consensus**

Consensus is a decision process that makes full use of available resources and resolves conflicts creatively. Consensus is sometimes difficult to reach, so not every group decision can be made in this way.

Complete unanimity is not the goal; it is rarely achieved. But each individual should be able to accept the group's decision on the basis of logic and feasibility. When all group members feel this way, a consensus has been reached and the judgment may be entered as the group's decision. Some guidelines to achieve consensus are as follows:

1. *Avoid arguing for your position.* Present your position as lucidly and logically as possible, but listen to the other members' reactions and consider them carefully.

2. *Do not assume that someone must win and someone must lose when discussions reach a stalemate.* Instead, look for the next most-acceptable alternative for all parties.

3. *Do not change your mind simply to avoid conflict.* When agreement seems to come too quickly and easily, be suspicious. Explore the reasons and be sure everyone accepts the solution for basically similar or complementary reasons. Yield only to positions that have objective and logically sound foundations.

4. *Avoid conflict-reducing techniques such as voting, averaging, and bargaining.* When a dissenting member finally agrees, don't feel that he or she must be rewarded by being allowed to win on some later point.

5. *Differences of opinion are natural and expected.* Seek them out and try to involve everyone in the decision process. Disagreements can help the group's decision, because with a wide range of information and opinions, there is a greater chance that the group will create a more adequate solution.

6. *Consider using an exercise that permits everyone to be involved, such as the "thumbs" exercise.* See Exhibit 10.6 for the thumbs exercise.

Tip: Ensure that everyone feels *permitted* to be involved in the process. The silent participants often have the best ideas.

initiatives in order for the decisions to be successfully implemented. The happiest employees are those who feel they have a role in the decisions that affect them. (See Exhibit 10.2 for a process on how to reach consensus.)

Better Understanding of Complex Problems and Issues

Meetings provide a forum for broadening employees' understanding of important organizational challenges by seeking everyone's point of view. Some organizations select someone to play the devil's advocate for meetings in order to broaden their perspectives. Of course, many medical practices already have team members who will present other points of view naturally.

More Thorough Follow Up and Follow Through

If the leader of the meeting makes assignments, the attendees have a better sense of why their individual contributions are important and how they fit into the big picture. In effectively run meetings, participants can learn how to manage conflict more productively, ask meaningful questions, and listen well.

Times When It Is Not Appropriate to Hold a Meeting

It is important for leaders to also recognize when issues are best addressed outside a meeting. Do not call a meeting when:

- The issues are human resource or personnel based (these are confidential);
- You have inadequate data or have not prepared adequately;
- The subject is better dealt with via a telephone call, an e-mail, or a one-to-one meeting;
- The subject matter is confidential;
- A decision has already been made;
- The subject matter is trivial, for example, where the summer picnic is to be held; and
- There is too much anger and/or hostility among the potential attendees.

TYPES OF WORKPLACE MEETINGS

The American Management Association describes seven types of meeting where you may participate on a regular basis in your organization:[53]

1. *Regular staff meetings.* This is the most common and traditional type of workplace meeting. A manager is often the one who plans and organizes this type of meeting.

2. *Project team or group meetings.* The common threads with these team or group meetings are:

   - The life of the team is limited to the length of the project;
   - The group is composed of people from various parts of the organization;

- The leader may not have supervisory authority over the team; and

  - Unique dynamics may have developed (the leader must assess group dynamics quickly to determine how to be productive).

3. *Cross-departmental meetings.* These meetings often have high levels of conflict. Leaders must ensure that conflict does not become destructive.

4. *Problem-solving meetings.* These meetings are called to address issues that have been causing difficulties to many within the organization. An outside facilitator may be needed.

5. *Information-sharing or update meetings.* These meetings are important because they communicate to and ensure that everyone within the organization knows the same key information. Usually people want to know not only the *what* of the change, but also the *why*.

6. *Combination meetings.* These meetings combine the elements of each of the preceding types of meetings. A staff meeting may involve problem solving and information sharing. Leaders must identify transitions to different types of meetings and help participants know how to participate.

7. *Impromptu meetings.* These meetings are usually 15 to 30 minutes long and focused on a single topic. Many medical practice groups hold *huddles* every morning to discuss the schedule for the day and anticipate special issues that may occur.

HOW DO YOU ORGANIZE AN EFFECTIVE MEETING?

When organizing a meeting to ensure that it will be effective, you need to consider a number of factors. These include:

- *Outcomes.* What do you want to accomplish during the meeting? Why are you holding this meeting? These need to be clear before moving to the next step.

- *Type of meeting.* What type of meeting do you want to hold?

- *Location and time.* Where and when do you want to hold the meeting? Ensure that you start on time and end on time.

- *Agenda.* What are the agenda items, how long will each item be discussed, and who is the person responsible for each? Circulate this information ahead of time. Good leaders ensure that the agenda and any supporting materials are accessible and publicized in advance, and that the discussion remains focused. Be prepared to cut off or table an unrelated conversation until a later time. Put these items in the "Parking Lot."

▲ *Meeting behavior.* Plan in advance for potential conflict and solicit help in dealing with it, if needed. Set ground rules for conduct and take them to the meeting. (See Exhibit 10.3 for a list of sample ground rules.)

▲ *Participants.* Who should to attend to achieve the desired outcomes? If not all decision makers are able to attend, do not hold the meeting until they are available (unless they give you their proxies to make decisions on their behalf). Limit attendees to those participants who have a stake in the outcome of the agenda items. Indicating "required" vs. "optional" attendance lets employees know when their participation and input is necessary and helps them prioritize their time. At the beginning of each meeting, welcome and introduce participants.

▲ *Physical arrangements.* What facilities, equipment, and room setups do you need? Who will sit where? Ensure that there are enough seats in the room for everyone. Leave time for setup and to resolve any potential pre-meeting technology challenges.

▲ *Role assignments.* Who will do what task? Assign a scribe, gatekeeper, leader, facilitator, and presenters.

EXHIBIT 10.3   Rules of Conduct for Meetings

▲ Own today's meeting — it is your meeting. Participate. Ensure that others do too.

▲ Keep discreet information confidential.

▲ Be engaged. Ensure that laptops, phones, iPods, etc., are turned off.

▲ Value all opinions and ideas; be respectful.

▲ Listen attentively without interrupting.

▲ No cursing, sarcasm, or personal attacks are tolerated.

▲ Say "I feel" vs. "You." Avoid "always" and "never" statements.

▲ Focus on the future; learn from past.

▲ Be specific with examples.

▲ Honor time commitments.

▲ Avoid sidebar conversations.

▲ Display positive body language.

▲ *Materials.* What are the materials you need (for example, flip chart, microphone, name tags, handouts, and refreshments)?

▲ *Evaluation method.* How will you evaluate the success of the meeting? Meetings are like any other part of business life, you get better only if you commit to it. An outstanding example for meetings management occurs at Charles Schwab & Co., the financial-services company based in San Francisco. In meetings, someone serves as an "observer" and creates what the company calls a *Plus/Delta list*. The list records what went right and what went wrong, and gets included in the minutes.[54] (See Exhibit 10.4 for a sample evaluation form.)

EXHIBIT 10.4   Sample Meeting Evaluation Form

1. Was rapport established with everyone present?
   ☐ No ☐ Yes

2. Were the meeting objectives stated up front?
   ☐ No ☐ Yes

3. Did each person agree with stated objectives of the meeting?
   ☐ No ☐ Yes

4. Did each person participate and state his or her position on
   ☐ No ☐ Yes

5. Were positions discussed, reviewed, challenged appropriately and respectfully so that each participant felt listened to and understood?
   ☐ No ☐ Yes

6. Was the meeting kept on track and on time?
   ☐ No ☐ Yes

7. Was there focus on both the task and the process?
   ☐ No ☐ Yes

8. Were important items summarized during the meeting?
   ☐ No ☐ Yes

9. At the conclusion of the meeting, did the leader summarize the decisions made and state the next steps?
   ☐ No ☐ Yes

10. Overall, I rate this meeting   1   2   3   4   5
                                  Not effective   Extremely effective

11. Comments:
    _____
    _____
    _____

    (Exhibit continues)

EXHIBIT 10.4 *(continued)*   **Sample Meeting Evaluation Form**

	Date: _____
	Start/End Time: _____
	Location: _____
Purpose of meeting:	
Leader:	
Time keeper:	
Scribe:	
Facilitator:	
Attendees and their roles:	
Unable to attend:	

AGENDA			
AGENDA ITEM	WHO	TIME	OUTCOME
1.			
2.			
3.			
4.			
5.			
6.			

ACTION ITEMS	DISCUSSION	ACTION	PERSON RESPONSIBLE	DEADLINE

PARKING LOT
1.
2.
3.

NEXT MEETING WILL BE:

▲ *Plan to finish strong.* Summarize the objectives of the meeting, accomplishments, and next steps. If anyone leaves the meeting wondering what the next steps are, you haven't done your job as meeting host. Allow time for people to ask questions, and determine who has responsibility for each follow-up item.

GROUP DYNAMICS IN MEETINGS

How do you decide the size of the group needed to best accomplish your meeting objectives? When deciding what kind of meeting to hold and what group dynamics you need to accomplish your meeting objectives, it is important to know how the group size affects the participation. You can conduct an information-sharing meeting with a large crowd of people. However, for meetings that include problem solving, decision making, and planning, the number of participants is important. It can be effective to have larger groups and segment the group into smaller groups for participation. See Exhibit 10.5 for a breakdown of number of participants vs. participation.

It is important that participants understand that no matter the size of the group, the most talkative member makes between 40 percent and 50 percent of the comments, and the second most talkative member makes between 25 percent and 30 percent. A strong leader and assertive participants can ensure that your meetings are more participative.

As Woody Allen said, "Eighty percent of success is showing up."[55] I say that when it comes to running effective meetings, "Eighty percent of success in meetings is showing up *prepared*!"

EXHIBIT 10.5 — Number of Participants vs. Participation Level

Number of Participants	Participation Level
3–6	Everyone speaks.
7–10	Almost everyone speaks. Quieter people say less. One or two may not speak at all.
11–18	Five or six people speak a lot; three or four others join in occasionally.
19–30	Three or four people dominate.
30+	Little individual participation is possible.

LEADER OR PARTICIPANTS CAN CAUSE MEETINGS TO FAIL

Meetings can fail because of the actions of leaders and/or participants. For leaders, the actions leading to meeting failure may include lack of agenda and purpose, a hidden agenda or rubber stamping of the plan, lack of direction, too much talk by the leader or not listening, no handouts, or no discussion of future plans.

The reasons that meetings may fail because of participants include poor performance, speech making, rambling, dominating, being silent or withdrawn, being argumentative, power-seeking, or inattentive listening.

During the meeting, the leader should be prepared to help the group:

- ▲ Maintain rapport;
- ▲ Find agreement on outcomes;
- ▲ Identify issues and discuss options;
- ▲ Evaluate the task vs. the process;
- ▲ Stay on track by managing competing conversations, rambling, and dominating participants;
- ▲ Summarize outcomes;
- ▲ Summarize agreements;
- ▲ Determine the next steps, who will do what by when;
- ▲ Thank the group; and
- ▲ Evaluate the meeting.

HINTS FOR LEADING EFFECTIVE MEETINGS

The following pointers can help you lead effective meetings, which in turn can improve your organization's culture — today:

- ▲ Ensure that participants know the outcomes.
- ▲ Create a comfortable environment.
- ▲ Ask open-ended questions.
- ▲ Redirect back to the group. (For example, rather than answering all the questions yourself, ask questions of the group, such as "What do you think about this?" "What concerns do you have?" or "What additional questions do you have?")
- ▲ Call on people by name.

▲ Use appropriate silence. Bear in mind the 17-second rule; that is, within 17 seconds of asking a question, someone in the group will respond. Be patient with silence!

▲ Use humor.

▲ Be flexible.

▲ Make decisions using the Rule of Thumbs shown in Exhibit 10.6.

 EXHIBIT 10.6 Decision Making Using Thumbs

When making decisions in a group, it can be difficult for everyone to voice their opinions. In meetings, there are often team members who are more talkative and others who are more reticent to speak. By voting using thumbs, all participants have an equal chance of being recognized.

The three positions of the thumbs for voting:
1. Thumbs up — Agree with the idea.
2. Thumbs down — Disagree with the idea.
3. Thumbs sideways — Willing to go along with the idea.

The goal of this process is have every participant's thumb be either pointing up or pointing sideways. Follow these six steps for voting with thumbs:

1. **Leader clearly and succinctly states the proposal.** For example, "The company picnic will be held July 1 at 4:00 p.m. at Lakeside Park. We will have it catered by the Gourmet Catering Company. Let's have a show of thumbs."

2. **The participants show their thumbs** —either thumbs up, thumbs down, or thumbs sideways.

3. **To those whose thumbs are pointing down, the leader asks, "What would it take for us to move your thumb position from thumbs down to thumbs sideways?" A response is made.** In this case, the response could be, "We've just had to reduce our staff because of budgeting constraints, so I'm not comfortable having the Gourmet Catering Company provide expensive food for our picnic. I think the picnic is a good idea, and I would move my thumb to the sideways position if we had a potluck picnic where we all brought our food to share. We could create a menu and have some of us bring appetizers, salads, entrees, desserts, and beverages. Then we could still have the picnic, bring our families, and demonstrate that we are being cost conscious."

4. **The leader then asks the team, "Shall we discuss this idea and then vote again?"**

5. **After discussion, the leader rephrases the proposal:** "The company picnic will be held July 1 at 4:00 p.m. at Lakeside Park. We will have a potluck picnic where we will all bring dishes and beverages."

6. **A new vote is taken. If thumbs are either pointing up or sideways, then the proposal is accepted.**

Tip: If everyone's thumbs are pointing sideways (instead of up), it is probably not a very good idea and it will only be half-heartedly implemented. Keep brainstorming!

HANDLING DIFFICULT MEETING SITUATIONS

Because meetings depend on personal interaction, it is inevitable that problem situations will occur. It is the leader's responsibility to ensure that meetings are productive and that the focus is kept on discussing the meeting objectives. There are three main types of participants who can make a meeting ineffective: side conversationalists, ramblers, and dominators.

Controlling the Competing Conversationalist

Side conversations are inevitable in a typical meeting and can be problematic if prolonged. As a leader, your primary objective is to stop the disruption and draw participants back into the meeting without causing embarrassment or discouraging future input. Some ways to handle competing conversations are to:

- Pause and look directly at conversers;
- Ask conversers to share their ideas with the group; or
- Restate the importance of the objectives and state that the group will accomplish more if one person speaks at a time.

Pitfalls to avoid in stopping competing conversations are to:

- Object to every slight whisper; or
- Scold or embarrass anyone in your attempt to stop the distraction.

Controlling the Rambling Participant

In almost every meeting, there is a participant who seems to take a long time to get to the point he or she is trying to make. The individual may go on tangents or fill in extra examples to illustrate his or her point of view. This can behavior can make your meeting run overtime as well as cause some participants to lose interest. Some ways to handle the rambling participant are to:

- Find a natural break or pause and intervene;
- Confirm your understanding of the point of the individual's story;
- If appropriate, state the urgency of the objectives and time constraints; or
- Direct a question to another participant or the entire group and refocus on the meeting objectives.

Pitfalls to avoid in controlling the rambler are to:

- ▲ Avoid sarcastic comments or rude cut-offs; or
- ▲ Listen carefully for the useful idea that might be contained in the rambler's story.

Controlling the Dominating Participant

A talkative person must not be permitted to dominate the discussion. Sometimes a person may assume a dominant role because of more seniority or more experience than other participants. Some ways to handle the dominating participant are to:

- ▲ Credit the speaker's knowledge of the subject and constructive contribution;
- ▲ State the need for opinions from other participants;
- ▲ Ask the group or an individual for views and reactions;
- ▲ Shut down personal attacks; and
- ▲ Include a flip chart, summarize the dominating participant's point, and refer to it as needed.

Some pitfalls to avoid in controlling the dominator are to:

- ▲ Avoid personal put-downs;
- ▲ Not to take sides in personal attacks; or
- ▲ Make it understood that you will not permit a one-sided discussion by stating firmly and clearly the need for others' opinions.

EFFECTIVE MEETINGS CAN MAKE OR BREAK AN ORGANIZATION

As a leader, it is your responsibility to ensure that meetings are effective. Without effective meetings, not only does work not get done or goals achieved, staff become demoralized and unproductive. You lead by example. If your meetings are respectful productive encounters, you and your staff will exceed personal and professional expectations.

CHAPTER PRESCRIPTIONS

- Consider posting in every conference room the four questions Intel displays:
    1. Do you know the purpose of this meeting?
    2. Do you have an agenda?
    3. Do you know your role?
    4. Do you follow the rules of good minutes?"
- How many meetings do you attend each month? Calculate the cost of your time spent in meetings? How much do your team meetings cost every month?
- Create an agenda for every meeting you lead. Circulate the agenda ahead of time for feedback and in order to prepare all participants for the meeting.
- At the end of each meeting, have attendees complete a meeting critique assessment. Determine ways you can make every meeting more meaningful.
- Reflect on the meeting participants who usually attend your meetings. Are some participants challenging, for example, rambling, dominating, and competing conversationalists? Use the techniques recommended in this chapter to get your meeting back on course to be effective and productive.
- Improve your medical practice culture today by improving your meetings!

CHAPTER 11

Creating a Coaching Culture

Did you ever hear the story about the boiling frogs? When researchers placed frogs in a boiling pot of water, the frogs immediately jumped out. When they placed frogs in lukewarm water and turned up the heat slowly, the frogs continued to sit in the water. From the frogs' perspectives, nothing really changed in their environment. Given enough time, the frogs boiled to death as the heat continued to rise, and the researchers had frog legs for dinner.

Dysfunctional organizational cultures can have a lethal effect on quality of care, team performance, and patient satisfaction. Like the boiling frogs, team members who have been in a negative environment for a while may not even realize the impact of their sour workplace culture. The stress of such a culture can cause the team to be sick and unproductive, and can cause customers to leave. New team members will turn over quickly, just like the frogs placed in a boiling pot of water.

Whether considering the culture of different countries, families, or medical practices, experts define culture as having 10 dimensions.[56] These are:

1. Sense of self and space;
2. Communication and language;
3. Dress and appearance;
4. Food and eating habits;
5. Time and time consciousness;
6. Relationships;
7. Values and norms;
8. Beliefs and attitudes;
9. Mental processes and learning; and
10. Work habits and practices.

What exactly is organizational culture? It's frequently defined as an organization's beliefs, knowledge, attitudes, and customs. It's the heart and soul of an organization that shapes how its people behave. Culture may result, in part, from senior managers' beliefs, but it also results from staff members' beliefs. It can be supportive or unsupportive, and positive or negative. It can affect a team member's ability or willingness to adapt or perform well. Some describe it as *the way we do things around here.*

CAN YOU CHANGE THE CULTURE OF YOUR ORGANIZATION?

Changing your organization's culture is not impossible, as many would believe. You just have to carefully evaluate and adjust the factors that influence culture, such as your systems (reward, information technology), structure (reporting, physical), policies, human resource practices (selection, training), communication, leadership style, and so forth. As Tom Peters says, "Culture change, that elusive goal, can be achieved one project at a time."[57]

A CULTURE CHECK PROCEDURE

At the hospital of the future that is discussed in Chapter 1, we developed a value-centered culture and created a formal system for conducting a culture check.[58] Every month, we selected two culture checkers from the facility who assessed the environment by visiting every unit, interviewing team members, and reporting their findings and recommendations to the senior management team. The first agenda item for every meeting throughout the facility, including medical staff meetings, was the culture check. The culture check was a procedure in our policy and procedure book that asked questions such as those listed in Exhibit 11.1.

Strong, trustworthy leadership is the key to creating a high-performing, goal-focused, coaching culture. The culture stems from the strategy, and the leaders drive the strategy. Every action the leaders take affects the culture. For example, every promotion of team members to new positions symbolizes what performance behaviors the leaders of the organization value. Every time a team member is terminated for cause, a strong message is sent by management about the behaviors they will not tolerate.

Gallup research has shown that engaged employees are more productive, profitable, safer, create stronger customer relationships, and stay longer with their company than less engaged employees. One Gallup poll found a disturbing lack of engagement among employees that is creating "cultures of disengagement."[59] Only about 33 percent of employees are actively

EXHIBIT 11.1   Culture Check Procedure

This is the way that we measure how things are or are not working within our environment. We ask, "How is it going?" and we mean "How is it going with regard to such things as:

▲ Are we preserving and protecting the service culture?

▲ Are we treating people well? This means patients, families, physicians, and each other.

▲ Are we cultivating the values, beliefs, philosophies, and concepts that are desired in our culture?

▲ Are we looking at ways to grow financially?

▲ Are we stimulating the expression of new ideas and looking for solutions to problems?

▲ Are we motivating team members to high levels of service, creativity, and performance and then rewarding these team members for their efforts?

▲ Are we working as a team?

OUR CULTURE IS THE ENVIRONMENT WE ARE CREATING TO PROMOTE:
SERVICE EXCELLENCE.

Note: This exhibit is available as an electronic file.*

engaged whereas 15 percent consider themselves *actively disengaged*. Gallup estimates the cost of their disengagement at $328 billion per year. Another key point for leaders to understand is that the more engaged the leader is, the higher the level of engagement among the employees.

WHAT DO MOST TALENTED TEAM MEMBERS NEED FROM THEIR WORKPLACE?

At a time when so many employees are disengaged, it's crucial that leaders explore ways to create a culture of engagement. Fortunately, there was an excellent research study from the Gallup organization that examined two questions: (1) What do the most talented employees need from their workplace? (2) How do the world's greatest managers find, focus, and keep talented employees?

Researchers Marcus Buckingham and Curt Coffman of Gallup captured answers to these two questions from interviews with 80,000 managers in 400 companies in their best-selling book, *First, Break All the Rules*. Buckingham and Coffman established 12 questions that can measure the core elements needed to attract, focus, and keep the most talented

---

*Instructions to access the electronic files are available in Appendix A.

employees. These 12 questions are the simplest and most accurate way to measure the strength of a workplace:[60]

1. Do I know what is expected of me at work?
2. Do I have the materials and equipment I need to do my work right?
3. At work, do I have the opportunity to do what I do best every day?
4. In the last seven days, have I received recognition or praise for doing good work?
5. Does my supervisor, or someone at work, seem to care about me as a person?
6. Is there someone at work who encourages my development?
7. At work, do my opinions seem to count?
8. Does the mission/purpose of my company make me feel that my job is important?
9. Are my coworkers committed to doing good quality work?
10. Do I have a best friend at work?
11. In the last six months, has someone at work talked to me about my progress?
12. This last year, have I had opportunities at work to learn and grow?

The questions clearly show that the front-line manager is the key to attracting and retaining talented employees. The immediate supervisor of employees affects — either positively or negatively — the employees' responses to these questions. No matter how generous its pay or how renowned its training, the organization that lacks great front-line leaders will suffer.

This cutting-edge research found that the manager's core role consists of four key activities:[61]

1. Selecting an employee for talent rather than skills or experience;
2. Setting expectations for the individual that define the right outcomes rather than the right steps;
3. Motivating people by building on unique strengths rather than fixing weaknesses; and
4. Developing people by finding the right fit for the individual — not the next rung on the ladder.

Buckingham and Coffman document the link between employee opinions and an organization's productivity, profit, customer satisfaction, and rate of employee turnover.

COACHING SKILLS ARE CRUCIAL FOR MANAGERS

These 12 questions from *First, Break All the Rules* demonstrate the critical nature of coaching skills for the front-line manager. Corroborating research by the Center for Creative Leadership® (CCL) found that 85 percent of the 4,500 participants thought that a coach or mentor was useful for their development. When asked, "Who would you prefer to have as a coach/mentor?" people of all generations responded that they want to find in their leaders the ability to coach and mentor.[62]

Additionally in the CCL study, there was agreement across all generations that learning on the job was important and that what people want to learn is the same:

- ▲ Leadership;
- ▲ Skills training;
- ▲ Team building;
- ▲ Problem solving; and
- ▲ Decision making.

What is coaching? Coaching is the key to developing people and is an essential leadership skill. It is the relationship between two people in which one person finds ways to enable and empower the other person to perform at increasingly higher levels or in a different role. Coaching is a complex process. The best coaching helps people determine why something should be done, what is to be done, how to do it correctly, when to do it, where to do it, and how much it should be done.[63]

IDENTICAL CHARACTERISTICS FOR TEACHERS AND MANAGERS

From my experience, I've found that when I've asked team members to describe the characteristics of their favorite teacher and then to compare those characteristics with those of their favorite manager, the lists are identical. Today, team members want their managers to believe in them, encourage them, trust them, listen to them, teach them skills, and give them attention and respect. We want our managers to behave as our favorite teachers behaved.

In the past, we accepted managers who were directing, telling, competing, and dictating, and who focused mainly on the financial bottom line. Today, team members expect their managers to guide, empower, listen, consult, trust, and focus on the team members (as well as the bottom line). Talented team members will no longer put up with old-school managers. This is especially true of Generation Xers and Millennials — they want to feel respected and to be coached in order to learn new skills as soon as possible.

Effective coaches challenge team members and don't accept the status quo. They delegate true responsibility along with authority to make things happen. They are confident enough in themselves and their own judgment that they know when to let go.

Why Do Some Managers Avoid Coaching?

There are a myriad of excuses that managers give for not coaching, such as:

- ▲ "I don't have time."
- ▲ "His performance is 'almost' acceptable."
- ▲ "Coaching feels awkward and I might fail — nobody ever coached me!"
- ▲ "I have too many employees."
- ▲ "That employee is motivated and doesn't need feedback."
- ▲ "My employees get defensive."
- ▲ "My standards are obvious — my employees should know what to do."

Additionally, many managers mistakenly believe that it's not important to coach their "star" team members. Try this exercise from Buckingham and Coffman:[64]

> On the left-hand side of a blank sheet of paper, write down the names of the people who report to you in descending order of productivity, with the most productive at the top and the least productive at the bottom. On the right-hand side, write down the same names, but this time record the names in descending order according to the "time you spend with them" — the most time at the top and the least time at the bottom. Now draw straight lines joining the names on the left with the appropriate names on the right.

Do your lines cross? They often do. Many managers find themselves spending the most time with their least productive people and the least time with those who are most productive. Investing in your least productive team members appears shrewd, yet the most effective managers do the opposite. When they join the names, their lines are horizontal. They spend the most time with their most productive team members. These managers reported that "investing in their best was, first, the fairest thing to do; second, the best way to learn; and, third, the only way to stay focused on excellence."[65]

Managers who operate with the erroneous philosophy of "no news is good news" are actually destroying the very behaviors you want to multiply for long-term excellence.

Employees join a company and leave a manager. When managers don't encourage the growth and development of their team, the talented members will leave that manager and find one who will encourage their growth and development.

WHAT ARE BENEFITS OF EFFECTIVE COACHING FOR MANAGERS?

Why should you hone your coaching skills? Coaching sets high standards of excellence and increases the likelihood of tasks being completed with high quality. Coaching holds team members accountable, builds trust and open communication, and increases productivity because team members know what the goals are and how to achieve them. It ensures positive recognition and regular feedback about performance — increasing the team's motivation and initiative.

A coaching culture develops team members and can make the manager's job easier as the team builds their skill levels and takes ownership in the success of the organization as goals are accomplished.

TO COACH OR NOT TO COACH: IS IT NECESSARY?

You may be wondering whether you really need to learn how to coach — in my view, you have no choice. Most people are managers, leaders, or associates of someone. Even if you have no responsibility for the work of others, I believe that you still need to be able to coach so you can help your team, whether it's by rapidly transferring your skills to others or motivating and supporting others on your team to reach new performance levels.

What's the Difference Between Coaching and Mentoring?

Today's successful leaders perform many roles simultaneously. They are leaders, managers, coaches, and mentors. Each of these roles is important for aligning the performance of their team with organizational goals.

Coaching describes a process that provides insight and perspective in aligning an individual's goals with those of the organization and involves a short to intermediate time frame. The coach focuses on job-related learning and development for the current or future job.

Mentoring describes a more long-term process that focuses on the protégé's career growth and personal advancement. Mentors deal with all life structures — family, career, and current work role. Mentoring is the focus of Chapter 12.

Trust Is Imperative in Coaching and Mentoring Relationships

Trust is the building block on which all relationships develop. The dictionary defines *trust* as "an assured reliance on some person or thing," "a confident anticipation in a person or thing," and "hope in the future."

Why is trust so important to the success of the coaching relationship? In all work environments, many people have been bruised from past encounters with their leaders and their associates. As a result of these shattered relationships, many people are reluctant to open up and discuss issues relating to work and the jobs they have to do. We humans avoid taking any risks if the environment isn't safe. In an unsafe environment, your team members won't be open to trying new and innovative ideas or to learning new things and problem solving. As a coach, leaders play a critical role in supporting and encouraging trust in the workplace. Without trust, it's virtually impossible to align team performance with organizational goals.

When employees perceive their manager to have high credibility, they are more likely to:

- ▲ Be proud to tell others they're part of the organization;
- ▲ Feel a strong sense of team spirit;
- ▲ See their own personal values as consistent with those of the organization;
- ▲ Feel attached and committed to the organization; and
- ▲ Have a sense of ownership.

When employees perceive their managers to have low credibility, they are more likely to:[66]

▲ Produce only if they're watched carefully;

▲ Be motivated primarily by money;

▲ Say good things about the organization publicly but criticize it privately;

▲ Consider looking for another job in tough times; and

▲ Feel unsupported and unappreciated.

As a leader and coach, you can enhance the development of trust employees perceive in you when you:[67]

▲ Do what you say you're going to do;

▲ Tell the truth and demonstrate integrity;

▲ Reinforce people when they offer ideas or opinions;

▲ Disclose your personal feelings;

▲ Listen to others;

▲ Prepare adequately;

▲ Allow people to make mistakes and learn from them; and

▲ Exhibit competence.

Studies of effective leaders show that integrity and competence are the most important leadership qualities that inspire teams into high performance. Associates need to believe you are competent in those areas when you demand trust. Team members quickly become disengaged when they perceive their managers are not competent in their roles and that they cannot be trusted. Refer to Chapter 6 for more information about developing trust as a leader.

THE COACHING CONTINUUM

The coaching process is a dynamic process that is never linear; coaches may be in several steps simultaneously. Many leaders develop coaching plans for their team members, and many leaders provide external coaches for their team. I've been serving as an external coach for clients for more than 15 years. The coaching process is the same process whether performing external or internal coaching.

I use a seven-step coaching process that includes the following components:

1. Set specific, measurable, achievable, results-oriented, and time-bound (SMART) goals and milestones.
2. Develop a coaching plan.
3. Train to build professional and interpersonal skills.
4. Build a two-way relationship based on trust.
5. Motivate.
6. Monitor performance at benchmarks.
7. Provide corrective feedback.

Step 1: Set SMART Goals and Milestones

The first step in the coaching continuum is to set SMART goals, and ensure that they are aligned with organizational goals. Although this is the most important step, it's often the most poorly done. (See Chapters 2 and 4 for more information about SMART goals.) What exactly does the protégé need to learn and by when? How does achieving these goals fit into the big picture of the organization's vision, mission, values, and goals? The coaching goals must be objective, measurable, provide clear direction, *and must be talked about all the time.*

After the goals are set, determine the milestones so both the coach and team member can measure progress toward achieving them. Another benefit of creating milestones is that it helps employees pace their energy and establish priorities. Coaches can help employees by asking the question, "What is the best use of this team member's time?"

A goals checklist for coaches and protégés to consider includes the following questions:

- ▲ What goals would the team member say have been agreed to?
- ▲ Are these the same goals that the coach would have identified?
- ▲ When was the last time the coach and team member talked about these goals? Is there a schedule for follow-up — daily, weekly, monthly?
- ▲ What systems are in place to measure progress toward achieving these goals?
- ▲ What performance factors are being used to measure progress?
- ▲ Do the coach and team member know how the coaching goals fit into the big picture of the organization's vision, mission, values, and goals?

Step 2: Develop a Coaching Plan

After the SMART goals have been developed, the next step is to jointly create the coaching plan with specific actions and outcomes. The coaching plans should include SMART goals, competencies, action steps, success measurements, resources needed, and a timeline. Please see a sample of a coaching plan format in Exhibit 11.2.

Step 3: Train to Build Professional and Interpersonal Skills

In the workplace, just as in sports, it's important that team members work to enhance their individual skills as well as strengthen their abilities to work together as a high-performing team.

There are two types of skills on the job: technical skills and people skills. Technical skills include how to operate equipment, computer programs, and telecommunication systems. The people skills are the interpersonal skills and customer service skills that include communication, conflict management, negotiation, and assertiveness.

Together, the coach and team member create a training plan that works well for the trainee. Training can include online training, seminars, shadowing, modeling, instructing, and reading assignments. You may choose veterans who are on your team to work side by side with your trainee.

When training your whole team, consider using the first 30 minutes of staff meetings for instruction. When training is conducted toward the end of the meeting, it may appear that the training is secondary to other agenda items, and the energy level may be lower.

Contrary to the popular belief that younger people want to learn everything on the computer, recent research indicates that all generations prefer face-to-face interactions, including peer and manager interaction and feedback. A high percentage of survey respondents said that coaching was a very suitable method for learning soft skills (such as conflict management, negotiation, and influencing). Even technical skills were viewed as best learned through methods other than computers.[68]

When a coach is instructing and teaching, there are four steps to follow:

1. Tell the protégé what the task is, how it fits into the broader context of the team and organization, how it's done, when it's done, and how well it's to be done. Don't ask "Do you understand?" Instead ask the individual to explain the process he or she will follow to accomplish the task.

| **EXHIBIT 11.2** | **Sample Coaching Plan** |

Name: _____   Coach: _____

STRENGTHS: Feedback from others, instruments, performance appraisals, self-perception.

_____

_____

GOALS/PERFORMANCE OUTCOMES	COMPETENCIES *Which competencies will give you the greatest leverage for success?*	ACTION STEPS *What do you need to do to accomplish your business goals?* *Multiple steps:* *• Formal learning/books/tapes* *• On-the-job training* *• Learning from others*
1. Development Goal		
2. Development Goal		
3. Development Goal		

(Exhibit continues)

---

2. Show how to perform the skills and explain the relevance of each task.

3. Have the protégé perform the task and have him or her explain each step.

4. Correct performance by providing feedback so that the individual can correct mistakes and reinforce accomplishments, which leads to building competence and self-esteem.

Step 4: Build a Two-Way Relationship Based on Trust

Coaching is a relationship between people — the coaches and the learners. The relationship between individuals is the essential component of coaching. Successful coaching is based on mutual trust, acceptance, and respect.

EXHIBIT 11.2
(continued)

Sample Coaching Plan

Manager:_____ Date:_____ Title:_____

AREAS FOR DEVELOPMENT: Self-perception, career goals, professional growth, feedback from others.

_____

_____

SUCCESS MEASUREMENTS	SUPPORT/RESOURCES	TIME LINES
How will you measure success? Include a variety of sources.	*Who will help? What do you need?*	*Identify target dates.*

Note: This exhibit is available as an electronic file.*

To build trust, the coach and protégé need to spend time together — trust takes time to build. People need to experience trust at the personal level so that they can openly discuss all aspects of the organization without fear of reprisal, especially those aspects that mitigate their individual performance or performance of the team. Effective coaches allow the protégé to feel comfortable about expressing feelings about his or her work experience.

A part of building the relationship is to hold regular coaching sessions where you can continue to build trust and respect for one another. The learner may not always like the feedback and discussions, but one of the goals is to keep respect for one another intact. Although sometimes coaching can be done by phone, the more time you can spend together, the faster the relationship will develop.

---

*Instructions to access the electronic files are available in Appendix A.

When I'm doing coaching with clients, I usually start with a four-hour face-to-face session to build rapport, trust, and respect early on. Now, with videoconferencing, phone coaching can work more effectively because more than the auditory system is involved. Trust can be built more quickly.

Step 5: Motivate

Coaches must understand what motivates others. So, how do we motivate others? Today there are at least 12 substantial motivational theories that experts espouse. Much time and effort has been expended attempting to find out "what turns people on," only to discover that there is no one thing, no motivational common denominator. The things that turn on an individual are his or her needs, desires, and expectations — not necessarily management's.

In the coaching process, I believe it's important to clarify what is driving the learner to attain the goal. It could be to develop promotional opportunities for him- or herself, to increase salary or bonus, to expand his or her skill level for the position currently held, or to develop leadership skills.

Can a coaching culture motivate people to stay with an organization? I believe so. When 18,000 people were asked why they stayed in an organization "for a while," there were only minor differences among functions, levels, genders, and ages. Following are the top 13 responses listed in order of frequency of response:[69]

1. Exciting, challenging, or meaningful work.
2. Supportive management or good boss.
3. Being recognized, valued, and respected.
4. Career growth, learning, and development.
5. Flexible work environment.
6. Fair pay.
7. Job location.
8. Job security and stability.
9. Pride in the organization, its mission, or product.
10. Working with great coworkers or clients.
11. Fun, enjoyable work environment.
12. Good benefits.
13. Loyalty and commitment to coworkers or boss.

What makes rewards effective as a motivation tool in coaching? Rewards are more effective when they are awarded close in time to the achievement. If you have to wait a year for your award, it can cut down your enthusiasm. Plus, reward systems are more effective when the coach is specific about the behavior that is being awarded and offers the reward sincerely.

How a coach communicates with his or her protégé can profoundly affect motivation and growth. Communication conveys how much you respect and care about others, and your level of compassion and concern. Words have the power to enhance or destroy self-esteem and confidence.

The coach's words should encourage and challenge. Your words should:

- *Enhance,* not destroy, your protégé's self-esteem, by using empathy and understanding with them.
- *Enable* you to deepen your connectedness with your protégé by acknowledging and recognizing him or her as a valuable person.
- *Empower* your protégé to be more competent and self-directed by helping him or her see the problems, create new options, and experiment with new behaviors.[70]

Step 6: Monitor Performance at Benchmarks

As a coach, it's important to monitor the performance of your protégé as an individual and as part of the team. There are several ways to do this:

- *Direct observation.* Watch your protégé as that individual develops his or her skill. As I monitor the people whom I coach, I frequently shadow them as they are performing. Additionally, I may audiotape them during phone conversations, during meetings, and during coaching sessions when they are working with their direct reports.
- *Third-party input.* Third-party input can be very important during the coaching process. Getting 360-degree feedback from peers, leaders, and others within the organization can be very helpful in monitoring progress.
- *Self-reporting.* Self-reporting by the learner can be very effective for growth and development. Asking Socratic-type questions can be helpful in self-discovery. I often ask my coaching clients to review how they believe they've performed. For example, if a client is developing skills in leading meetings, I'll ask questions such as "How do you believe the meeting went? What went better in this meeting than in your other meetings? What did the participants get out of the meeting? What went well? What could have gone better? What will you do differently next time?"

Step 7: Provide Corrective Feedback

The goal of feedback in the coaching process is to create an environment in which the coach and protégé can discuss openly and supportively how to increase the chances for success. During the coaching process, it's important to give feedback that is both positive — what the learner is doing right — as well as constructive as to what the learner is doing wrong. The challenge is to provide feedback that is both relevant and useful for enhancing learning and performance.

Some guidelines for providing corrective feedback during coaching are:

- ▲ Give FAST feedback — feedback that is frequent, accurate, specific, and timely.
- ▲ Give feedback immediately, as closely as possible to the event. This is called the *educable moment.*
- ▲ Have the learner point out what he or she is doing well.
- ▲ Provide the learner with alternative behaviors.
- ▲ Make sure the feedback describes what the person is doing — that it's critical about the activity, not the person.
- ▲ Whenever possible, provide corrective information before errors occur.[71]

Cycle Back to Step 1 and Set New Goals

After an employee is able to perform at the desired levels, the coaching process cycles back to Step 1 and new goals are set. In summary, by reviewing the seven steps in the coaching process, it is apparent that ineffective coaches:

- ▲ Lack direction and goals;
- ▲ Fail to praise or effectively use rewards;
- ▲ Fail to give feedback; and
- ▲ Criticize performance without providing clear direction.

WHAT ARE COACHING OPPORTUNITIES?

There are many opportunities for managers to coach their team members. Coaching opportunities exist when managers are:

- ▲ Orienting and training a new team member;
- ▲ Teaching a new job skill;

⊿ Making the needed simple corrections to enhance performance;

⊿ Recognizing when goals and business conditions change;

⊿ Following up on a training session;

⊿ Helping a team member who wants to become a peak performer; and

⊿ Supporting a team member who needs self-confidence to be developed.

C-O-A-C-H

Coaching in its essence is excellent communication. An acronym from the word *coach* conveys the central role of communications in the process of coaching:[72]

C — Caring. Caring for another is hard work. It involves knowing and supporting what the other needs and wants. It necessitates self-discipline and self-control so as not to impose your own needs and requirements on the other.

O — Openness. To be in a relationship that enhances another person, you must be open, both in the sense that you are able to listen and that you are able to share.

A — Awareness. To facilitate growth, to nurture another, you must understand the uniqueness of the person's needs and requirements.

C — Commitment. Coaching is not a one-time encounter; it is a relationship built on commitment and feelings.

H — Honesty. You cannot be helpful if you cannot be truthful. Many times you will observe that your associate's behavior is not helpful, and when you do, you must be willing to say so.

Coaching is *c*aring with *o*penness, *a*wareness, *c*ommitment, and *h*onesty.

Coaching and Listening Skills

One of the most important skills for coaches and leaders is listening. In Exhibit 11.3, you can examine how you rate as a listener. Please rate yourself from 1 to 5.

EXHIBIT 11.3   Listening Quiz

10 ANNOYING LISTENING HABITS
How do you rate as a listener?

	Frequently				Rarely
1. Interrupting the speaker and taking over the conversation.	1	2	3	4	5
2. Acting defensively and debating every point.	1	2	3	4	5
3. Topping the speaker's story: "You think you have it bad…" "That's nothing, when that happened to me."	1	2	3	4	5
4. Responding in lecturing manner: "Yes, but…," "Don't you realize…"	1	2	3	4	5
5. Finishing the speaker's sentences.	1	2	3	4	5
6. Not maintaining eye contact with the speaker.	1	2	3	4	5
7. Fidgeting, squirming, acting restless and disinterested.	1	2	3	4	5
8. Evaluating speaker's comments: "You should know better." "You are wrong."	1	2	3	4	5
9. Devaluing or dismissing the speaker's point of view: "Don't worry, you'll get over it." "You don't really feel that way."	1	2	3	4	5
10. Rushing the speaker and acting like speaker is wasting your time.	1	2	3	4	5

SCORING: Total your score.
- If you scored from 40 to 50, you're listening well.
- If you scored 10 to 39, you may want to learn more about listening because leaders, coaches, and team members need to excel at this skill.

Now, ask those who live and work with you how they perceive your listening skills!

ONE SUCCESSFUL LEADER'S REPORT CARD

An impressive leader whom I met in one of my seminars shared the following story with me. He was very serious about improving his leadership capabilities and wanted to identify the leadership areas where he needed coaching. So, he created a questionnaire with 10 questions for his team to answer, hoping that he would learn which skill sets he needed to improve.

He distributed it to his team members and emphasized that it was to be returned anonymously, thinking that would encourage honest responses and input. He was quite surprised when everyone in his department signed their names — no one chose to be anonymous.

The employees wanted things that the manager did not expect — they wanted more coaching and mentoring — more career counseling, training, and scheduled conferences, more mutual goal setting, and more recognition of accomplishments. Following are the questions that my colleague asked his team. He called it "Rating My Service to You":

1. Is our work environment one in which you feel you can succeed?
2. Is our communication with each other as often and as free as you would like?
3. Is our organization designed as it should be?
4. Is quality being promoted in our area?
5. Are your questions answered promptly and satisfactorily?
6. Is advice given as desired?
7. Is attention given to your training and development?
8. Are performance appraisals conducted as you desire?
9. Is my leadership as it should be?
10. When you submit something for my approval, do I properly consider it?

CHOOSING YOUR LEADERSHIP BRAND

Branding is an important aspect of any business. It is what make products and services distinctive and different from others. Your brand is your promise to your customer and tells the customer what they can expect from you. A brand is what a product, service, or medical practice is known for — its reputation. Your brand is derived from who you are, who you want to be, and who people perceive you to be.

In fact, a brand can elicit an emotional response in people. How do you respond when you think about Microsoft vs. Apple? Coke vs. Pepsi? New York vs. Vancouver? Nike vs. Adidas? Nike's advertising strategy is to select spokespeople who are star athletes hoping that customers will transfer their emotional attachment from the athlete to the product. Have you noticed that Nike rarely advertises the features of the shoe or golf ball? It's about the emotional enthusiasm for the athlete.

Peters developed the idea 20 years ago that people can have brands too. In fact, he believes that whether or not you proactively choose your brand, others have already branded you. He calls it your "default brand."[73] As leaders, it's important to know your default brand and then to select the brand that you want and grow into it.

Helping leaders choose their leadership brand is one of my favorite activities as a consultant. The first part of the process is to find out what their default brand is. The assignment is to ask four people who know them professionally to provide four words that describe them. This can be illuminating. One woman asked me what she should do with some comments that she received during this exercise because two of the words people provided for her were "short" and "nice." I asked her if she wanted those two comments to be the first words that people think about when they think of her. She said, "No!" So, the next steps for her were to proactively choose what she wanted her brand (reputation) to be and then develop a strategy to re-brand herself.

During this exercise to explore their default brand, my clients have received the following comments: "mentor, creative, short-tempered, judgmental, trustworthy, knowledgeable, quality-focused, customer-focused, good listener, and stubborn." Listen for the not-so-positive comments too, because oftentimes others do not want to give you negative feedback face-to-face.

My leadership brand is four attributes for which I want to be known: wit, wisdom, experience, and approachable. Those are the four qualities that I want people to associate with me, and I work hard to have them as part of my reputation. What is your leadership brand?

MEASURE YOUR ORGANIZATIONAL CULTURE

If you want to find out the dominant characteristics in your organizational culture, there is an excellent instrument called the R!CP (Re-imagine!SM Corporate Productivity). To date, it is the most reliable and valid instrument for measuring culture. It was created by three professors from the University of California, Berkeley; Stanford University; and Santa Clara University. It measures the 54 characteristics that are a part of every organization culture and identifies which are the most prevalent: innovation, stability, respect for people, results orientation, aggressiveness, detail orientation, and team orientation. This instrument is excellent for showing how aligned an organization is around the strategy and mission of the organization.

CHAPTER PRESCRIPTIONS

- A strong practice requires you to be a strong leader. Keep in mind that strong, trustworthy leadership is the key to creating a high-performing, goal-focused, coaching culture.
- Give your employees what they need — a coach who is also willing to be their mentor. Creating a unified and goal-oriented environment is essential for a productive practice.
- Reflect on the qualities of your favorite teacher — relay those same traits to your employees. You will foster a trustworthy, goal-oriented environment.
- A big part of being an effective coach or mentor is spending the bulk of your time with your most effective employees. Remember that you want to promote and advance the type of work that you expect.
- Create a strong coaching culture and enable your team members to feel more invested in the team. They will inevitably feel like a bigger part of the successes as well.
- Use the seven-step coaching plan, and constantly focus on the process of coaching. Cycling back to Step 1 and setting new goals is vital as you remember the cyclical nature of the steps, which are constantly in flux.
- In short, rest assured that coaching is caring with openness, awareness, commitment, and honesty.
- It is important that leaders understand their default brand — their reputation. Then you can determine what you'd like your brand to be and create a strategy for becoming the brand that you want. Ask four people who know you professionally to provide four words that describe you. Start working on your leadership brand today.

CHAPTER 12

Mentoring

As a Chinese proverb says, "To know the road ahead, ask those coming back." The word *mentor* comes from Homer's *The Iliad* and *The Odyssey*. As Odysseus was preparing to fight the Trojan War, he realized he would leave behind his one and only heir, Telemachus. Because "Telie" was only in junior high, Odysseus recognized that his son needed coaching on how to be king while he was off fighting the Trojans. He hired a trusted family friend named Mentor to be Telie's "king-ship" tutor. Since then, the term, *mentor*, has come into our language to mean "a wise advisor, a teacher or coach."

"Everyone Who Makes It Has a Mentor" was the title of a classic 1978 *Harvard Business Review*[74] article, and the interest in using mentoring as a technique for developing talent has increased significantly since then. *Mentoring* can be defined as a significant, long-term, beneficial effect on the life or style of another person, generally as a result of personal one-on-one contact. A mentor is one who offers knowledge, insight, perspective, or wisdom that is especially useful to the other person.[75]

WE NEED MENTORS

The *millisecond millennium* is how I refer to this time in history. "The ability to learn faster than your competition may be the only sustainable competitive advantage," says Arie de Geus, the former director of Shell International and author of *The Living Company*.[76] Today, we all need mentors, no matter what our title or skill level, and most of us can readily name people throughout our lives who have served as our mentors.

Who provided an "aha!" experience for you that allowed you to find meaning in some event? I think of my friend, Pam, an artist who taught me to *really see* the leaves on the ground. Luckily, I met Pam when I was a freshman in college, so I've seen the beauty in nature for many years. Who gave you a quote that influenced your thinking? Wayne Gretzky, the hockey star, once said, "You miss 100 percent of the shots you don't take."[77] Even though I've never met Gretzky, he served as a mentor to me through his quote. When I'm trying to figure out whether to take a risk about something, I frequently recall, "You miss 100 percent of the shots you don't take," and I say to myself, "Susan, go for it!" Another mentor of mine was the comedian, Jack Benny, who said, "Always play up to the audience."[78] When preparing presentations, I often reflect on Benny's quote. Who helped you discover a talent or ability that you had not recognized? Dr. Pat Heim has served as a mentor to me. Many years ago, she said, "I think you'd be great giving presentations about gender differences. You're funny, and also sensitive." Then Pat started letting me share the speaking platform with her, and we even wrote *In the Company of Women* together.[79]

There are times when we are mentoring others and may not realize it. Recently, Mike, a long-time client of mine said, "Susan, 10 years ago you said something to me that changed my life. You said, 'It's important to stay approachable as a leader. By being approachable, your team and others will feel comfortable telling you about mistakes they've made that need to be corrected, ideas they have for improving things, and feedback to you when you're doing something that blocks progress.' For 10 years, I've tried to end conversations on a positive note so that the other person feels a bridge between us rather than a wall." So, through my comments a decade before, I had served as a mentor to Mike — and I did not even realize it.

PHYSICIANS WANT MENTORING

New physicians want mentoring and seek organizations that offer mentors. Most physicians (61 percent) assign a mentor to newly recruited physicians. Physician-owned groups (77 percent) are significantly more likely to do so. Among those who assign mentors, 66 percent assign the mentor from the same department, 27 percent report that the assignment may vary among departments, and 7 percent report that the mentor is from another department.[80]

Many physicians (74 percent) believe mentoring reduces turnover. Medical practices have expanded to include the mentor's spouse engaging with the new recruit's family in 24 percent of cases.[81]

Physicians and physician organizations understand the importance of getting up to speed quickly. The lightning fast changes in technology, the expanding global economy, and changes in the workforce have dramatically impacted our work lives. Mentorship is more critical than ever.

Representatives from the Northern California region of Kaiser Permanente Medical Group address their new physicians in the following way:[82]

> Because we are operating in such a competitive healthcare arena and physicians are our most valuable and expensive commodities, we must invest in you to a degree that surpasses the efforts professional sports teams put into coaching their top draft picks. We believe that the mentoring relationship is one of the most personal, influential, and long lasting relationships that we will ever forge with you. It is our first and best opportunity to influence and mold you — our star recruits — into providers who will have long, successful, and satisfying careers with us. Therefore, one of our medical group's top priorities is to dedicate the time and resources needed to develop and execute an industry-leading mentoring program.

TYPES OF MENTORING ASSISTANCE

We can be helped by mentors in several facets of our lives: professional, technical, financial, family, physical, and/or spiritual. Mentoring can be done at any time and by anyone — it can be a one-time experience or a lifelong relationship; it can be part of a formal system or it can be informal. Mentoring is a partnership built on respect and trust — it's not about power and leverage. It's a process where a mentor and mentee work together to provide the mentee with knowledge and to sharpen skills, develop latent abilities, and hone thinking.

Some mentors are looking for a cookbook to dictate how to mentor, when to do it, and what to say next. Mentoring is not merely a training program — mentoring takes us beyond the bookwork and adds special insights, understanding, intuition, and caring to the mentee. Some of the abilities and skills that successful mentors employ are coaching, active listening, counseling, providing information, exploring options, effective confrontation skills, managing conflict, and positive reinforcement. Mentors learn to read the verbal and nonverbal messages that their mentees send. They can tell a lot about their mentee's frame of mind by the mentee's tone of voice, how rapidly he or she is speaking, facial expression, and body posture.

Research about mentoring reveals that there are seven types of mentor assistance. These are:

▲ *Type 1* — Helping a person shift his or her mental context;

▲ *Type 2* — Listening when the mentee has a problem;

▲ *Type 3* — Identifying mentee feelings and verifying them (feedback);

▲ *Type 4* — Confronting mentee's negative intentions or behaviors;

▲ *Type 5* — Providing appropriate information when needed;

▲ *Type 6* — Delegating authority or giving permission; and

▲ *Type 7* — Encouraging exploration of options.

Mentors need not be worried that they may not be able to serve all the needs of their mentees. Mentors are there to help at important junctures with key needs — when the mentee needs help resolving a problem or making a decision.[83]

QUESTIONS TO ASK AT THE BEGINNING

At the start, there are several questions to ask that can add clarity for the mentor:[84]

▲ Does the mentee have a goal?

- What are the mentee's goals, and are they aligned with what the mentor is willing and able to provide?

- What ideas does the mentee have in terms of where he or she wants to be at the peak of his or her career?

▲ Can this be a win–win relationship?

- What will the mentor gain from the relationship?

- What are the specific ways the mentor can be of assistance to the mentee?

▲ What do your first impressions say about the mentee?

- How does the mentee's nonverbal communication style (that is, eye contact, body language, energy) check out?

- Does the mentee have — or does he or she have the potential to develop — that special something or executive presence?

⬧ Is this mentee a winner or a whiner? Does the mentee describe problems and challenges in his or her career and job constructively?

SUCCESS OR FAILURE OF MENTORING

The number 1 reason for success or failure of mentoring is mentor commitment. No matter how talented or enthusiastic a mentee might be, mentoring can fail when mentors are not committed 100 percent. Research reflects the following reasons for mentor–mentee success and failure:[85]

Succeed	Fail
Solid mentor commitment	Lack of mentor commitment
Devoting enough time	Lack of time
Compatible personality	Poor personality fit
Similarities in age, specialty	Communication issues
Compensation for the mentor	
Communication/training	
Responsive to questions/problem resolution	

WHAT'S IN IT FOR MENTORS?

Although the relationship usually begins because of the belief that the mentee can benefit from a relationship with the mentor, mentors often gain from the relationship as well. Because it can be a major investment of time and energy, I've found it beneficial for both parties to explore how the mentor may gain from this relationship too.

Many mentors savor the intrinsic benefits of mentoring. The most common are satisfaction from helping someone else; the excitement that comes from working with a talented, energetic junior; and a sense of personal rejuvenation. I'll never forget the satisfaction I experienced when, Greg, one of my very successful mentees, introduced me at an awards banquet as "the person who taught me to be a leader." The extrinsic, tangible benefits may include visibility, development of a loyal support base, recognition, respect, financial incentives and rewards, enhancement of the mentor's network, reduction in workload, and technical assistance. Some younger mentees are doing reverse mentoring in order to help their Baby Boomer mentors learn more about high-tech equipment.

CONSEQUENCES OF MENTORING

Is there a downside to serving as a mentor? At first glance, the largest cost is the mentor's time and energy. Other potential costs are high visibility, mentee failures, sabotage or undermining by disloyal mentees, and animosity from other professionals who feel threatened or jealous. As the deep mentoring bond develops, it can impinge on the mentor's personal life and can create confusion, discord, and jealousy among the mentor's family members and close friends. Mentors should recognize their motivations for mentoring, and then remain vigilant and proactive with regard to the possible costs to their professional and personal lives.

MENTEE BENEFITS

What do mentees gain from their mentoring relationships? Research indicates that mentees receive career support in areas such as promotion opportunities; pay raises; job and career-related feedback; challenging assignments; access to resources, information, and people; and exposure and visibility. On the personal and emotional side, mentees may attain interpersonal growth and receive sponsorship and protection, counseling and guidance, friendship, and support and confirmation.

RETURN ON INVESTMENT FOR MENTORSHIP AND COACHING

In 1977, the international consulting firm Heidrick & Struggles was the first organization to seriously examine the mentor–mentee relationship. Their study found that 1,000 executives who had mentors earned more money at a younger age, were better educated, were more likely to follow a career plan, and, in turn, sponsored more mentees than executives who did not have a mentor. The study concluded that "those who had a mentor are happier with their career progress and derive somewhat greater pleasure from their work."[86]

Now, more than 30 years later, researchers are able to quantify the benefits for mentors and mentees, and thousands of studies have been conducted. A 2007 study found the both mentors and mentees were at least five times more likely than non-mentoring or non-mentored employees to be promoted and approximately 20 percent less likely to leave an organization than non-mentoring or non-mentored employees.[87] This study also showed that mentoring significantly affects key return on investment (ROI) factors, such as retention and employee productivity, by a factor of four to six times over the control groups. In a 2001 survey[88] of 140 companies in which executives worked with coaches and mentors, the average ROI was more than 5:1. Another 2001 study of 43 executives found that those who received coaching had a ROI of 5.7 times the financial investment.[89] At Nortel Networks Inc. in 2002, the ROI for executive coaching and mentoring was 788 percent when using productivity gains, quality, cost control, and product development time.[90]

CLARIFYING EXPECTATIONS AND GOALS

Most of us have heard this characterization of *assume*: Assuming makes an "ass" out of "u" and "me." The same danger can occur when a mentor and mentee have assumptions about expectations for the relationship. Mentoring relationships work best when the mentee is clear about what he or she would like from the experience and negotiates with the mentor so both partners have the same expectations.

When the mentor and mentee have agreed to a relationship, it's time to develop the scope that defines the expectations. One way that I've seen work well is for the mentee to write his or her expectations of what an ideal relationship would produce in the short term and longer term, and present these goals to the mentor for negotiation. Then together they can determine the outcomes and goals of the partnership, and make sure both agree on the focus. What exactly is the mentee trying to learn or change? Will the mentor give input and/or warn the mentee about impending problems? How will they work together?

A colleague of mine asked me to mentor her in communication skills because her team thought she didn't listen to them. We agreed that whenever I was in meetings with Gerry that I would give her feedback after the meeting regarding what I saw her do well in the meetings and specific areas where I perceived she could do better. We also developed a signal to use in the meetings if I witnessed signs that Gerry did not appear to be listening. It worked well because we had a plan for how we'd work together.

Other ideas for defining the mentor–mentee expectations include:

- ▲ *Defining* the roles and responsibilities for the mentor and mentee.
- ▲ *Discussing* the areas in which the mentee would like support and new knowledge.

▲ *Deciding* the frequency of contact, such as one hour per week, and in person or by phone.

▲ *Agreeing* on the acceptability of communication. Is it okay to call at work? Is it okay to call at home? Contact by e-mail?

▲ *Projecting* the length of the relationship.

▲ *Determining* how frequently they will meet to assess their progress. Should it be every 30, 60, or 90 days? Should it be every six months?

▲ *Agreeing* on the issue of confidentiality and the boundaries.

▲ *Sharing* with the mentor how the mentee would like to receive feedback and support, and how he or she would like to handle disagreements.

GROUP MENTORING

Although most mentoring is between one mentor and one mentee, group mentoring can be appropriate when one mentor provides ongoing mentoring to small groups of mentees. Group mentoring can work well when one mentor has special knowledge and experience that he or she can impart to several mentees or when the number of mentees far exceeds the available mentors.

Group mentoring can foster a sense of camaraderie among mentees and lead to peer mentoring. There are many advantages to group mentoring, but it should not be relied on exclusively because mentees may not be able to address confidential or sensitive issues that they are facing when there are other individuals in the sessions.

Role of the Mentor

The mentor's role is to:

▲ Be a positive, professional role model;

▲ Introduce the mentee to others, and assist mentee in developing professional networks;

▲ Guide the mentee in developing skills of reflection and learning from experiences;

▲ Challenge assumptions and the status quo;

▲ Provide constructive feedback when asked;

▲ Encourage independent decision making;

- Assist the mentee to set professional career goals;
- Provide a listening ear;
- Help the mentee identify potential personal and professional development opportunities;
- Be aware of personal values and beliefs and ensure that these are not imposed on the mentee;
- Support, encourage, and inspire the mentee;
- Help solve problems and identify potential solutions and relevant resources;
- Be empathetic; and
- Assist the mentee in deciding which issues are appropriate to be addressed in mentoring and which should be referred to another person.

Role of the Mentee

The mentee's role is to:

- Bring forth professional and career issues for discussion;
- Make decisions;
- Be prepared to take risks;
- Look for new challenges;
- Set professional goals;
- Take appropriate advantage of professional development opportunities suggested by the mentor;
- Share openly with the mentor;
- Accept constructive criticism and use feedback wisely; and
- Disclose frustrations and concerns.

EIGHT STEPS FOR DESIGNING A MENTORING PROGRAM

"Prescribing mentoring is kind of like prescribing friendship," said Barbara Lazarus of Carnegie Mellon University.[91] It takes more than assigning a mentor to protégés and then assuming that mentoring will happen naturally; it won't. Dr. Carol Muller, founder and CEO of MentorNet, cites eight essential components to mentoring programs. MentorNet is a mentoring network for diversity in engineering and science.[92] The eight components to a successful mentoring program are:

1. **Research and planning.** This includes establishment of objectives, metrics, and expected outcomes. Establishing expectations includes such things as the duration of relationships, communications, interactions; and establishing the protocols for the program, which are listed in the following components 3 through 7.

2. **Resource development.** It is important to evaluate and establish the resources necessary to ensure a successful program. This can be staff, funding, evaluation procedures, pre-program surveys, and possibly information technology support. Program protocols and implementation are important for components 3 through 7.

3. **Participant recruitment.** Organizations must ask questions about how mentors and protégés will be recruited, and about target populations and whether there would be an adequate number of participants (and if not, how more people will be recruited).

4. **Matching strategies.** It is not critical or likely that there will be an exact match of the backgrounds, gender, race, or areas of interests between mentors and mentees. This is not usually a problem, and can lead to excellent matches, with more diverse viewpoints shared between participants. Organizations must consider the process by which matches are being made. It is not uncommon for participants to fill out a profile on paper and have matches made through an examination of interests and expressed needs.

5. **Training.** It is extremely important that training is a component. Most people can be excellent mentors — they just need training. Training can be ongoing and available through many means, such as in-person courses; online courses; mentoring books; and personal, one-on-one training.

6. **Coaching and communication.** This should take place throughout the mentoring relationship. Participants need to understand what their role is as mentor or mentee, what to expect, and how to deal with any concerns during their mentoring process.

7. **Closure.** There should be a plan for continuing, changing, or ending the relationship. "I don't believe in a relationship that lasts for more than one year." There is a natural ebb and flow in the mentoring process.

8. **Evaluation.** This is critical to providing feedback by which leaders can modify their mentoring programs to best meet the needs of the organization. Establish measures of your outcomes and measure the things your stakeholders want to know. Stakeholders include

the mentors and mentees, but also the leaders of the organization, from department chairs to boards-of-director members.

ROLE OF THE PHYSICIAN MENTOR IN CLINICAL PRACTICE

Kaiser Permanente Medical Group in Northern California, for which I consulted for many years, is a leader in physician mentoring and describes a physician mentor as someone designated to be a teacher and friend. Initially the mentor's job is to make the newly hired physician feel welcome and wanted. Ultimately, his or her goal is to empower the new physician to mature into a productive and satisfied member of the medical group. What specific things do physician mentors at Kaiser do for mentees?

- ▲ They get to know the mentee personally in important areas such as the mentee's social history, educational background, favorite food, birthday, and even astrological sign.

- ▲ Physician mentors focus on developing skills in the following areas:

  - Good listening skills. Successful physician mentors serve as role models as they listen to mentees, patients, colleagues, and team members. They teach active listening techniques to others.

  - Thoughtful and cost-effective medical decision making, including asking themselves questions such as "Why am I ordering this test? What will I do with the results? How will this improve the patient's outcome?"

  - Collegial and courteous relationships with physician colleagues, ancillary providers, and staff; that is, how to get along with others.

  - An understanding of and commitment to innovative ideas and programs that result in better patient outcomes. For example, introduce mentees to information about classes and programs available for patients to attend, so patients can learn more about their health, chronic illness, and lifestyle choices.

  - Flexibility and teamwork in dealing with daily operational challenges, such as covering for colleagues on vacation, assisting the nurse practitioner, and answering all phone messages.

  - A positive and constructive approach to working with major change projects (which are sometimes less than perfect) within the practice or the practice community. Mentors should teach mentees how to be open minded about change and positive about the possibilities.

▲ Physician mentors take the time to directly observe mentees by seeing patients and offering suggestions for providing more efficient and better care.

▲ Physician mentors provide a confidential "safe haven" for mentees' questions and concerns.

Exhibit 12.1 describes the wide variety of activities that physician mentors perform.

EXHIBIT 12.1   Physician Mentor Activities

PHYSICIAN MENTORS PERFORM A WIDE VARIETY OF ACTIVITIES

Regularly Scheduled Meetings
- Meetings regularly with new hire
- Proactive calls or discussions to check in
- 1:1 meetings twice daily for first month
- Phone calls
- Meetings weekly to discuss integration/ patient care
- Meetings monthly for first few months, then as needed

Reviews
- Productivity review meetings quarterly
- Performance review
- Chart review and training
- Monitoring of performance

Go-to Role
- 24/7 availability for questions
- Being available to source questions, concerns
- Feedback, go-to person
- Coaching, answering questions
- Availability to answer questions
- Counseling/guiding new doctors
- Advice
- Available to answer any and all questions
- Feedback assisting in access to resources for personal, professional, and family needs
- Go-to person for questions, touch base frequently during the first few months

Clinical and Practice Management
- Hospital rounds, clinic work, and documentation review
- Assistance with operational matters
- Answer questions about financials, practice specifics, assist with transition
- Review charts and patients with new doctors, assist with efficient work flow

Policy
- Cover unstated rules, clinic policy, coding issues
- Policy orientation
- Oversight/counseling about culture
- Political land mines to avoid
- Review policies, answer questions

Orientation
- Shadowing for 1/2 day on 1st day employment
- Orientation to clinic culture
- Shadowing in first few weeks

Social
- Socials for physician and family
- Lunch socials
- Dinners
- Introductions at medical staff meetings
- Introductions to staff, community, and senior leadership/management

Cejka Search and American Medical Group Association (AMGA), *2006 Physician Retention Survey* (St. Louis, MO: Cejka Search, and Alexandria, VA: AMGA, 2007), 31. Used with permission.

MENTORING FOR ASSISTANT PROFESSORS AND INSTRUCTORS

Although the Kaiser mentoring program focuses on clinical and practice management, physicians in academic environments also want mentoring. To respond to this need, I worked with Stanford University School of Medicine and the leaders at the Lucile Packard Children's Hospital at Stanford to create a dynamic mentoring program for assistant professors and instructors in the Department of Pediatrics. This pediatrics mentoring program is dedicated to the academic enrichment and success of early career investigators in the Department of Pediatrics.

Mission of the Stanford Mentoring Program

The mission of this program is to promote the career development of early career investigators (assistant professors and instructors) in the Department of Pediatrics at Stanford through a formal mentorship program and creation of the stable of mentors as described in the following section.

Goals of the Stanford Mentoring Program

The program seeks to actively guide and promote the career development of assistant professors and instructors in the Department of Pediatrics and supplements existing assigned primary mentors. There are two key components of the program. The first component is an eight-member *stable of mentors*, who are specifically chosen for their expertise in supporting early career investigators. The second component is that the mentors are intentionally assigned outside of the mentees' division to provide a relationship without conflict of interest and one free of a supervisory influence.

These mentors work together to provide targeted mentorship for the 35 new physicians who are early career investigators. Since 2007, 79 mentees have participated. Each member has notable coaching skills and expertise in one of four key development areas: academic, research, clinical work and clinical teaching, and work–life balance:

- ▲ *Academic* — Understanding milestones in the academic career pathway, including academic organizational structure, promotion criteria, and negotiation strategies.
- ▲ *Research* — Understanding progress from supervised investigator to independent investigator, identifying internal and external funding resources, developing networks and collaborations, and providing objective review of grants and manuscripts.

▲ *Clinical work and clinical teaching* — Understanding the key elements of clinical work and clinical teaching, including responsibilities of faculty, improvement of teaching abilities and becoming a mentor, and management of difficult clinical or teaching situations.

▲ *Work–life balance* — Recognizing the importance of healthy balance to global personal success, as well as institutional success through ensuring diversity and productivity of workforce.

Objectives of the Stanford Mentoring Program

Key objectives of the Stanford program are to:

▲ Improve the academic trajectory of early career investigators and the academic profile of the Department of Pediatrics;

▲ Provide training and orientation for mentors and mentees;

▲ Customize mentoring needs through specialized developmental areas: academic, research, clinical work and clinical teaching, and work–life balance; and

▲ Have a positive effect on recruitment, retention, and job satisfaction as the academic employer of choice.

This new program provides training and orientation for mentors and mentees through workshops, team-based activities, one-on-one meetings, and peer mentoring. There is formal protected mentoring time through members of the stable of mentors.[93] Exhibit 12.2 is a progress review form for mentors.

GETTING STARTED: PHYSICIAN MENTOR–MENTEE SUGGESTIONS

Kaiser Permanente Medical Group recommends several ideas for getting started. The framework Kaiser uses is a time budget of up to four hours per month for the initial two months, and two hours per month for the next six months for the mentor and mentee to meet formally. Because the medical group trusts their mentors to be innovative and recognizes the diverse needs of each newly hired physician, it wants to give each mentor–mentee pair a good deal of freedom in how they use their time together. The group provides some general guidelines for meeting formats and content:

EXHIBIT 12.2   Progress Review for Mentors

How often do you and your mentee meet? _____

Indicate where you usually meet?

_____ in your office   _____ by phone

_____ in your mentee's office   _____ by e-mail

_____ over a meal   _____ on the job/shadowing

_____ other (please explain) _____

How long have you been mentoring your mentee? _____

Did you and your mentee have clear expectations and goals for what you both wanted as outcomes? Please explain._____

_____

What has been the most valuable part of mentoring for you? _____

_____

What are the traits that your mentee has that have positively contributed to this experience for you? _____

_____

When considering the personalities of you and your mentee, are your personalities similar or different?_____

Has your mentee met or exceeded your initial expectations? If not, please explain.

_____

What has been the best aspect of this mentoring experience for you? _____

_____

What ideas and input do you recommend to enhance the mentoring program? _____

_____

_____

Will you want to be a mentor again through this program? _____

Additional comments: _____

_____

Adapted from the *Mentoring Progress Review*, Workplace Toolbox. Workplace Toolbox is an online resource used by professional practice managers and business owners around the world. www .workplacetoolbox.com.

1. **Initial meeting.** Start by scheduling a one-hour meeting, preferably first thing in the morning when mentor and mentee will not be interrupted by patient care.

   - Establish agreements around confidentiality and other areas of trust (for example, what is discussed will remain confidential);

   - Determine and prioritize development needs (for example, have mentor list his or her top five areas for success and have the mentee list the areas in which he or she would like direction); and

   - Determine which modalities will best promote learning and development (for example, coaching, shadowing, seeing patients together, chart review).

2. **Format.** The format depends on specific needs of the pair, but it is suggested that the mentor–mentee pair:

   - Meet at least once per week, preferably to start the day or to start the afternoon;

   - Set aside adequate time for major projects such as shadowing (two hours) or chart review (one hour); and

   - Set aside 15 minutes per day for questions and answers during weeks when there will not be long meetings.

3. **Content.** The following topics, as a minimum, should be specifically reviewed:

   - *Patient communication style* (for example, greeting patients, being a good listener, and ending the visit by asking if there is anything else you can do for the patient);

   - *Charting* (for example, keeping an updated, stable events summary and medication list in the chart; taking note of personal or social issues that are important to the patient, and asking them about those issues at the follow-up visit);

   - *Phone medicine.* Learn how to stay on top of and close out your phone messages, when to call back vs. send lab test or X-ray results, and the art of how to leave messages with either voice mail or someone else other than the patient who answers the phone;

   - *Task matching.* Work with other members of the healthcare team to ensure a good match of task to team member. For example, let clinical pharmacist review medications, calculate formulary conversions for patients on multiple medications who are new to health plan;

- *Information technology (IT).* Use IT services to improve patient care (for example, access important patient care information before going into the exam room when the chart is not available or using e-mail to send prescriptions to the pharmacy when appropriate);

- *Resource utilization.* Ordering of lab tests, radiology studies, and specialty consults. Use them appropriately, wisely. Think about what results are wanted and whether using resources will change management of the patient or the health outcome;

- *Records review.* Consider reviewing together the mentee's copies of lab test, X-ray, and specialty service referrals. Use phone consults when appropriate (the patients often like this much better);

- *Performance feedback and utilization reports.* Review and aid in the interpretation of peer review data, patient complaints, and utilization data;

- *Panel management.* Review importance of healthcare maintenance and point out how IT and team members can help; and

- *Time management.* Review patient schedule and make changes as necessary. Do the best to run on time. Stay on top of mail, e-mail, refill requests, phone messages, charting, and correspondence. Leave the office at a reasonable hour.

Exhibit 12.3 is a sample work plan that Kaiser Permanente Medical Group provides to individuals who are mentoring new physicians.

Excellent Mentors Listen Actively

Excellent mentors actively listen, and mentees rank listening as high among traits of ideal mentors. Unfortunately, people in mentoring roles often mistakenly rush to offer advice, provide suggestions and answers, or tell their own story without really listening to what their mentees' real concerns are. What can mentors do to show active listening? Mentors can use nonverbal responses; that is, nodding, maintaining eye contact, smiling in conjunction with their verbal prompts to encourage the mentee to continue, such as "yes," "tell me more about that," and "uh huh." They don't interrupt until the mentee has finished his or her presentation of ideas. They let the mentee know what they heard by paraphrasing what the mentee just said.

EXHIBIT 12.3   **Sample Work Plan for Mentoring New Physicians**

Physician Name:_____Date:_____

Communication Style
• Develop communication and listening skills.

Charting
• Keep updated stable of events and medication.
• Note personal and social issues of importance to the patient.

Phone Medicine
• Stay on top of messages with effective triage.
• Return calls regarding lab and X-ray results when necessary.

Time Management
• Review your schedule with your medical assistant.
• Strive to run on time.
• Timely follow up of e-mail, phone messages, charting, correspondence, refill requests.
• Leave the office at a reasonable hour.

Effective Use of Health Care Team
• Utilize other team members to assist with work load.

Information Technology for Patient Care
• Access clinical laboratory profile for patient information.
• Use e-mail to send prescriptions to pharmacy.

Resource Utilization
• Use lab, radiology, and specialty consults appropriately.

Performance Feedback
• Interpret member and patient surveys and peer review data.
• Follow up on patient concerns.
• Internet utilization data.

Panel Management
• Review importance of health care maintenance and population management.
• Highlight how information technology and team members can assist.

KPMGroup, KPMG Physician Mentoring Program: A Template for On-going Learning. Used with permission.

When a mentee is describing his or her problems, the most effective mentors:

▲ Provide ideas or information that the mentee can use to develop his or her own solution, when the mentee asks for your input.

▲ Agree early on as to how the mentor will give advice. Should it be given only when the mentee specifically asks for it? Or would the mentee be receptive to being asked, "Could I give you a suggestion?" and waiting for the mentee to say "yes" before continuing.

▲ State advice and feedback in the first-person singular. Many of us are tempted to start with "you ought to ..." or "you should ..." because everyone likes to give advice. Unfortunately, these statements can raise defenses and cause resistance. Try "what I've found helpful ..." and "what works for me is ....". By referring to ourselves, we don't sound critical or judgmental of the mentee. We're merely giving him or her the benefit of what we've learned or experienced, not telling the mentee what he or she should do. Adults seldom want to be told what they should or shouldn't do or how to do it, but an idea or a bit of information offered in a neutral way becomes something they can identify with and use.

▲ Let the mentee know which emotions you're sensing from the mentee (for example, try "you sound frustrated," "you sound upset," or "you sound disappointed").

▲ Avoid "why" questions. Direct communicators use "why" to help them get the picture. Many women and some men are indirect communicators. "Why?" instantly puts an indirect person on the defensive. The individual may feel judged and vulnerable when queried in this manner. If, as the mentor, you are curious, try: "Help me understand ..." This can be much less disconcerting.

Some other useful questions the mentor might ask are:

▲ "What have you learned about your project that you didn't expect to discover?"

▲ "How is this project different from the last one you managed?" "How is it similar?"

▲ "If you could handle that situation again, what would you do differently?"

Traits of Excellent Mentors

In addition to active listening, mentees rank a good sense of humor as one of the top traits of ideal mentors. People who have a good sense of humor are often more approachable and fun to be around. They remind us not to take ourselves so seriously, even though we take our work seriously. Excellent mentors take care to use humor appropriately and are careful to never laugh *at* or belittle the mentee.

Additionally, mentees prefer mentors who are trusting and trustworthy, interpersonally warm and sensitive, unconditionally accepting, respectful of values, and nonjudgmental. The best mentors have a high emotional intelligence quotient (EQ), which is described in Chapter 6. Those with a high EQ are self-aware and understand how their emotions and drive affect other people; have self-control over their reactions to emotions; are intuitively linked into the emotional makeup of others; are superb at reading verbal and nonverbal cues; and build social networks with mentees, colleagues, and superiors. Additionally, excellent mentors serve as role models in the area of self-care and strive to balance their roles at work and home.

Negative Behaviors to Avoid

As mentors who are eager to help our mentees be successful, effective, productive, and happy, we often fall into the same trap that parents do. We rush to rescue, give advice, and, at times, criticize. Research on mentoring reflects that we should sparingly dole out advice and criticism, and resist the temptation to rescue mentees.

As described in Chapter 9, negative reinforcement (that is, criticism) almost always has negative repercussions. When we're providing criticism, we're usually trying to be helpful. However, the criticism usually generates defensiveness, damages self-esteem, and causes negative self-talk and poor listening by the receiver. Criticism makes people feel judged and misunderstood. Just as with the employees described in Chapter 9, when the mentee has gotten off target, there is a gap between the current performance and the goal. When your mentee's performance is unacceptable, instead of criticizing him or her, provide information and refocus the mentee on the goal.

It's easy to convince ourselves that giving a lot of advice to mentees shows that we are being an active mentor. On the contrary, it does not. In fact, effective mentors allow the mentees to solve most of their own problems. The drama triangle, as illustrated in Exhibit 12.4, demonstrates how giving advice can hurt relationships.

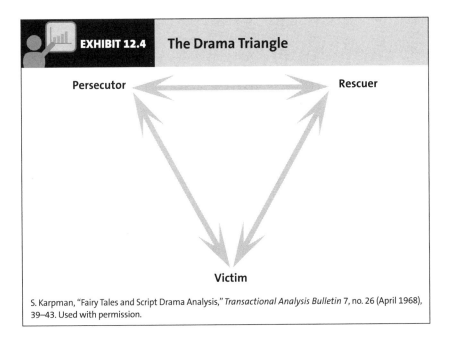

EXHIBIT 12.4   The Drama Triangle

Persecutor   Rescuer

Victim

S. Karpman, "Fairy Tales and Script Drama Analysis," *Transactional Analysis Bulletin* 7, no. 26 (April 1968), 39–43. Used with permission.

Dr. Stephen B. Karpman, a teacher of transactional analysis, described the drama triangle 40 years ago, and I believe that almost every dysfunctional interaction in our professional and personal lives takes place in this triangle. By remaining cognizant of the three roles in the triangle, mentors and mentees can maintain a healthier relationship. All three roles — victim, persecutor, and rescuer — can be held by both the mentor and mentee.

Here's what can happen in a mentoring relationship. The mentee has a problem and feels like a victim because he or she feels unable to solve it. Next, the mentee seeks the help of the mentor whom the mentee believes is more adept at handling the situation. When the mentor (rescuer) offers advice such as, "I recommend that you ..." or "If I were you ...," oftentimes the mentee will reject that advice because the mentor doesn't really know all aspects of the complex problem and the mentee has probably already rejected all the easy solutions to the problem. The mentee says, "Yes, but ..." to stall the conversation and the mentor continues to make suggestions for the mentee. There's a good chance the mentee may not follow any of these suggestions. The mentor then becomes frustrated by the rejections and thinks, "This person really doesn't want to solve this problem." Resentment can build in both parties — the victim feels misunderstood and looked down on. Because of feeling looked down on, resentment can build in the victim. It can also build strong emotion in the rescuer, exemplified by the statement, "after all I've done for you!" Some retaliation can follow, perhaps by both parties. They may both take on the persecutor role to "get even" (often in a passive-aggressive manner) and to feel they're intact and okay. The relationship becomes damaged.

WHEN THINGS GO WRONG IN THE MENTORING RELATIONSHIP

Mentorships are special relationships and, because they are subject to human foibles, sometimes have a dark side. They can become unhealthy, dysfunctional, and emotionally destructive. How do mentors and mentees know when their relationship is in trouble?[94]

Three warning signs are:

1. The mentor or mentee does not believe that some of the important developmental or professional needs are being met;
2. The mentor or mentee senses that the cost of the relationship outweighs the benefits; and
3. The mentor or mentee feels distressed or harmed by the relationship.

I believe it is up to the mentor to take the lead in addressing problems quickly and attempting to restore the relationship. However, when the relationship can't be restored or when continuing the relationship is not in the best interest of the mentee, mentors must take responsibility for ending the relationship.

Some of the most typical causes for mentor–mentee trouble include poor matching between mentor and mentee (that is, dissimilar backgrounds, interests, personality style), faulty communication, incongruent expectations, role conflicts (that is, evaluative or supervisory vs. helping roles), exploitation, abandonment or neglect, mentor incompetence (technically or relationally), boundary violations, problematic attraction, and unresolved disputes.

Throughout my career, I've had several hundred mentees and have developed a good track record as a mentor. Along the way, I met Christine, who asked me to mentor her as a private client. She felt that she was being undermined by a male coworker and found work to be very stressful. During our first few sessions, Christine developed strategies for dealing with the coworker, and she said she felt more empowered in how to handle the situation. As I got to know her better, Christine began telling me that others were undermining her at work, and then she started telling me that I didn't support her and that I was trying to undermine her too.

This is an extreme example, but when I realized that Christine seemed to perceive that many people, including me, were undermining her, some red flags went up. I met with her and told her that I'd noticed a pattern developing where she believed many people were undermining her. After some serious discussions, I recommended that she consider formal counseling with a healthcare professional and provided her a referral. In Christine's case, it was up to me as the mentor to address the problems in our relationship and change directions for Christine's sake.

FIRST, DO NO HARM

When a relationship is becoming difficult, there are steps that the mentor can take. As with the Hippocratic Oath of physicians, "First, do no harm," some guidelines for avoiding harm include the following:

- ▲ Mentors own the responsibility for ensuring that the relationship benefits the mentee;
- ▲ Mentors must continue to treat mentees with dignity, respect, and compassion, even if they become disappointed with the mentee; and
- ▲ Mentors must stay committed to the mentee and must also stay accountable to the organization that is sponsoring the relationship.

So, when things go wrong, mentors should tell the mentee the truth. When mentors don't provide critical, honest, and constructive feedback — whether it's because they are phobic about confrontation, fearful of hurting feelings, or anxious about rejection, they are doing a disservice to their mentees. Although most mentoring relationships work well, on the rare occasions when they fall apart, it's good to have documentation about the development of the conflict. Document mentorship information throughout the process, including expectations and goals, periodic assessments of achievements and concerns, plus information about how the mentoring relationship is developing.

CROSS-GENDER MENTORING

Until recent years, mentors were primarily male because men held most of the positions of power in organizations. Research has shown that women who have been mentored gain higher rewards (higher salaries and bonuses and more promotional opportunities) than their nonmentored colleagues. Male mentors for women can be very successful, especially when they empathize with their female mentees and try to see the world through a woman's eyes. Women often prefer nonhierarchical, more egalitarian relationships and want to share power. Male mentors to women can learn to be sensitive to the many stressors that women experience, including stereotyping, higher levels of marriage–work conflict, lack of access to information about networks, and so forth.

Conversely, male mentees often require special considerations when mentored by women. Because men are accustomed to hierarchical relationships, they may find egalitarian or subordinate relationships with women to be disconcerting. An area that women mentors can be especially helpful for male mentees is in the area of work–family balance where many men are now struggling. Women mentors can help men learn about the significance of providing for their families emotionally as well as financially.

The key to success in cross-gender mentoring is open communication between the mentor and mentee about gender differences. There can be great synergy as mentor and mentee bring complementary strengths. There can also be sexual tension because of mutual liking and admiration. The mentor must take the lead and set boundaries around these issues of professional behavior to prevent damage to mentee, mentor, and the organization.[95]

One of my male mentees once told me how much he enjoyed "the sexual tension between us." Not only did John's comment take me by surprise because I had not experienced any sexual tension, but it also put me on alert that I'd better start paying attention to those cross-gender dynamics. I gently and respectfully redefined our mentor–mentee expectations and goals, and became more reserved around John. Fortunately, we were able to move forward in a professional relationship and stay focused on his growth and development. If at any time I felt that our professional relationship was compromised, I would have been up-front with him and would have terminated my role as his mentor.

LETTING GO WHEN MENTORING IS OVER

Preparing to say good-bye to a mentee is an important step in successful mentoring — and it is often skipped. Excellent mentors find creative ways to recognize and honor good collaboration, friendship, and professional growth in their mentees. I recommend scheduling a formal celebration, such as lunch, dinner, or coffee, during which the mentor offers salient highlights of the mentee's journey, accomplishments, and development. The mentee may want to do the same so that both are sharing reflections, feelings, thoughts, and gratitude for one another and the impactful mentoring experience.

HOW TO FIND A MENTOR

To continue the analogy I used in Chapter 9 about achieving goals, airplanes are constantly making course corrections because the wind turbulence blows them off their flight path. Just like airplanes, we humans are also blown off course, even when we know where we're headed. It's simply smart business to identify a mentor who will help you get to your destination by limiting how much time you stray from your goals.

How do you find a mentor? The following pointers can help:[96]

▲ *Determine your goal and/or destination.* Clarify which skills need development. A professional mentorship will help you improve as a leader, project manager, communicator, team player, and/or meeting facilitator. In which areas do you need advice?

▲ *Look for experts in this area.* Potential mentors are all around you: a peer, a boss, someone in another area of your organization, and even someone in another organization or someone you've met at a professional association.

▲ *Contact the individual you've chosen.* Call him or her. Meet for lunch. Talk about why you would like help in a specific area, and why he or she would be the ideal helper. It is quite an honor to be selected as a role model. If the person you've chosen is unable to assume the mentor role, take heart. Even if your first candidate declines your request, you have increased the feelings of goodwill toward yourself because you acknowledged him or her as someone you admire. Ask who else he or she might recommend who has the skill or knowledge you're seeking to develop.

▲ *Agree on how your relationship will work.* The role of the mentor is to support not to rescue. Relying on a mentor to rescue you can lead to codependency, which is a dysfunctional relationship. When I mentor clients, we initially meet for several hours to define the goals. Then I usually follow up with weekly phone calls or face-to-face meetings to discuss progress, situations that have arisen in which the new skill has been used or is about to be used, client insights, my feedback, and plans for further development. Discuss with your mentor the mechanics of your relationship: how often you will meet, what you will focus on, how you are to receive feedback, and so on. You might also ask your mentor to recommend a list of books, tapes, or periodicals to enhance your insights into your area of interest. Libraries and video rental stores can be inexpensive resources for your learning.

▲ *Celebrate success as partners on a team.* In *Going to the Top*, organizational psychologist Carol Gallagher recommends that you seek out more than one mentor, supporter, or advocate.[97] "Although your boss may be a great advisor and supporter," she explains, "it can be an ineffective strategy to limit yourself to just this one individual. Develop a broad range of supportive relationships."[98] This is especially true if you align yourself too closely to one individual. In that case, you run the risk of falling into the *sidekick* syndrome. You may never be taken seriously because you'll always be in this more powerful individual's shadow, and, unfortunately, should your mentor find him- or herself in serious trouble, your career may become endangered too.

PIE — THE BEST MENTORING ADVICE EVER!

A few years ago, while working with a client in the automotive industry, I met Dave, a longtime sales manager who has mentored thousands of professionals. Dave told me that he always has the same advice for his mentees — "PIE":

▲ Performance;

▲ Image; and

▲ Exposure.

By focusing on those three words, his mentees continuously improve their professional brand and they remain visible and available for new assignments and promotion opportunities. Now, I share Dave's PIE with mentees every day, as well as ensure that I practice PIE too.

CHAPTER PRESCRIPTIONS

- Mentoring is a partnership built on respect and trust; it's not about the mentor being in control of the mentee. Focus on building a relationship where a mentor and mentee work together to provide the mentee with knowledge as well as to sharpen skills, develop latent abilities, and hone thinking.

- Although the mentor–mentee relationship seems to focus on providing the mentee with essential skills and knowledge, ensure that the mentor enters into the partnership with a keen eye on what he or she can gain from the affiliation as well.

- Expectations are a major component to a successful mentoring relationship. Be clear about what the mentee would like from the experience and discuss those expectations with the mentor so that both partners are working toward the same goals.

- The logistics of the relationship should be defined clearly for both mentor and mentee. Consider the duration of the relationship, frequency and type of communication that will be used, frequency of interaction, and the like.

- People are not good mentors just because they are successful in their careers. Train mentors in the skills of communication, coaching, leading, and especially listening. Plus, good mentors have a good sense of humor.

- Remember that having a mentor with a great sense of humor allows for a level of camaraderie and comfort to be forged. Trustworthiness is another vital characteristic — the mentee should feel as if he or she can fully confide in the mentor.

- Establishing closure after the mentoring process has ended is a key element for both mentor and mentee. Set aside a special time to reflect on the journey, allowing both parties the ability to qualify the hard work each has contributed, especially as they review their intended goals and how they were reached.

- Remember that an effective mentor doesn't protect the mentee from working on his or her own. A mentor must allow a mentee to make decisions and learn from those choices — a mentor is a tutor, not a parent.

- Remember PIE in mentoring: performance, image, exposure.

CHAPTER 13

Wellness for Leaders

"In case of turbulence, an oxygen mask will fall from the ceiling. Put the mask on yourself first, before helping those around you." This important announcement, made routinely by flight attendants, is also instructive for leaders. For example, I often see healthcare leaders acting like emotional service stations. Anyone at any time drives up to the pump, and the leaders fill up the gas tank, even when their own gauge is operating close to empty.

As Benjamin Franklin said, "An empty bag can't stand up straight."[99] While there are blood types of A, B, and O, leaders often operate as type E, giving *e*verything to *e*veryone *e*very day. It is crucial for leaders to be healthy and in top shape, to ensure that they are wearing their oxygen masks during today's turbulent healthcare environment. When you focus on being well and living life in a healthy manner, you influence your team to focus on their wellness.

I believe that life is 5 percent what happens to us and 95 percent what we do with that. Each of us is born with a destiny, and it is our personal responsibility to find out what our destiny is and how to achieve it. We must set our own goals for our lives, and these goals will be different for each of us. So how can leaders create a healthy, fulfilling life wherein they can take charge of their destiny? As we discussed at the beginning of this book, all successful enterprises use strategic planning to develop a road map for success. It is critical for leaders to clarify in what direction they want their organizations to go and then develop the strategy to get them there.

STRATEGIC PLANNING FOR YOUR LIFE

The same tools and processes for discovering an organization's purpose, values, goals, strengths, and obstacles can be applied to your journey through life. You are the producer, director, and actor of your life. What you do every day is important, because you are trading a day of your life for it.

What can you do each day to ensure that you are on track to manifesting the destiny you have been created to fulfill?

A Ten-Step Prescription for a Creating Healthy, Meaningful Life

My business partner, Jasenka Sabanovic, and I developed a successful life-changing program for professionals titled "Add *Life* to Your Years." This program has created breakthrough results for thousands of professionals. In the next sections, I outline our 10-step prescription for creating a life that is worthwhile, meaningful, fulfilling, and as healthy as possible. The tools in these steps offer the strategic building blocks that will ensure that you live your life purposefully! I believe that discovering what your destiny is and then fulfilling it is crucial to having a meaningful life. Strategic planning for your life is a dynamic process, which is not finished until you take your final breath. As Peter Drucker said, "The best way to predict the future is to create it."[100]

Step 1: Define Your Purpose

One way to define your purpose is to "begin with the end in mind"[101] as suggested by the late Stephen Covey in *The 7 Habits of Highly Effective People*. Close your eyes and imagine your funeral. What are the mourners saying about you? How did your actions affect their lives? As a leader, what effect did you have on those who followed you? What difference have you made because you lived?

Create a bulleted list of the comments you heard and what you *wish* you had heard, and use this list to develop your mission statement. My own purpose is "to serve as a catalyst in the optimum development and performance of people and their organizations. I am driven to help people to reach their goals and fulfill their potential and create harmonious, positive, loving, peaceful relationships."

Developing your mission statement is the most critical part of your strategic planning process because it will serve as your foundation, driving your decisions from now on.

Step 2: Clarify Your Values

What do you stand for? What principles and values are important to you? How much do you value them? "Things which matter most must never be at the mercy of things which matter least," wrote the philosopher Goethe.[102]

Just as with business enterprises, if you define your purpose and clarify your values for yourself, it is easier to set goals and make decisions throughout your life's journey. My own top values include kindness, authenticity, being a contributor, family, leadership, hope, teamwork, self-support, optimism, trustworthiness, courage, wisdom, spirituality, joy, and health.

Step 3: Define Your Current Reality

The Wheel of Life is used by life coaches everywhere to help clients benchmark how satisfied they are in the different areas of their life and where they want to start goal setting (Exhibit 13.1).

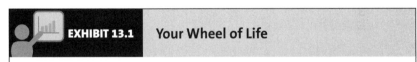

EXHIBIT 13.1   Your Wheel of Life

The eight sections in the wheel represent different aspects of your life. Regard the center of the wheel as 0 and the outer edge as 10, then rank your level of satisfaction with each area of life by drawing a curved line to create a new outer edge.

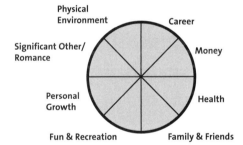

Physical Environment: Do you like the areas in which you live and work? How well do you like your car? Is your home comfortable and safe?

Career: How satisfied are you with your career? Your job? Does it reflect your values?

Money: Are you planning for financial freedom? Do you earn and save enough?

Health: How is your physical, emotional, mental health? Are you generally fit and well?

Family and Friends: Do you have valuable, relationships with your family and friends? Are you close to them?

Fun and Recreation: Do you take time to relax and enjoy life? How often do you have fun?

(Exhibit continues)

EXHIBIT 13.1
(continued)   **Your Wheel of Life**

Personal Growth: Are you continuing to learn new things and develop as a person? Are you growing spiritually and emotionally?

Significant Other/Romance: Do you have/want a partner and soul mate? Do you share values and intimacy?

Rate each of the areas 1–10 and then connect the lines to form an inner wheel.

EXAMPLE

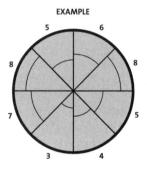

Physical Environment	5	Family and Friends	4
Career	6	Fun and Recreation	3
Money	8	Personal Growth	7
Health	5	Significant Other/Romance	8

The new perimeter represents the wheel of your life. If this were a real wheel, how bumpy would the ride be?

This gives you an idea of how balanced your life is. This is not about getting all 10s. It's about a smoother ride.

1. What areas are going well? In what areas are you ready to make a change?
2. How bumpy would the ride be if this were a real wheel?
3. What would a fulfilled life look like in each area?
4. How would you raise it from 4 to 6? What will you do to make it more fulfilling?

Why you need balance in your life. As a healthcare leader, especially in this ever-changing environment, you have a strong influence over the culture of your team. If you are out of balance, your organization's culture will be out of balance. You are a role model who sets an example for your team and your patients.

Each area of the Wheel of Life is important. Imagine neglecting your health for a few years while you are focusing only on your work. The areas of the Wheel of Life reinforce each other. You can advance your career by being

EXHIBIT 13.2   Roles We Play in Life

Self	Employee	Spouse
Parent	Leader	Professional association member
Colleague	Board member	Sibling
PTA member	Son/Daughter	Church member
Friend	Neighbor	Manager
Other		

healthy, having good social connections, and receiving support from your family. We all play many roles in life. What roles do you play? See Exhibit 13.2 for some of the roles we play in life.

Step 4. Uncover Your Beliefs

How you think is everything. Your thoughts drive your actions. Both your conscious and subconscious mind are critical to success because you become what you think about. Throughout history, philosophers, historians, and poets have written about the power of the mind. The Bible proclaims, "If thou canst believe, all things are possible to him that believeth."[103]
Even 2,500 years ago, Buddha said, "All that we are is the result of what we have thought."[104]

Norman Vincent Peale, the author of *The Power of Positive Thinking,* said, "Change your thoughts and you change your life. If you think in negative thoughts, you will get negative results; if you think in positive terms, you will achieve positive results. In three words, 'believe and succeed.'"[105]

People act as they think. You become what you think about. Your thoughts determine your character, your career, your everyday life. If you think about a concrete goal, you become that goal. If you do not have goals and your thoughts are confused and full of fear and doubts, your life becomes full of confusion, fear, and doubt.

The Magic of Believing by Claude Bristol[106] is an excellent resource for understanding the power of our minds. Bristol wrote about the importance of both our conscious and subconscious mind in reaching goals — our conscious mind is the source of *thought,* and our subconscious is the source of *power.* The subconscious works constantly while you are awake and asleep. It can actually fast-forward and see you already being successful! Bristol believed that powers of our subconscious include intuition, emotion, inspiration, imagination, organization, memory, and dynamic energy. Our subconscious assimilates all that is needed for us to reach success; you just need to keep focused on the goal without letup, no matter how long it takes — learn to be patient.

Examine self-limiting beliefs. An important aspect of our subconscious is that it does not have a sense of humor. It can't take a joke! Every time your conscious mind says, "I can't do that," or "That's too hard," your subconscious mind concurs, "You're right!" Every negative thought you have becomes a goal. If you say "I'll never be promoted," or "I'll never finish college," or "I'll never find love," your subconscious says, "That's right."

Because you may be negatively influencing your health, life, and business in ways that are unconscious, it is important to examine your self-limiting beliefs. Dr. Bruce Lipton, a molecular biologist and former professor of medicine at Stanford University found that the unconscious mind operates at 40 million bits of data per second, whereas the conscious mind processes at only 40 bits per second.[107] The unconscious mind is *much* more powerful than the conscious mind, and it is the unconscious mind that shapes how we live our life. (Exhibit 13.3 lists what I've found to be the top 10 self-limiting beliefs of my clients.)

Managing your thoughts is the key to achieving peace and happiness. Unmanaged thoughts lead to tension, conflict, and stress. Managing your thoughts leads to confidence, strength, security, and serenity. Lipton

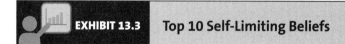

EXHIBIT 13.3   Top 10 Self-Limiting Beliefs

I have found the top 10 self-limiting beliefs to be:
1. I've already tried everything.
2. I don't have the willpower.
3. I'm too old.
4. I'm not smart enough.
5. It's selfish of me to want more.
6. I don't feel that I really deserve it.
7. I'm not educated enough.
8. I'm afraid of trying and failing.
9. I have to have money to make money.
10. All the good ones are taken.

believes that if we interpret things in a positive way, we start living healthier and better quality lives, regardless of our genetic makeup.[108] A new attitude, positive or negative, sends new messages to the cells in our body and can actually reprogram their health and behavior. Positive thoughts can even change cellular structure, turning diseased cells into healthy cells.

Meditation, hypnotherapy, exercise, drug therapies, and prayer are becoming mainstream approaches to integrated health. In my practice, I have been helping clients examine their perception of stressful events. Have you noticed how people can experience the same stressful event and have totally different reactions to it? Two people can be stuck in the same traffic jam: one flies into road rage, and the other remains calm. The effect of stress can be how you *process* the stress you experience. I have heard that Elvis Presley experienced stage fright before performing, while Bruce Springsteen considers the warmup music before his concert his "get ready music"!

I believe optimism is a critical component of a positive mental attitude. Negative thoughts can be extremely powerful and get in the way of progress toward meeting goals and achieving success. Research performed by academics Emily Heaphy and Marcial Losada indicated that for every negative comment, there needed to be 5.6 positive ones to encourage effective leadership.[109] Negative thoughts and comments can negatively affect our performance.

Did you know optimists live two years longer than pessimists? Optimism and enthusiasm can be contagious. Optimists look ahead to see opportunities on the horizon, while pessimists often keep their heads and eyes focused downward. One way to turn from being pessimistic to optimistic is to change our self-talk (Exhibit 13.4). I recommend that pessimists wear a rubber band around their wrist, and when they start thinking or saying negative things, immediately say "Cancel!" and snap the rubber band.

Remembering Eleanor Roosevelt's quote, "No one can make you feel inferior without your consent,"[110] can be helpful when your subconscious thoughts try to take over.

Step 5: Uncover Your Negative Patterns and Habits, and Develop Mindfulness and Gratitude

Many of us are prone to worry, and this can impede our journey toward wellness. "Worry does not empty tomorrow of its sorrow. It empties today of its strength," wrote Corrie Ten Boom, author of *The Hiding Place*.[111]

EXHIBIT 13.4   Assess Your Outlook

Apply the following scoring indicators to the statements below.

A	B	C	D	E
Strongly Agree	Agree	Neutral	Disagree	Strongly Disagree

It's important that I keep learning new things. _____

In changing times, I usually expect the best. _____

I get upset easily. _____

If something can go wrong for me, it will. _____

I have a good sense of humor. _____

I'm always optimistic about my future. _____

I have goals for the future. _____

I hardly ever expect things to go my way. _____

I expect more good things to happen to me than bad, overall. _____

Scoring:
Subtotal your points for items 1, 2, 5, 6, and 9: A = 4; B = 3; C = 2; D = 1; E = 0
Subtotal your points for items 3, 4, and 8: A = 0; B = 1; C = 2; D = 3; E = 4

What does your score mean? I believe those who have an optimistic outlook can thrive during change, whereas those who are pessimistic are more prone to have difficulty when life throws them a curve ball. Optimists, far from protecting their fragile vision of the world, confront trouble head on, whereas pessimists bury their heads in the sand of denial.

© 2016 Susan A. Murphy, MBA, PhD

Note: This exhibit is available as an electronic file.*

In his book *The Little Book of Letting Go,* Hugh Prather calls worry "mental debris" or "a mental pollutant." Although Prather believes that worry is natural, he says so are tooth decay, accidents, and jealousy, but that does not mean worry is useful or beneficial. Worry "fragments the mind, shatters focus, distorts perspective, and destroys inner peace."[112] Just because you might have a tendency to worry doesn't mean you have to feed or nourish that tendency. Worry comes from the Greek words "to divide the mind." You are dividing your mind between the present and the future. "Worrying

---

*Instructions to access the electronic files are available in Appendix A.

is like a rocking chair. It gives you something to do but doesn't get you anywhere."[113]

A still mind can assess a situation more accurately than an anxious mind, and is therefore less likely to overlook a present danger. Breathe through your fears and meditate. As your breath becomes deeper, you are more able to control fears and anxieties. Deep breathing reaches deep into the body's core, reducing stress and relaxing the mind. You will find yourself squarely in the present moment; you will experience mindfulness. Watch your breath and make it your go-to best friend. Fearful thoughts will dissipate, and your balance and happiness will take center stage in your life.

I have found several effective methods to deal with my own worries, fears, and stress. First is staying in the present. Twice per day (at least) I say to myself, "What's happening *now*?" and stay focused on the present for at least one minute. Second, by focusing on breathing, you can significantly affect your mindfulness. One exercise for breathing in a mindful way is to breathe four times per minute for 5 minutes. Usually, you breathe 20 times per minute. In this exercise, inhale for 5 seconds, hold for 5 seconds, exhale for 5 seconds. Then repeat. At first, it may seem impossible for you, but once you start doing this several times per day, you will become more mindful and live in the present during the exercise. Try it while stopped at a red traffic light and soon you might even look forward to those pesky red lights! Additionally, practicing gratitude daily is a powerful way to be mindful. It is difficult to be grateful and worried simultaneously. I have stickers posted throughout my home that list six things for which I'm grateful: God, health, husband, family, friends, and career. Several times each day I'm reminded of my gratitude.

Another mindful exercise that can be effective is the emotional freedom technique (EFT) tapping exercise. The EFT exercise is based on the idea that the cause of all negative emotions is a disruption in the body's energy system. It follows, then, that energy disruptions are the reason we have any kind of emotional issue such as grief, anger, guilt, depression, trauma, and fear. Because both physical and performance issues often have emotional roots, it also follows that clearing energy disruptions can be useful for those as well. Once we find those energy disruptions, we use the tapping process to correct them. The EFT tapping points exercise involves repetitively touching nine points on your own body with your fingertips (Exhibit 13.5). More information about EFT is available on several free Internet sites.[114]

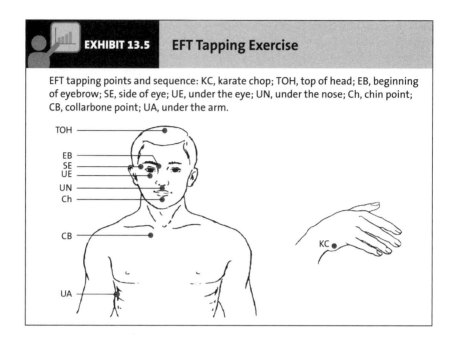

EXHIBIT 13.5   EFT Tapping Exercise

EFT tapping points and sequence: KC, karate chop; TOH, top of head; EB, beginning of eyebrow; SE, side of eye; UE, under the eye; UN, under the nose; Ch, chin point; CB, collarbone point; UA, under the arm.

It takes time to change and grow. Humans are slow learners. You often have to relearn a lesson 40 or 50 times to really get it. How often have you reprimanded yourself and thought, "Not again! I've already learned that"? You need repeated exposure.

We also have a lot to unlearn. It requires hard work to remove bad habits and replace them with good ones. The Bible calls this work, "taking off the old self" and "putting on the new self."[115] Growth is often painful and scary. Every change involves a loss. Even if your old ways were self-defeating, they were at least comfortable and familiar, like a worn-out pair of shoes.

Finally, good habits take time to develop. You can't claim to be kind unless you are habitually kind. You must practice them — and that takes time!

Fears can sabotage success. We all have both conscious and subconscious fears, some of which may be sabotaging us from achieving greatness and success in careers, businesses, health, and relationships. The only fears you were born with are fear of loud noises, fear of falling,[116] and fear of bright lights. All other fears must be learned. It is important to uncover those exact fears, deal with them, and remove these obstacles blocking your success. Some examples of fears and their consequences include:

⏶ *Fear of failure* keeps you from trying;

⏶ *Fear of success* sabotages your every effort;

⏶ *Fear of looking foolish* keeps you from speaking up;

⏶ *Fear of speaking* keeps others from seeing your brilliance; and

⏶ *Fear of loneliness* pushes you into unhealthy relationships.

Step 6. Do a Strengths, Weaknesses, Opportunities, and Threats Analysis

Businesses perform SWOT analyses, and so can you. (A SWOT analysis is a formal process by which an organization considers its strengths, weaknesses, opportunities, and threats.) After all, your life is your most important business.

Be introspective about *you*. What are your strengths and talents? Take a look at all the things you've done while in school and during your career. What have you accomplished? What did you enjoy most? Where have you excelled? What areas have not been enjoyable? What drained your reservoir of personal energy?

Richard Bolles' best-selling book, *What Color Is Your Parachute?*,[117] is an excellent resource for this process. Additionally, there are many self-assessment instruments available to help you better understand your career aptitude, style of leadership, conflict management, and workplace preferences.

EXERCISE What Makes You Different?

Identify your excellent talents.
Identify those talents and traits that make you unique.
Identify the skills, talents, and areas where you do not excel.

Discover and assess your gaps in knowledge, skills, and behaviors. What are the hard and soft skills you need for the next part of your life's journey? Seeking honest feedback from people who know you well can be insightful. One exercise is to ask people close to you, "What are four words that describe me?" Reflect on whether the four words those individuals use to describe you match the view you have of yourself personally and professionally.

Step 7. Set SMART Goals for Each Area of Your Life

Decide what you really want. It is easy to be persuaded to set goals that others want for you. Your spouse may want you to become a good golfer, but if you don't want to, you will not reach that goal. Be clear on what you want and why you want it. The *why* is important because if you don't have a good reason for achieving the goal, you will easily get off track.

Limit your goals and spread them out. Start small and easy, especially if you have not been successful in reaching your goals in the past. Consider starting with something you already do occasionally but want to do daily. Your self-confidence will grow as you reach these initial goals, and this will help prepare you for achieving future goals. One of my client's resolutions was to develop a closer relationship with his young daughter, so his goal was to take his daughter for pancakes the first Saturday of every month. Start working on one goal in January, then write in your calendar the start date for the next one (for example, June 15).

Write down your goals and make them SMART. SMART is the acronym for specific, measurable, achievable, results-oriented, and time-bound (for example, "My cholesterol will be less than 180 by May 1" or "Family cruise will be enjoyed by November 30"). The date of completion is critical, because otherwise your destination becomes *someday else*, which translates into merely wishful thinking.

Post your goals in visible sites around your home. My family posts three sets of goals: my goals, my husband's goals, and team goals. We check off goals that we accomplish and save the list from year to year. This builds our confidence that we are successfully achieving the goals we set. We annually clarify our family's mission, values, and goals, which is unifying and creates a team atmosphere. See Exhibit 13.6 for a seven-step process for setting SMART goals and Exhibit 13.7 for a goal planning worksheet.

Step 8. Select a Personal Board of Directors

Keep only supportive, positive people on your personal board of directors. This is the time to remove toxic people from your inner circle. Consider your closest relationships and decide who should stay, who should be reclassified, and whom else you can support to recruit you. When you were a kid, your parents probably told you not to hang out with the wrong crowd. As adults it is easy to forget these words of advice; however, it remains true.

EXHIBIT 13.6	Seven-Step Process for Setting SMART Goals
Step 1: Identify the goal.	Write a clear description of what you want to achieve.
Step 2: List the benefits.	Write out what reward, benefit, or positive outcome you will achieve when you achieve your goal.
Step 3: List obstacles that could get in your way.	These obstacles can be things such as having enough time or having limited resources.
Step 4: List the skills and knowledge you need to reach your goal.	Write down the additional skills and knowledge you will need to acquire.
Step 5: Identify the people who can help you.	Don't be afraid to ask for help.
Step 6: Develop a plan of action.	Write out each step or task that you'll need to complete in order to reach your goal as well as the action you will take to achieve each task.
Step 7: Set a deadline.	Set a deadline based on your plan of action. Without a deadline, your goal is merely a wish and you may never get around to accomplishing your goals.

Who resides in your inner circle has a strong effect on whether you achieve your goals. To paraphrase Jim Collins, "Keep the right people on your bus, in the right seats of your bus, and ask the people who are not supporting you to disembark from your bus as soon as possible."

Step 9. Evaluate, Reflect on Your Progress

Keep yourself accountable and stay on course with your personal strategic plan. Just as you do with managing your business strategic plan, you need to review your personal due dates and goal milestones. Many leaders hire coaches to hold them accountable for their commitments to their growth and development. I belong to a Mastermind group that keeps me accountable to live my purpose, exhibit my values, and achieve the goals that I set for my growth and development.

Step 10. Celebrate Successes with Rewards and Recognition

A way to encourage yourself to continue working toward your goals is to give yourself an incentive or reward (for example, a massage, golf lesson, tickets to a concert) to celebrate your successes toward your goal.

EXHIBIT 13.7   Goal-Planning Worksheet

Goal (specific, measurable, attainable, results-oriented, time-bound): _____

_____

Benefits (from achieving this goal): _____

    Possible Obstacles   Possible Solutions

1. _____   _____

2. _____   _____

3. _____   _____

Skills and knowledge you need to reach your goal: _____

Identify the people who can help: _____

Action Steps	Who	Target Date	Date Completed	Resources Needed
1.				
2.				
3.				
5.				
6.				
7.				
8.				
9.				

Is it worth the time, money, and effort to reach this goal?   ___Yes ___No

Write the goals for each area of your life:

Physical Environment	1.	
	2.	
Career	1.	
	2.	
Money	1.	
	2.	
Health	1.	
	2.	
Family and Friends	1.	
	2.	
Fun and Recreation	1.	
	2.	
Personal Growth	1.	
	2.	
Significant Other/Romance	1.	
	2.	

A PERSONAL STORY ABOUT SELF-CARE

About 20 years ago, my purpose, vision, and goals saved my job. I had already developed my purpose and values, which included "contributing, self-supporting, and optimistic." At the time, I was an internal corporate consultant with a large Fortune 500 corporation that was experiencing a lot of layoffs. For several years, I had seen many of my colleagues laid off, and I had always escaped the dreaded reduction in force. One year when it was time for my performance review and also time to review my goals for the next year, my director said, "This is the toughest thing I've had to do but your position has been eliminated. The cutbacks have hit our department hard, and I've got to cut your position."

I was shocked. Suddenly my thoughts and my intuition kicked in. My vision for myself did not include a layoff! All of a sudden, I heard myself saying, "That decision just doesn't make sense. I'm the only one in the department who has hospital experience, and this is a healthcare company! Why would the company lay off the one person who understands what our employees need and our clients expect? Here are the goals and action plan I developed for next year to meet the needs of our clients…"

I just kept talking for I'm not sure how long. When I stopped, I looked at my stunned boss whose face appeared frozen, his mouth open. He finally said, "Well, let me reassess this. At this moment, you're not laid off. I'll get back to you."

As it turned out, not only did I stay employed at the organization for several more years, I got a raise. So between being clear about my *vision* and listening to my *intuition*, I was successful in staying *self-supporting*, *contributing*, and *optimistic*.

STAY HEALTHY FOR YOU AND YOUR TEAM

As a leader, it is critical for you to stay healthy physically, mentally, and emotionally for both yourself and your team (Exhibit 13.8).

Physical Health for Leaders

Experts have recommended healthy low-fat diets and exercise regimens for years. Walking can be an excellent way to attain physical well-being. One area often overlooked in the literature is the importance of

 **EXHIBIT 13.8**   **What Is Your Personal Distress Level?**

The following are 40 symptoms of distress. Place a checkmark next to all of the signs (physical, emotional, and mental) that you are experiencing:

PHYSICAL SIGNS
___ Heart pounds or skips a beat
___ Tightness in chest
___ Breathing is rapid and shallow
___ Dry throat, mouth, and lips
___ Tight muscles; pain especially in neck, shoulders, and lower back
___ Muscular tics or twitching
___ Frequent headaches
___ Urinary frequency
___ Rash
___ Hemorrhoids
___ Frequent indigestion, diarrhea, or constipation
___ Insomnia
___ Elevated blood pressure
___ Feel tired throughout the day
___ Easily catch colds or develop the flu
___ Grind teeth when sleeping
___ Herpes simplex
___ Loss of appetite
___ Loss of sex drive
___ Cold, clammy hands

EMOTIONAL SIGNS
___ Irritable, easily annoyed, and angry
___ Indecisive
___ Jealous
___ Overeating
___ Aggression
___ Crying
___ Isolation
___ Blame others
___ Self-critical
___ Abuse alcohol or drugs
___ Nagging

MENTAL SIGNS
___ Low concentration
___ High degree of worrying
___ Low creativity
___ No fantasies
___ Living in the past
___ Feelings of worthlessness and depression
___ Forgetfulness
___ Unsure of yourself in routine situations
___ Apathy

SCORING:
Add all the checkmarks. If you score:

   More than 32, *you are highly distressed.*
   20–32, *you are moderately distressed.*
   Less than 10, *you are calm and peaceful.*

rest and taking breaks. Rest is different from sleep. Research shows that students who study for 50 minutes and take a break for 10 minutes during a four-hour study period learn more than those who cram for four hours straight. Relaxation exercises, which include deep breathing, can revitalize even the most stressed leaders.

Emotional Health for Leaders

Rediscover your sense of humor. During times of change, we are either the change agent or the target of the change. Some days you're the bug, and some days you're the windshield. Laughter increases your endorphin level and makes you feel better. In fact, endorphins have 200 times the power of morphine. Try reading the comics first before you tackle the newspaper headlines.

Get a little help from your friends. This support, however, does not include the team you manage, because as the leader, providing support to them is *your* role. A common mistake is seeking all your emotional support from one person, often from our significant other. There are many individuals who can help us. Look outside your organization for people to provide comic relief, advice, comfort, or consulting support. Finally, consider strengthening the spiritual side of yourself, whatever this means for you. This often gives leaders an inner strength to face stressful changes in both their personal and professional lives.

Mental Health for Leaders

Stay current with the latest theories and ways to stay balanced during times of change. The Chinese character for change includes a symbol for crisis as well as a symbol for opportunity. The Serenity Prayer is said at Alcoholics Anonymous meetings because it provides a mental solution to change: *God grant me the serenity to accept the things I cannot change, courage to change the things I can, and the wisdom to know the difference.* We often spend our time, energy, and spirit trying to change things over which we have no control. Determine which parts of changes you can control, which parts you can influence, and which parts are completely out of your control and influence. Share this exercise with your staff members to help them determine where to focus their energies.

ENJOY THE JOURNEY

Continue to focus on the positive every day — no matter where you are on your career path. There is always an opportunity to affect those in your circle in a positive way. As Maya Angelou said, "My mission in life is not merely to survive, but to thrive; and to do so with some passion, some compassion, some humor, and some style."[118] Are you thriving now? If not now, then *when will you start?* Your team and your organization are depending on you! (Exhibit 13.9)

 **EXHIBIT 13.9**   **What Is Success?**[119]

To laugh often and much

To win the respect of intelligent people and affectionate children

To earn appreciation of honest critics

To endure the betrayal of false friends

To appreciate beauty

To find the best in others

To leave the world a bit better whether by a healthy child, a garden patch, or a redeemed social condition

To know even one life has breathed easier because you have lived.

This is to have succeeded.

CHAPTER PRESCRIPTIONS

- As the leader, commit to being healthy and encourage your team members to be healthy as well.
- Perform strategic planning for your life. Start by *defining your life purpose* and *clarifying your values*.
- Complete the exercise for your Wheel of Life. Determine your level of satisfaction with each of the eight sections of your Wheel of Life.
- Write two SMART goals for each of the eight sections for your Wheel of Life.
- Examine your self-limiting beliefs. Assess your outlook: Are you more optimistic or pessimistic?
- Practice having the attitude of gratitude every day. Choose five things in your life for which you are grateful and start and end each day by focusing on them.
- Perform a SWOT analysis on yourself. Capture your strengths, weaknesses, opportunities, and threats on paper just as successful organizations perform a self-assessment. Which areas can you celebrate?
- Keep only supportive, positive people on your personal board of directors. This is the time to remove toxic people from your inner circle. Consider your closest relationships and decide who should stay, who should be reclassified, and whom else you can recruit to support you.
- Keep yourself accountable and stay on course with your personal strategic plan. Just as you do with managing your business strategic plan, you need to review your personal due dates and goal milestones.
- Keep your mirror handy. Reflect on the state of your health: Are you healthy physically, mentally, emotionally, and spiritually? As a leader, it is critical for you to stay healthy for yourself and your team. Your team and your patients are depending on you!
- Enjoy the journey. Continue to focus on the positive every day — no matter where you are on your career path. There is always an opportunity to affect those in your circle in a positive way. To paraphrase Maya Angelou, "It's not how to survive, but how to thrive with passion, compassion, humor, and style."

ENDNOTES

1 P. Drucker, *The Essential Drucker: In One Volume the Best of Sixty Years of Peter Drucker's Essential Writings on Management* (New York: HarperCollins, 2001).

2 W.G. Bennis and B. Nanus, *Leaders: The Strategies for Taking Charge* (New York: Harper & Row, 1985).

3 Proverbs 29:18.

4 Bennis and Nanus, *Leaders*, 28.

5 J.C. Collins and J.I. Porras, *Built to Last: Successful Habits of Visionary Companies* (New York: HarperBusiness, 1994), 233–234.

6 D.J. Boorstin, *The Americans: The Democratic Experience* (New York: Vintage Books, 1974), 548.

7 Collins and Porras, *Built to Last*, 233–234.

8 W. Manchester, *The Last Lion* (Boston: Little Brown, 1988), 686.

9 "Albert Schweitzer Quotes," BrainyQuote, accessed Nov. 17, 2015, www .brainyquote.com/quotes/quotes/a/albertschw112973.html.

10 Bennis and Nanus, *Leaders*, 36.

11 "Responding to Shifts in Employee Values," *The Wirthlin Report* (March 2001), 2.

12 "Responding to Shifts in Employee Values," 3.

13 "Aligning Employees with a Unified Vision," *The Wirthlin Report* (August 2004), 2; Conference Board, *CEO Confidence Survey, 2nd Quarter 2004* (New York: Conference Board, 2004), 2.

14 "Aligning Employees"; *CEO Confidence Survey*, 2.

15 "Aligning Employees"; *CEO Confidence Survey*, 2.

16 "Aligning Employees."

17 "Albert Schweitzer Quotes."

18 A. Mehrabian, "Communication Without Words," *Psychology Today* (September 1968), 52.

19 E. Bormann, William S. Howell, and George Shapiro, *Interpersonal Communication in the Modern Organization*, 2nd ed. (Englewood Cliffs, NJ: Prentice Hall, 1982), 183.

20 G.Z. Laborde, *Influencing with Integrity: Management Skills for Communication and Negotiation* (Palo Alto, CA: Syntony, 1983), 30.

21 J. Shaffer, "Say It, Do It: A Leader's Guide to Credibility," *Strategic Communication Management* (December/January 1998), 18.

22 Shaffer, "Say It, Do It," 18.

23 Bennis and Nanus, *Leaders*, 152.

24 G. Lowe, "Best Workplaces 2006: Trust is Tops — Building a Better Workplace Culture," *Canadian Business* (Apr. 10, 2006), www.canadianbusiness.com/ business-strategy/best-workplaces-2006-trust-is-tops-building-a-better -workplace-culture/.

25 Bennis and Nanus, *Leaders*.

26 Peter Salovey and John D. Mayer, *Emotional Intelligence* (Amityville, NY: Baywood, 1990), www.unh.edu/emotional_intelligence/EIAssets/Emotional IntelligenceProper/EI1990%20Emotional%20Intelligence.pdf.

27 D. Goleman, *Working with Emotional Intelligence* (New York: Bantam Books, 1995).

28 Goleman, *Working with Emotional Intelligence.*

29 J. Collins, *Good to Great* (New York: HarperCollins, 2001).

30 Shaffer, "Say It, Do It."

31 David M. Shedd, "Quotes on Change," *Move Your Company Forward* (blog), July 3, 2010, http://moveyourcompanyforward.com/2010/07/03/quotes-on-change/.

32 "Mark Twain Quotes," BrainyQuote, accessed Nov. 17, 2015, www.brainyquote .com/quotes/authors/m/mark_twain_2.html.

33 S.R. Covey, *The 7 Habits of Highly Effective People: Powerful Lessons in Personal Change* (New York: Simon & Schuster, 1989).

34 C. Heath and D. Heath, *Switch: How to Change Things When Change Is Hard* (New York: Crown, 2010).

35 P. Hersey and K.H. Blanchard, *Management of Organizational Behavior: Utilizing Human Resources,* 8th ed. (Englewood Cliffs, NJ: Prentice Hall, 2000).

36 Hersey and Blanchard, *Management of Organizational Behavior.*

37 Ken Blanchard, *The Heart of a Leader* (Colorado Springs, CO: Cook, 2007), 39.

38 "George S. Patton Quotes," BrainyQuote, accessed Nov. 17, 2015, www .brainyquote.com/quotes/quotes/g/georgespa159766.html.

39 E. Raudsepp, "Are You Secure Enough to Delegate Effectively?" *CareerJournal Europe.com* (1995).

40 B. Tulgan, *Managing Generation X* (Santa Monica, CA: Merritt, 1995).

41 Ken Blanchard, Thad Lacinak, Chuck Tompkins, Jim Ballard, *Whale Done! The Power of Positive Relationships* (New York: Free Press, 2002).

42 W.I. Zangwill, *Success with People: Theory Z Approach to Mutual Achievement* (Homewood, IL: Dow Jones-Irwin, 1976).

43 Kenneth Blanchard and Spencer Johnson, *The One Minute Manager* (New York: Berkeley, 2003), 57.

44 A. Bandura and D. Cervone, "Self-Evaluative and Self-Efficacy Mechanisms Governing the Motivational Effects of Goal Systems," *Journal of Personality and Social Psychology* 45 (1983), 1017–1028.

45 B. Tulgan, *The Manager's Pocket Guide to Generation X* (Amherst, MA: HRD Press, 1997), 42–43.

46 T.F. Fischer, "The Chemical Side of Failure," *Ministry Health* 112 (2004); G. Cowley and A. Underwood, "A Little Help from Serotonin," *Newsweek* (December 29, 1998).

47 B. Nelson, *1001 Ways to Reward Employees* (New York: Workman, 1994).

48 B. Kaye and S. Jordan-Evans, *Love 'Em or Lose 'Em* (San Francisco: Berrett-Koehler, 2005), 166.

49 K.H. Blanchard and S. Johnson, *The One Minute Manager* (New York: William Morrow, 1982).

50 Kaye and Jordan-Evans, *Love 'Em or Lose 'Em.*

51 *Merriam-Webster's Learner's Dictionary,* s.v. "meeting," accessed July 5, 2015, www.learnersdictionary.com/definition/meeting.

52 Michael Weiss, "Managing Meeting Madness," *Robert Half Management Resources* (June 5, 2014), www.roberthalf.com/management-resources/blog/managing-meeting-madness.

53   American Management Association, *The Importance of Workplace Meetings*, 9, accessed Nov. 17, 2015, www.flexstudy.com/catalog/schpdf.cfm?coursenum= 96026.

54   Eric Matson, "The Seven Sins of Deadly Meetings," *Fast Company* (April/May 1996), www.fastcompany.com/26726/seven-sins-deadly-meetings.

55   "Woody Allen Quotes," BrainyQuote, accessed Nov. 17, 2015, www .brainyquote.com/quotes/quotes/w/woodyallen145883.html.

56   P.R. Harris and R.T. Moran, *Managing Cultural Differences* (Houston: Gulf Press, 1979).

57   T. Peters, "What Is It Worth to Understand Culture?" *Tom Peters! Times* (July 2007).

58   R.L. Kennedy, *The Orders of Change: Building Value-Driven Organization* (New York: McGraw-Hill, 1995).

59   Gallup, "Employee Engagement Index," *Gallup Management Journal* (2006).

60   M. Buckingham and C. Coffman, *First, Break All the Rules: What the World's Greatest Managers Do Differently* (New York: Simon & Schuster, 1999), 43–45.

61   Buckingham and Coffman, *First, Break All the Rules*, 66.

62   R. Plettinx, *Emerging Leaders: Implications for Engagement and Retention* (Brussels: Center for Creative Leadership, 2006).

63   O.G. Mink, K.Q. Owen, and B.P. Mink, *Developing High-Performance People* (Reading, MA: Addison Wesley, 1993), 20.

64   Buckingham and Coffman, *First, Break All the Rules*, 155.

65   Buckingham and Coffman, *First, Break All the Rules*, 155.

66   J.M. Kouzes and B. Posner, *The Leadership Challenge* (San Francisco: Jossey-Bass, 2002)

67   Mink et al., *Developing High-Performance People*, 88.

68   Gallup, "Employee Engagement Index."

69   B. Kaye and S. Jordan-Evans, *Love 'Em or Lose 'Em*, 5th ed. (San Francisco: Berrett-Koehler, 2014), 8.

70   Mink et al., *Developing High-Performance People*, 161.

71   Mink et al., *Developing High-Performance People*, 155.

72   Mink et al., *Developing High-Performance People*, 163.

73   Tom Peters, *Reinventing Work: The Brand You 50: Fifty Ways to Transform Yourself from an "Employee" into a Brand That Shouts Distinction, Commitment, and Passion!* (New York: Knopf, 1999).

74   E.G. Collins and P. Scott, "Everyone Who Makes It Has a Mentor," *Harvard Business Review* 56 (1978), 89–101.

75   G.F. Shea, *Mentoring* (Menlo Park, CA: Crisp, 1997), 9.

76   A. de Geus, *The Living Company* (Boston: Harvard Business School Press, 1997).

77   Paul B. Brown, "'You Miss 100% of the Shots You Don't Take': You Need to Start Shooting at Your Goals," *Forbes* (Jan. 12, 2004), www.forbes.com/sites/actiontrumpseverything/2014/01/12/you-miss-100-of-the-shots-you-dont-take-so-start-shooting-at-your-goal/.

78   Susan King, "Kelsey Grammer: Cheers for Jack," *Los Angeles Times*, Nov. 26, 1995, http://articles.latimes.com/1995-11-26/news/tv-7133_1_kelsey-grammer-salutes-jack-benny.

79   P. Heim and S. Murphy with S.K. Golant, *In the Company of Women* (New York: J.P. Tarcher/Putnam, 2003).

80   Cejka Search and American Medical Group Association (AMGA), *2006 Physician Retention Survey* (St. Louis, MO: Cejka Search and Alexandria, VA: AMGA, 2007).

81   Cejka Search and the American Medical Group Association (AMGA), *2010 Physician Retention Survey* (St. Louis, MO: Cejka Search and Alexandria VA: AMGA, 2010).

82   Kaiser Permanente, *TPMG Physician Mentoring Program Booklet* (Roseville, CA: Kaiser Permanente, 2001), 1.

83   Shea, *Mentoring*, 43.

84   E. Ensher and S. Murphy, *Power Mentoring* (San Francisco: Jossey-Bass, 2005), 128.

85   Cejka Search and AMGA, *2006 Physician Retention Survey*, 31.

86   Ministry of Small Business and Entrepreneurship, *The Mentoring Advantage* (Ontario, Canada: Queen's Printer, 2007).

87   Triple Creek Associates, *Mentoring's Impact on Mentors: Doubling the ROI of Mentoring*, 1st ed. (2007), www.3creek.com/resources/research/Mentor_Impact.pdf.

88   K. Pate, "Coaches Help Execs Get Comfortable in New Roles," *Denver Post*, Sept. 2, 2001.

89   J. McGovern, M. Lindemann, M. Vergara, S. Murphy, L. Barker, and R. Warrenfeltz, "Maximizing the Impact of Executive Coaching: Behavioral Change, Organizational Outcomes, and Return on Investment," *The Manchester Review* 6, no. 1 (2001).

90   J. Phillips, *In Action: Implementing On-the-Job Learning* (Alexandria, VA: ASTD Press, June 2002).

91   "Celebrating the Legacy of Barbara Lazarus—Educator, Mentor, Activist," *Carnegie Mellon Today* (2003), accessed Nov. 17, 2015, www.cmu.edu/cmnews/extra/031007_blazarus.html.

92   C. Muller, "Success Through Mentoring: A Workshop on Mentoring Research and Practice in Collaboration with the SACNAS National Conference — Science for America's Future," (SACNAS National Conference, Denver, CO, Sept. 29, 2005).

93   Developers of the Stanford pediatric mentoring program are Dr. Christy Sandborg; Dr. Hannah Valantine; Linda McLaughlin; Mary Chen, MS, MBA; Dr. Hayley Gans; Dr. Laura Bachrach; and Dr. Susan Murphy, MBA, PhD.

94   B.W. Johnson and C.R. Ridley, *The Elements of Mentoring* (New York: Palgrave Macmillan, 2004), 109.

95   Johnson and Ridley, *The Elements of Mentoring*, 77.

96   Heim et al., *In the Company of Women*.

97   Carol A. Gallagher and Susan K. Golant, *Going to the Top: A Road Map for Success from America's Leading Women Executives* (New York: Viking Adult, 2000).

98   Gallagher and Golant, *Going to the Top*.

99   [Benjamin Franklin], *Poor Richard: An Almanac, 1740* (Philadelphia: Printed and sold by B. Franklin, 1739).

100 "Peter Drucker Quotes," BrainyQuote, accessed Nov. 17, 2015, www.brainyquote.com/quotes/authors/p/peter_drucker.html.

101 Stephen R. Covey, "The 7 Habits of Highly Effective People: Habit 2: Begin with the End in Mind," accessed Nov. 17, 2015, www.stephencovey.com/7habits/7habits-habit2.php.

102 "Johann Wolfgang von Goethe Quotes," Think Exist.com, accessed Nov. 17, 2015, http://thinkexist.com/quotation/things_which_matter_most_must_never_be_at_the/180010.html.

103 Mark 9:23.

104 Max Müller and Max Fausböll, *Sacred Books of the East, Vol. 10: The Dhammapada and Sutta Nipata* (1881), accessed Nov. 16, 2015, www.sacred-texts.com/bud/sbe10/sbe1003.htm.

105 "Norman Vincent Peale Quotes," Good Reads, accessed Nov. 16, 2015, www.goodreads.com/author/quotes/8435.Norman_Vincent_Peale.

106 Claude M. Bristol, *The Magic of Believing* (New York: Pocket Books, 1991).

107 Anando, "It's Now a Proven Fact: Your Unconscious Mind Is Running Your Life," Lifetrainings.com, accessed Nov. 17, 2015, www.lifetrainings.com/Your-unconscious-mind-is-running-you-life.html.

108 Anando, "It's Now a Proven Fact."

109 Jack Zenger and Joseph Folkman, "The Ideal Praise-to-Criticism Ratio," *Harvard Business Review* (March 15, 2013), https://hbr.org/2013/03/the-ideal-praise-to-criticism.

110 "Eleanor Roosevelt Quotes," BrainyQuote, accessed Nov. 17, 2015, www.brainyquote.com/quotes/quotes/e/eleanorroo161321.html.

111 Corrie Ten Boom, *The Hiding Place* (1971; repr., New York: Bantam, 1984).

112 Hugh Prather, *The Little Book of Letting Go* (Newburyport, MA: Conari Press, 2000).

113 "Van Wilder," *National Lampoon's Van Wilder* (Myriad Pictures, 2006).

114 "The Basic Tapping Procedure: The Centerpiece of EFT," Official EFT Tutorial, accessed Nov. 17, 2015, www.emofree.com/eft-tutorial/tapping-basics/how-to-do-eft.html.

115 Ephesians 4:22–24.

116 "Ronald Rood Quotes," Think Exist.com, accessed Nov. 17, 2015, http://thinkexist.com/quotes/ronald_rood/.

117 Richard N. Bolles, *What Color Is Your Parachute?* (Berkeley, CA: Ten Speed Press, 2013).

118 Lindsay Deutsch, "13 of Maya Angelou's Best Quotes," *USA Today*, May 28, 2014, www.usatoday.com/story/news/nation-now/2014/05/28/maya-angelou-quotes/9663257/.

119 Adapted from Bessie Anderson Stanley's poem "Success?" (1904).

PART 3

Building and Rewarding Your Team

CHAPTER 14

The Role of Compensation and Incentives in Engaging the Team

Laura Jacobs, MPH, GE Healthcare Camden Group,
and Mary Witt, MSW*

We all remember the oft-quoted phrase "Follow the money." This mantra is never truer than when it comes to translating organizational goals from words to desired behavior and outcomes. As the backbone of any medical practice, physicians set the tone for the culture and operating environment of the organization (the "system"), and engaging physicians in the process of strategic planning as well as establishing goals and performance expectations is critical. Just as critical, however, is translating those priorities into a compensation and incentive structure for physicians and staff members, which ensures that the desired attributes and outcomes are appropriately rewarded.

This chapter explores the ways in which compensation systems can be structured to ensure that the financial (and other) incentives fit with the desired vision, strategies, and goals of the practice. Too often, physician compensation and incentives become the focus of attention because of a need to react to a negative influence: the need for a financial turnaround, competitive threats of physicians leaving the group, internal jealousies between physicians, and so forth. And even more frequently, physician compensation and incentives are designed in a vacuum, without regard to

* Contributing authors are Laura Jacobs, MPH, of GE Healthcare Camden Group, and Mary Witt, MSW. For more than 25 years, Witt and Jacobs have each led strategic development, compensation redesign, and operational performance improvement of medical groups across the country.

team member incentives. As discussed throughout this book, the interdependencies of the systems of the practice must be acknowledged and addressed to achieve success. And there's nothing more obvious than incentive systems to illustrate what the organization values. This includes the benefits that are offered. Increasingly, physicians are as interested in the lifestyle they can enjoy in the practice as they are in the income they will derive while practicing there.

Designing and implementing a compensation structure for physicians, however, is not for the faint-hearted. As described later in this chapter, the process of designing or modifying a compensation plan is nearly as important as the result, because the outcome must have the support and understanding of management and physicians. Although much has been and will continue to be written on compensation structures for physicians, this chapter focuses on the key elements of compensation design that support the engagement of all team members to jointly support the achievement of the medical practice's goals and desired culture.

THE CONTEXT FOR PHYSICIAN COMPENSATION

It's important to frame the environment that influences physicians' outlooks and perspectives on compensation. Physicians are facing increasing financial pressure because reimbursement increases are not keeping up with practice expense increases. Exhibit 14.1 illustrates the increasing proportion of dollars going to pay for operating expenses, as indicated by MGMA surveys of multispecialty groups. This economic reality puts a strain on compensation systems, because there tends to be a shrinking pool of dollars available to pay physicians in the group.

At the same time, we are facing a period where there are shortages of physicians in many specialties. Particularly critical is the supply of primary care physicians, as shown in Exhibit 14.2. This trend puts pressure on compensation and benefits, because with demand exceeding supply, pure economics would indicate that compensation levels will increase. This is in direct conflict with the preceding point that there are fewer dollars available to pay physicians. So one can see why physician compensation discussions are about as appealing for most practice administrators as enduring a root canal.

If this weren't difficult enough, the regulatory climate puts restrictions on how physicians can get paid, even within a medical group. The federal Stark law regulations limit how physicians get paid for ancillary services

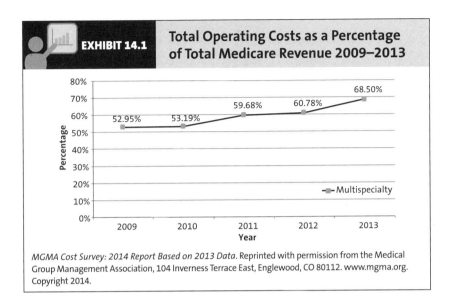

EXHIBIT 14.1 — **Total Operating Costs as a Percentage of Total Medicare Revenue 2009–2013**

MGMA Cost Survey: 2014 Report Based on 2013 Data. Reprinted with permission from the Medical Group Management Association, 104 Inverness Terrace East, Englewood, CO 80112. www.mgma.org. Copyright 2014.

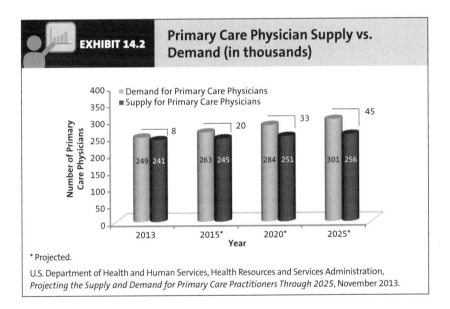

EXHIBIT 14.2 — **Primary Care Physician Supply vs. Demand (in thousands)**

* Projected.

U.S. Department of Health and Human Services, Health Resources and Services Administration, *Projecting the Supply and Demand for Primary Care Practitioners Through 2025*, November 2013.

(laboratory, radiology, durable medical equipment) production as well as putting strict guidelines in place for physicians employed or compensated by hospitals. Any compensation model, particularly one that is productivity based, must also be concerned with compliance with fraud and abuse regulations; there must be adequate protections in place to ensure that physicians are billing not only what is documented in the medical record but what is medically appropriate as well.

Adding new challenges and complexity in compensating physicians are the changes occurring in the way payers are paying medical groups. Historically, payers paid medical groups on a fee-for-service basis, that is, the volume and type of services a physician provided to patients. Payers are now moving to alternative payment methodologies based on fee-for-value. Examples of value-based payment methodologies include payment and penalties for quality reporting, accountable care organizations, bundled payments, and care management fees. Catalyst for Payment Reform reported in 2015 that 40 percent of commercial payments to doctors and hospitals are value based.[1] Medicare has set a target for 2018 that 90 percent of their payments will be linked to quality and 50 percent to alternative payment models. This means that payers and employers will pay more for superior performance on quality and other measures, and less for those providers (hospitals and physicians) who score below average. So, as much as physicians and others may argue over the appropriateness of the measures, the fact is that payments will increasingly depend on the performance of the practice on certain quality, patient satisfaction, and efficiency measures. For the purposes of designing a compensation plan, then, it will be important to introduce measures and incentives that match the reward structures established by payers. (Remember: "Follow the money.")

WHAT PHYSICIANS WANT

Physicians want what all of us want: fair and reasonable compensation and a workplace that allows them to use their skills in the most effective way possible. They also want to be surrounded by colleagues who share a similar outlook and culture. But within those generalities, differences are emerging as the generation gap between Baby Boomer and Generation X and Millennial physicians is demonstrated in work styles and expectations. The "I had to work my way to the top" outlook of Baby Boomers just doesn't compute with the Generation Xers (Gen Xers) or Millennials.

And the 60-plus-hour workweeks of the Baby Boomers don't mesh with the youger generations' need for work–family balance. These conflicts tend to come out in discussions about compensation: Gen Xers are interested in the paid-time-off policy, whereas the Baby Boomers are interested in the productivity formula.

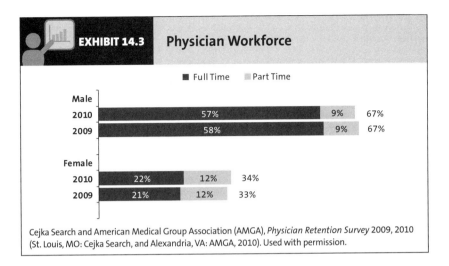

EXHIBIT 14.3   Physician Workforce

Cejka Search and American Medical Group Association (AMGA), *Physician Retention Survey* 2009, 2010 (St. Louis, MO: Cejka Search, and Alexandria, VA: AMGA, 2010). Used with permission.

Another demographic trend to be factored into compensation models is the growing percentage of female physicians. As shown in Exhibit 14.3, women now comprise 34 percent of the physician workforce, a growth of 1 percent from 2009 to 2010 according to a survey conducted by Cejka Search and the American Medical Group Association (AMGA). This survey also showed that while 9 percent of male physicians work part time, 12 percent of female physicians work part time. This trend is expected to continue, as the proportion of new medical school graduates who are female has risen to 47 percent.[2] Therefore, compensation structures that allow for part-time physicians will be a necessity, if they aren't already.

Given that turnover at 6.8 percent remains at its highest levels since 2004, according to the 2013 Cjeka Search and AMGA Physician Retention Survey,[3] it is important to focus on all aspects of the practice environment, not just compensation. Medical groups often report that flexible scheduling, part-time practice, and job sharing are important components in physician retention as are cultural fit, regular feedback, and performance reviews. We will cover the importance of feedback later in this chapter. Those physicians at a practice fewer than three years are the most vulnerable to turnover, reinforcing the need for effective onboarding, feedback, and efforts to actively integrate new physicians into the practice. The important point in this discussion is that a group's compensation plan must take into consideration the expectations of the current and potential recruits to the practice. This means weighing all key issues, such as the balance of benefits and cash, flexibility in work hours, feedback mechanisms, as well as the degree to which compensation is *incentive driven*.

WHAT ELSE INFLUENCES COMPENSATION DESIGN?

We have discussed the general trends that are affecting not only compensation design but physician perspectives on compensation. But there are many other factors to consider when designing a compensation plan. Exhibit 14.4 illustrates some of these factors.

Internal Factors

The most important factors on the list in Exhibit 14.4 are (1) financial position and (2) strategic objectives. Why? The financial position of the group will influence the amount of compensation that must be incentivized. If the group is stable, it may be okay to have a high percentage of compensation driven by set salaries, with incentives driven by a profit pool. Conversely, a group that must turn around financial performance must put greater pressure on physicians to engage in the turnaround, meaning that a greater proportion of the compensation should be driven by factors that will affect financial performance, such as productivity, expense management, and success in a value-based payment environment.

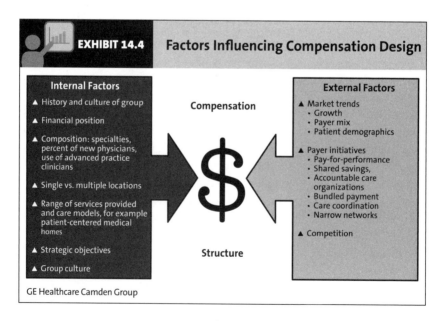

EXHIBIT 14.4   Factors Influencing Compensation Design

Internal Factors

▲ History and culture of group

▲ Financial position

▲ Composition: specialties, percent of new physicians, use of advanced practice clinicians

▲ Single vs. multiple locations

▲ Range of services provided and care models, for example patient-centered medical homes

▲ Strategic objectives

▲ Group culture

Compensation

$

Structure

External Factors

▲ Market trends
 • Growth
 • Payer mix
 • Patient demographics

▲ Payer initiatives
 • Pay-for-performance
 • Shared savings,
 • Accountable care organizations
 • Bundled payment
 • Care coordination
 • Narrow networks

▲ Competition

GE Healthcare Camden Group

The strategic objectives of the group are the starting point for setting the goals of the compensation plan. How does the group wish to reposition itself for the future? How does the group need to change its approach in order to take responsibility for a population of patients? By increasing patient volume, changing payer mix, improving quality or patient service, delivering more efficient care, changing its care model (for example, a patient-centered medical home [PCMH]), providing new services, or expanding into new markets? Are there operational goals or cultural goals that require change in physician behavior? The size and composition of the group is next in importance — what works for a small, single-specialty group is not likely to work for a larger multispecialty group.

External Factors

Also to be considered are market factors that influence both the competition for physicians as well as the structure of reimbursement to physician groups. For example, if there are many large groups in the market that offer a rich benefit package (pension, vacation, etc.), even small groups will have to think about how to structure their compensation package to provide a competitive alternative. If payers in the region are beginning to move to pay for value (for example, quality, patient experiences, cost efficiency) then the group must consider how to motivate individual physicians to achieve top performance within the measures used by payers. (Did we say, "Follow the money"?)

WHAT INCENTIVES ARE THE RIGHT INCENTIVES?

Before determining what to incentivize, the practice should determine what its core expectations are for physicians. That is, what behaviors are expected and required of all practice physicians in order to remain in the practice? These could be foundational, such as treating peers, staff, and physicians with respect, or more operational, such as clinical hours required and participation in marketing the practice.

The first question regarding incentives should be "How much of the physician's compensation should be 'at risk'?" That is, how much is base (or fixed) salary vs. variable? The smaller the group, the more variable compensation tends to be, because the group will merely split the net income (collections minus office expenses) among the physicians in the group according to a predetermined formula. Larger groups tend to set a base salary, to be

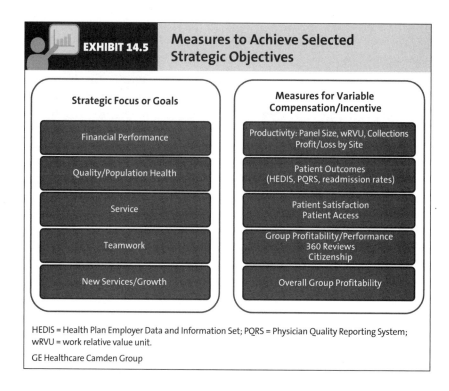

EXHIBIT 14.5 Measures to Achieve Selected Strategic Objectives

Strategic Focus or Goals	Measures for Variable Compensation/Incentive
Financial Performance	Productivity: Panel Size, wRVU, Collections Profit/Loss by Site
Quality/Population Health	Patient Outcomes (HEDIS, PQRS, readmission rates)
Service	Patient Satisfaction Patient Access
Teamwork	Group Profitability/Performance 360 Reviews Citizenship
New Services/Growth	Overall Group Profitability

HEDIS = Health Plan Employer Data and Information Set; PQRS = Physician Quality Reporting System; wRVU = work relative value unit.

GE Healthcare Camden Group

adjusted by the various incentives (productivity, collections, expense management, patient satisfaction, quality, etc.); this comprises the variable compensation. We avoid the use of the word *bonus*, because all of the compensation is for work completed; the variable portion is just more sensitive to actual performance. At a minimum, variable compensation should comprise no less than 10 percent of total cash compensation (excluding benefits). Anything less than 10 percent is of mild interest, which may get physicians' attention to monitor performance, but isn't likely to truly drive change.

The next question is "What should we measure and tie to compensation?" Exhibit 14.5 provides some examples of measures that help to achieve selected strategic objectives.

The following case studies provide some illustrations of how the compensation structure fits the strategic position and goals of the medical group. We've also provided a brief analysis of the advantages and disadvantages of each model.

EXHIBIT 14.6	Advantages and Disadvantages of the Egalitarians Model

Advantages	Disadvantages
▲ Promotes teamwork	▲ Difficult to allow for part-time physicians (or partial retirement)
▲ Promotes focus on overall group profitability and positioning	▲ Does not work as well in larger groups
	▲ Does not work when there is variation in physician performance

GE Healthcare Camden Group

The Egalitarians Model

The egalitarians model is illustrated in a four-person cardiology group that has existed for 20-plus years. The last person to join the group joined five years ago. The egalitarians group grew from a two-person practice and includes physicians that provide a variety of cardiac services — two are interventional cardiologists and two are noninvasive cardiologists. Members of the egalitarians decided long ago that it was important to bring in physicians with a variety of talents, but that the whole group should benefit by the multidisciplinary nature of the practice. That is, although the invasive cardiologist might benefit from higher reimbursement from the procedures he or she performs, it is because the physician is in a group that allows him or her to concentrate on those procedures. This group highly values teamwork and the *all-for-one-and-one-for-all* mentality. As a small group, there is visibility on the performance of each member, so it was never a concern that physicians might not hold their own. The advantages and disadvantages of this model are presented in Exhibit 14.6.

Individual Accountability Model

The individual accountability model is illustrated in a multispecialty medical group composed of 40 physicians, predominately primary care, but with approximately 10 specialists. They operate in a partially managed care environment and have been primarily salary based for most of their 15-year history. They want to increase physician accountability and, at the same time, ensure that the medical group excels in pay-for-performance programs that local payers are rolling out. Here's how they designed their plan:

EXHIBIT 14.7 | Advantages and Disadvantages of the Individual Accountability Model

Advantages	Disadvantages
▲ Provides a range of incentives that match the goals of the group — from individual productivity to quality and patient service. The fact that the indicators are measured is often a driver for performance, regardless of the amount of money at risk.	▲ Requires good measurement tools and reporting structures for feedback.
	▲ A relatively small amount of money may be at risk for quality and service performance, which could be interpreted that these are not really "valued" by the group.
▲ The overall pool is driven by the group's profitability, which helps to promote a group focus on performance.	▲ May not promote teamwork to the degree desired.

GE Healthcare Camden Group

▲ Base salary — 80 percent of market rate.

▲ Incentive pay — Pool driven by group profitability. Incentives paid based on individual performance in:

- Productivity, measured by weighted panel size (health maintenance organization and fee-for-service patients) as well as work relative value units (wRVUs);

- Patient satisfaction, measured by access (third next available appointment), continuity (degree to which primary care physicians see their own patients), and patient surveys; and

- Quality and teamwork, measured by the Health Plan Employer Data and Information Set (HEDIS) scores, staff and peer satisfaction (360-degree surveys), and medical record reviews.

Productivity measures account for 80 percent of the incentive, with patient satisfaction and quality and teamwork each at risk for 10 percent. The group believes that over time, a greater share of the incentive will go to the service and quality measures as the pay-for-performance programs from payers increase their potential payments. Exhibit 14.7 notes the advantages and disadvantages of this model.

Focus on Finance Model

The focus on finance model is illustrated by a multisite, single-specialty group that has had recent financial troubles and is concerned about

EXHIBIT 14.8 | Advantages and Disadvantages of the Focus on Finance Model

Advantages	Disadvantages
▲ Physicians become very engaged in managing both the revenue stream and expenses of their practice. ▲ Fairly allocates expenses where they are used.	▲ Can create competition within the group; does not promote teamwork. ▲ The focus on individuality can lead to a breakdown in group initiatives — physicians are not likely to want to go to a new location, particularly if the payer mix is not as attractive. ▲ May prevent advancing new care models (for example, patient-centered medical home) that require investment in new staff or technology.

GE Healthcare Camden Group

engaging its physicians in the financial turnaround. It has put in place a compensation program that mirrors how the physician would function as if he or she were in private practice in a fee-for-service environment. Collections are allocated to the physician who performed the work, and expenses are allocated depending on whether they are fixed, variable, or individual. For example, rent and administrative costs are distributed equally among each of the physicians; supply costs are variable; individual expenses, including extra staffing, are charged to the individual physician. Exhibit 14.8 outlines the advantages and disadvantages of this model. As a practice's environment moves toward fee for value, this practice will likely find the need to move toward the individual accountability model as it adds other incentives to better align with payer payment methodologies.

As these case study examples show, there are almost as many ways to design compensation programs as there are medical groups. The important thing to remember is to match your group's situation and goals with the drivers of the compensation plan; wherever there's a mismatch, you're likely to be frustrated with the results. Did we mention, "Follow the money"?

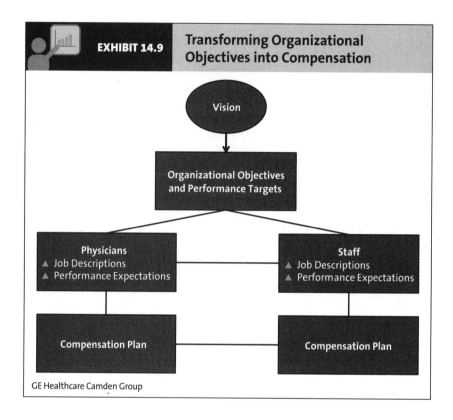

EXHIBIT 14.9   Transforming Organizational Objectives into Compensation

GE Healthcare Camden Group

DRIVING EXCELLENCE — SETTING EXPECTATIONS

Extraordinary medical practices are not afraid to set expectations and measure performance. As discussed earlier in this book, excellence starts with a vision that drives organizational objectives and performance targets. Without clearly defined performance targets at all levels of the organization, it becomes difficult, if not impossible, to create an approach to compensation that appropriately aligns incentives with the organization's mission and vision. Exhibit 14.9 illustrates the relationships among vision, organizational objectives, performance targets, and compensation.

Physicians are highly goal-directed, as demonstrated by their years in medical school and residency, so clearly articulated goals and performance standards help them focus their energies and activities to achieve success. Because physicians place high value on autonomy and independence,[4] it is important to involve them in the setting of the performance targets to achieve buy-in. Performance standards should be based on a set of criteria that defines the responsibilities and expectations. Exhibit 14.10 displays the qualities of effective expectations.

Of course, creating a performance target is not sufficient in and of itself to drive performance. It is critical that targets are routinely measured to monitor progress, positive or negative variances are identified, and action plans to address negative variances are quickly implemented. As already stated, feedback is an important physician satisfier, so they should receive regular feedback about their success in meeting targets.

Feedback on performance targets can and should be provided through a variety of approaches. Monthly physician dashboard reports inform physicians of their individual performance and also can show them how they compare to other physicians within the organization.

Because physicians are highly influenced by data, the use of dashboard reports can be a particularly effective way to gain physician attention. Physicians highly value the respect of their peers, so sharing of the data among all physicians can be an effective method for motivating physicians to improve their performance as compared to others. We believe that transparency is key here — sharing the names of physicians and their performance is better than blinded results. That way, physicians with less-than-average performance can seek the advice of the top performers, or at least observe what they might be doing differently. Most physicians assume they are performing at high levels of performance, so providing comparative (reliable) data is important to drive performance improvement across the medical group.

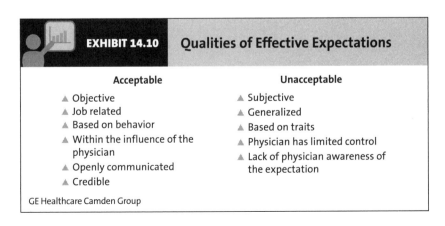

EXHIBIT 14.10   Qualities of Effective Expectations

Acceptable	Unacceptable
▲ Objective	▲ Subjective
▲ Job related	▲ Generalized
▲ Based on behavior	▲ Based on traits
▲ Within the influence of the physician	▲ Physician has limited control
▲ Openly communicated	▲ Lack of physician awareness of the expectation
▲ Credible	

GE Healthcare Camden Group

Regular group and one-on-one meetings also aid in monitoring and reinforcing physician performance. Group meetings provide a forum to publicly
recognize those physicians who have gone above and beyond, as well as to
review organizational performance against targets, especially the physician
dashboard report. It also provides an opportunity to engage the physicians
in brainstorming and discussion about critical medical group issues.
Moreover, these meetings provide a venue in which to strengthen physician
knowledge through education.

One-on-one meetings provide an opportunity to review an individual physician's performance as compared to targets to provide feedback, discuss
problem areas, and solve problems. In addition, they ensure that physicians
have an opportunity to provide their feedback and input to physician leadership. These meetings are an effective vehicle by which to mentor and
coach new physicians. Meeting frequency should be determined by the
amount of time the physician has been with the medical group, their practice maturity, and performance. For young physicians, those new to the
medical group, or those with performance issues, meetings should occur at
least monthly. If there are performance issues, a weekly schedule may provide a better opportunity to monitor progress and ensure compliance.
Quarterly meetings with established physicians may be sufficient. Regardless
of meeting frequency, it is incumbent on physician leadership to provide
physicians with the data necessary to monitor their own performance as
well as other opportunities for two-way communication. It is important
that physicians have the opportunity to share their issues and concerns as
well as be updated on the activities of the medical group as a whole.

Clear expectations provide direction to physicians, establish a mechanism
to create accountability within the organization, and provide a marker for
management to assess the contribution made by the individual to the success of the organization. The following example demonstrates how clearly
defined expectations can assist both the physician and the organization in
achieving their goals.

Case Study: Use of Performance Targets

Johnstown Medical Group recruited a new physician, Dr. George, and his
practice had grown much more slowly than anticipated. During the recruitment process, the medical group emphasized that Dr. George would have to
actively market his practice in order to maintain his income level after his
salary guarantee ended, but there was no discussion about specific

expectations. At six months, Dr. George felt frustrated, misled, and unsupported, while the medical group believed that Dr. George wasn't meeting expectations because he hadn't done the marketing they expected.

If the medical group had identified specific performance measures, Dr. George would have had clear direction on how he was to market and what the medical group expected from him. At the same time, the medical group would have had measurable standards with which to hold Dr. George accountable. Unfortunately, instead, they were left to argue about what was meant by "marketing."

To resolve the issue, the medical group and Dr. George agreed to mutually identify specific performance expectations related to marketing. The specific expectations identified were:

- Dr. George will schedule at least one luncheon per week with potential referring physicians.
- Dr. George will speak at least monthly at a community service organization, school, employer, or other group in venues that provide opportunities to introduce himself to the community. The medical group will provide Dr. George with a list of organizations to contact regarding speaking engagements.
- Dr. George will join one service organization and become an active participant.
- Dr. George will contact the local newspaper and offer to write a monthly column. If the offer is accepted, the administrator will interview Dr. George on the topic of the column and do the actual writing.
- The administrator and Dr. George will meet weekly to review progress. Dr. George will meet with the lead physician monthly.

Dr. George now had a clearly defined road map to guide his marketing efforts, and he knew what support he could expect from the medical group in this effort. The medical group had a set of measurements by which to assess Dr. George's performance. A mechanism to monitor (weekly and monthly meetings) and discuss performance was implemented. These meetings provided a forum in which both parties could hold the other accountable for achieving the growth required to sustain the practice. As a result of defining expectations and behavior for both parties, Dr. George succeeded in achieving the required growth target within two months of the original target date.

FORMAL PERFORMANCE EVALUATION

Formal performance measurement is critical to the success of any organization. As Jim Collins states in his book *Good to Great*,[5] great organizations make sure they have the right people on the bus in the right positions. Unless specific individual performance standards have been created and a formal process to evaluate performance exists, it becomes difficult to identify and address getting the right people on and off the bus.

Performance targets, dashboard reports, and regular meetings to provide feedback on performance are key components of a formal evaluation process. The additional elements include use of an evaluation tool and a formal meeting between physician and supervisor for review of and feedback on performance.

In creating an evaluation tool, it is beneficial to include a self-evaluation section, thereby providing the opportunity for the physician to provide input into the formal evaluation. Use of a self-evaluation portion can provide an effective vehicle by which to identify specific physician motivators, explore opportunities for integrating the physician's personal goals with organizational objectives, and to problem solve areas that need improvement. It also can provide a reality check to measure the congruence of the assessment by the individual with that of others.

In addition to self-evaluation, the evaluation tool should include quantitative data on productivity, patient relations and satisfaction, quality (patient outcomes), efficiency (resource utilization), dependability, and teamwork. The physician dashboard report can, and should, provide the basis for this section of the evaluation tool.

Many organizations also have added a component called the *360-degree evaluation*; this tool is especially useful as practices move to a team-based care model, such as PCMH, because it provides a formal process to enable team members to provide feedback to each other in a structured manner. The 360-degree evaluation is a multi-rater approach whereby physicians and staff who frequently work with the physician and/or are part of the same care team are asked to provide feedback on the physician's or team member's performance. The purpose of this tool is to measure strengths in working with others to care for patients and meet organizational objectives. Those completing the evaluation could include other physicians in his or her call group, other clinical providers such as nurse practitioners and physician assistants, his or her medical assistant, front office staff, other care team members, and/or medical group management. In using this tool, it is important that evaluators are only asked to evaluate those traits or criteria with which they have personal experience. The rating system should be easily understood, and careful instruction should be given to evaluators on how to apply the rating system in order to achieve consistency of application.

The meeting for the formal performance review provides an opportunity to review the past year and to plan for the upcoming year. It should build on data and feedback that has been provided to the physician during the past year. There should be no surprises. These meetings can facilitate collaboration, enhance communication, and establish mutually acceptable goals and performance targets for the year to come.

PHYSICIAN LEADERSHIP AND ACCOUNTABILITY

Organizational and physician excellence is impossible to achieve without effective physician leadership. Successful physician leaders articulate a vision, create a culture of accountability, instill confidence, and effectively manage change. They translate vision into performance targets, they recognize the need to continually monitor progress in achieving those targets, and they don't hesitate to address failures in accountability. The need for effective physician management is increasing as more and more physicians are becoming employed and struggling with the loss of autonomy and decision-making authority that is involved. Physician leaders who can effectively articulate the value of being in a group, translate that value into culture, and effectively mentor and manage physicians are critical to retaining those new physicians and driving group success.

As critical as the role of the physician leader is, medical groups often have difficulty in determining whether they have the right physician leaders in place because they lack the tools to evaluate performance. Physician leadership effectiveness is tied to the leader's ability to effectively relate to and communicate with the physicians, management, and staff within the medical group. It is important to evaluate leadership performance as well as that of individual physicians, but medical groups are often reluctant to address leadership inadequacies, thereby seriously handicapping the medical group as it tries to enhance success. Exhibit 14.11 provides a simple tool to assess the performance of your medical group leaders. The 360-degree tool can be

| | | EXHIBIT 14.11 | How Do You Know If You Have the Right Leader? |

	Consistently No				Consistently Yes
	1	2	3	4	5
1. The leader is skilled at influencing others and promoting an idea or vision.	☐	☐	☐	☐	☐
2. The leader is readily available and approachable.	☐	☐	☐	☐	☐
3. The leader is good at varying his or her approach based on the situation.	☐	☐	☐	☐	☐
4. The leader listens carefully to the medical group's physician, management, and staff.	☐	☐	☐	☐	☐
5. The leader is willing to accept different viewpoints.	☐	☐	☐	☐	☐
6. The leader confronts others skillfully and tactfully.	☐	☐	☐	☐	☐
7. The leader works actively to problem solve rather than blame.	☐	☐	☐	☐	☐
8. The leader has the ability to persuade while maintaining a collaborative relationship.	☐	☐	☐	☐	☐
9. The leader accepts feedback and responds well to feedback.	☐	☐	☐	☐	☐
10. The leader is decisive.	☐	☐	☐	☐	☐

GE Healthcare Camden Group

a particularly valuable approach to assessing leadership performance since it involves a variety of constituencies.

NONMONETARY INCENTIVES

In reviewing physician values and what they want from work, it quickly becomes clear that compensation is only one component of what they are seeking from work. Although competitive pay is a must in this era of physician shortages, compensation alone rarely attracts, motivates, or retains physicians.

Physicians and other team members evaluate their relationship with their work by comparing what they give at work (time, work effort, loyalty) to what they receive (pay, recognition, sense of accomplishment). Today's younger physicians seek a practice lifestyle that allows for life outside of the practice, and most are coming into practice with large debts from medical school.

Older physicians may be more focused on productivity, retirement benefits, and recognition for their years of service. All generations want recognition for their contributions as well as the opportunity to influence decisions.

In response to these needs, medical groups are continually reexamining their recruitment packages, benefit structures, physician scheduling, partnership and ownership options, and governance. Recruitment packages may include income and practice expense guarantees, student loan repayment, signing bonuses, and, in some cases, housing loans.

Physician benefits routinely average between 9 percent and 15 percent of their cash compensation.[6] Benefits generally include health and disability insurance, retirement, and paid time off. Physician time off averages approximately six weeks per year for vacation and continuing medical education. More medical groups are exploring the feasibility of offering deferred compensation plans to address the needs of those older physicians concerned about retirement.

Physician work and call schedules are more likely to become a point for negotiation as physicians seek to limit their work hours and improve their quality of life. As more women become physicians, the demand for part-time schedules has increased. Medical groups are struggling to find innovative ways to meet these demands while ensuring patient care and minimizing the financial impact on the medical group. Solutions include:

- Flexible scheduling, that is, expansion of clinic hours to allow for morning or evening shifts, and this approach also has the added benefit of meeting the needs of the working patient and improving patient access;
- Practice job sharing whereby two physicians or an advanced practice clinician (APC, such as nurse practitioner or physician assistant) share a practice;
- Increased use of registered nurses and APCs to provide first call to limit disruptions to personal life when on call; and
- Hiring of hospitalists to assume care for those patients requiring hospitalization.

As mentioned earlier, there can be an inherent tension as physicians join groups and struggle to maintain the autonomy and independence they have always valued. Therefore, medical groups may want to identify decisions at the local individual practice level where physicians can exercise some autonomy and independence of judgment within parameters established by the medical group governance structure.

The ability to achieve partnership or shareholder status may also influence physician satisfaction. While many younger physicians are less interested in partnership or ownership, those who have an interest are less willing to tolerate partnership or shareholder tracks that exceed three years. At the same time, new physicians often lack the capital to pay large amounts to become medical group owners. Consequently, medical groups often spread the purchase price (if there is one) over several years to address this issue.

HOW DO WE REDESIGN COMPENSATION?

Autocratic or dictatorial compensation redesign is rarely successful — in fact, many administrators have found it to be a lethal career-limiting move. Instead, successful redesign should be a team effort, but team members cannot be just anyone. It generally is not helpful to include all of the physicians in the organization unless the organization is small. It also should be a physician-led initiative and should begin with the medical group governing body. Although administrative staff can support the redesign process, physicians must drive the process in order to create credibility for the process and facilitate physician buy-in.

Before beginning redesign, it is important to understand the efficacy of the existing compensation plan. The assessment of the current plan should begin by examining how it contributes to organizational success. By asking key questions, leadership can determine if physician and medical group incentives are aligned and answer whether the plan is driving successful performance on those factors critical to the success of the organization. Exhibit 14.12 provides a quick diagnostic tool to help start this evaluation.

An effective compensation redesign team starts with the medical group's governing body and may include a compensation committee. The governing body should set the direction for compensation redesign based on organizational and financial goals. In larger groups, it should also make the final decision regarding the compensation plan, whereas smaller groups will more likely rely on unanimous consent. Exhibit 14.13 illustrates the role of governance, management, and physicians in the redesign process.

The governing body may wish to create a compensation committee to perform the detailed work of compensation redesign as well as to regularly

---

EXHIBIT 14.12   Checklist for a Compensation Checkup

	No 1	Sort of 2	Yes 3
1. We conduct a market comparison of physician compensation, including benefits, annually.	☐	☐	☐
2. Our physician compensation is generally competitive with market norms for cash compensation and benefits.	☐	☐	☐
3. Most physicians could describe how our incentives are calculated.	☐	☐	☐
4. Physicians are provided feedback on a variety of performance measures regularly (for example, monthly productivity, annual patient satisfaction, quality, and efficiency).	☐	☐	☐
5. Our physician incentives are aligned with our organizational goals, strategic priorities, and culture.	☐	☐	☐
6. Our physician incentives are aligned with the performance goals of our management team and staff members.	☐	☐	☐
7. Our physician compensation structure is aligned with our sources of revenue (payer mix, pay-for-performance initiatives).	☐	☐	☐
8. Our compensation structure makes allowances for flexible work hours (for example, part time or flexible hours).	☐	☐	☐
9. Once the incentives and total compensation are calculated, the variances between physicians seem appropriate, given performance, specialty, or other considerations.	☐	☐	☐
10. Our leadership group has reviewed the overall compensation structure and its fit with internal and external factors within the last 18 months.	☐	☐	☐

GE Healthcare Camden Group

---

monitor the plan's effectiveness. This committee would discuss and review potential options and their effect on the medical group. Based on direction from the governing body, it can make recommendations regarding the compensation methodology and identify the potential outcomes. The committee should be representative of the various physician constituencies, such as specialties and/or clinical sites, to ensure that various viewpoints are considered in the decision-making process. At the same time, it is important to the credibility of the process that representatives be perceived as acting without self-interest; that is, their primary obligation should be to the welfare of the medical group as a whole rather than to their own interests. Management representation is also key, to ensure that the mechanisms exist to regularly measure and report the data necessary for incentives and related measures.

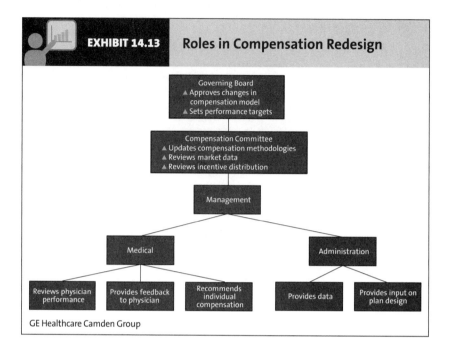

EXHIBIT 14.13   **Roles in Compensation Redesign**

Governing Board
▲ Approves changes in compensation model
▲ Sets performance targets

Compensation Committee
▲ Updates compensation methodologies
▲ Reviews market data
▲ Reviews incentive distribution

Management

Medical

Administration

Reviews physician performance

Provides feedback to physician

Recommends individual compensation

Provides data

Provides input on plan design

GE Healthcare Camden Group

COMMUNICATION, COMMUNICATION, COMMUNICATION

Compensation redesign often creates high physician anxiety, so frequent communication during the process is a must in order to manage physician concerns and expectations. The governing body can agree on a well-designed compensation methodology and still have the compensation plan fail because the plan was not appropriately communicated.

Communication of the process and the plan must begin with the governing body. It should introduce the redesign process as it begins and provide updates as the process moves toward completion. After it approves the plan, the governing body should present it to all physicians by clearly explaining the rationale for redesign and placing the new methodology in the context of how it supports success in achieving organizational goals. Individual leaders, such as the medical director, site medical directors, department chairs, and compensation committee members, should then be responsible for meeting with each physician to discuss the plan's potential effect on each individual.

It is helpful to model compensation by physician under the new methodology in order to address individual physician concerns about how it will affect them, but those discussions have to occur within the framework of organizational requirements. If the redesign is a significant change in methodology, the medical group may wish to run a shadow plan for several months before implementation to allow physicians to adjust to the new approach. Of course, this assumes that the medical group is not in a financial crisis and can implement the new plan over time.

Under a shadow plan, physicians continue to be paid under the old compensation methodology for a period of time (generally three to six months) while also seeing and adjusting to what their compensation would look like under the new compensation plan. When moving to a new compensation plan, some practices choose to either, or in conjunction with shadowing, implement a "risk cap," whereby the physician is protected from his or her compensation decreasing by more than a certain percentage, usually 10 percent to 15 percent. Another option is a blended approach, whereby the new plan is blended with old. For example, in the second quarter, the new compensation plan is blended with the current plan at 25 percent and 75 percent respectively; in the third quarter, it is blended at 50/50 percent; the fourth quarter is blended 25/75 percent; and at one year, the new compensation plan is fully implemented.

It is important to remember, however, that effective medical groups do not stop communicating when compensation redesign is completed. Successful medical groups develop ways to solicit regular physician input and feedback. Physician surveys, opportunities to participate in governance and decision-making, as well as group and one-on-one physician meetings provide opportunities to solicit physician advice and input.

PROMOTING PHYSICIAN–STAFF TEAMWORK

Physicians do not work in a vacuum. Without staff support, it is unlikely that performance targets can be met — staff behavior affects physician efficiency, and patients judge their satisfaction with care by their interactions with staff members as well as with physicians. Therefore, organizational goals, performance targets, and compensation must reinforce physician–staff teamwork.

As new care models are being created, roles are changing, and care teams are being created, staff and physician job descriptions become increasingly important in ensuring that everyone understands their responsibilities, accountabilities, and performance expectations. Staff member job descriptions should reflect their roles in ensuring timely patient throughput and volume, creating patient satisfaction, managing expenses, and facilitating physician efficiency. Physician job descriptions should acknowledge their roles as team members. It is useful to have a code of conduct that addresses treatment of others; timeliness and tardiness standards need to be consistently applied to both physicians and staff members, because inconsistent applicability of performance standards can lead to conflict and legal challenges.

Managing the Human Resource Component

Optimizing teamwork between physicians and staff members often introduces a human resource component, so clarity of roles, responsibilities, and reporting relationships is a necessity. Although physicians have a role to play in providing feedback about staff member job requirements and performance, their role is generally not that of supervisor. Physicians can create or magnify problems with staff when they attempt to intercede. It is not unusual for a staff member to attempt to play the physician against the supervisor to get what he or she wants when the individual senses that there is disunity between the supervisor and the physician. Exhibit 14.14

EXHIBIT 14.14 | **Management and Physician Team Member Roles as Related to Staff**

Management	Physician
▲ Develops staff job descriptions and performance standards	▲ Provides input into staff job descriptions and performance standards
▲ Leads recruitment and selection of staff	▲ Participates in selection of key clinical support staff; may also provide input into selection of certain supervisory/management staff
▲ Provides direction on nonclinical tasks	
▲ Provides guidance on clinical tasks based on physician — established standards	▲ Provides direction/guidelines on clinical tasks
▲ Supervises staff job performance	▲ Provides feedback on staff performance
▲ Determines staff compensation	

GE Healthcare Camden Group

delineates the difference between the role of management and the physician team member as it relates to staff.

Linking Financial Incentives

As medical groups strive to increase physician efficiency and manage operating expenses, they are often linking physician and staff compensation through the creation of incentive programs based on practice profitability. Under such arrangements, both physicians and staff receive variable compensation if profitability targets are met. However, it is weighted differently based on the ability of each to affect the profitability targets.

As with physician compensation, if the group wishes to structure performance incentive compensation for team members, the expectations for performance must be clear at the outset. Even if there isn't a staff bonus structure, letting the staff know how physician compensation is structured — at least what the performance measures are — will allow staff to support physician achievement.

Some medical groups have focused on targets in specific areas; for example, access, patient throughput, efficiency, operating expense, and/or patient satisfaction targets. With the advent of value-based reimbursement, medical groups also are considering ways to reward both physicians and staff for achieving quality goals. When linking incentives between staff and physicians, it is important to clearly delineate the roles and responsibilities as well as the ability to influence the outcome to ensure proper recognition and rewards for specified behaviors. Incentives can quickly become disincentives if any party is penalized or held accountable for items outside of their responsibility or control.

In linking incentives, it is important to recognize that physicians and staff play different roles in achieving organizational targets, and their effect or influence on specific targets may be significantly different. So although the target may be the same, clarity on how the outcome can be affected by individual performance must be communicated to each team member, based on his or her roles and responsibilities. For example, one metric that could drive variable compensation for both staff and physicians is patient satisfaction. And although both staff and physicians influence response time to patient requests or phone calls, their responsibilities vary, and their locus of control over the outcome also differs. The receptionist is responsible for quickly answering a patient's call, taking an accurate message, and giving it to the physician, although the physician must return the call. Both could be rewarded for contributing to achieving expectations for patient satisfaction, but there must be individualized communication about how each can impact the result.

SUMMARY

As described here, the process, structure, and implementation of compensation plans is a critical link to facilitating the achievement of the medical practice's goals. It is a fundamental component to keeping the system working as one — all oars are pulling in the same direction. The incentives and other components that drive the compensation structure are a telling sign of what the group's leadership truly values. Despite what may be written in the strategic plan, if the strategic priorities don't translate into evidence as illustrated in the workplace structure, monetary incentives, benefits, team objectives, or individual performance measures, then all efforts to craft a meaningful direction for the medical group will be in vain. Remember, "Follow the money."

CHAPTER PRESCRIPTIONS

- Evaluate your group's compensation plan for both physicians and staff. Do its design and incentives support your organizational goals?
- Set performance targets for physicians and provide them with regular feedback on how their actual performance compares to the targets. Consider using monthly dashboard reports.
- Use formal performance evaluation tools for physicians just as you would with staff members. They need feedback from medical leaders on how to improve performance; otherwise you're limiting your potential to reach your group's goals.
- Assure staff members that performance expectations support the goals you have set for physicians. This includes supporting practice growth, profitability, and patient satisfaction, or other targets that have been set for overall group performance.

CHAPTER 15

Interviewing and Hiring

Jim Collins, author of the best-selling book *Good to Great*,[7] found that great companies (1) get the right people on the bus, (2) get the right people in the right seats, (3) get the wrong people off the bus, and (4) put who before what.

THE RIGHT PEOPLE ON THE BUS AND IN THE RIGHT SEATS

Great companies have rigorous selection processes for getting new people on the bus. They invest substantial time in evaluating each candidate, making systematic use of at least three evaluation devices, for example, interviews, references, examination of background, meeting members of the family, and testing. "When in doubt, we do not bring the person on the bus."

NEVER, EVER RUSH!

Never rush into a hiring decision! Sure, that position's been open a long time, and you're worn out from pulling weekends and late evenings trying to keep it all together. However, putting the wrong person in the wrong job can make things even worse — and for a long, long time.

There are important benefits for making good hiring decisions. One of the primary reasons is that you can strengthen the culture you're creating by screening and hiring someone who emulates the values and behaviors in which you believe. The people whom you hire and the people whom you fire communicate clearly to your team the values that you believe are important. By making good hiring decisions, you will have fewer staff performance problems, fewer interruptions in workflow, and can elevate your organization closer to the lofty vision you and your team have developed. Good hiring decisions reduce the high costs of turnover. Replacing a staff member can cost 50 percent to 150 percent of his or her annual salary in recruitment and orientation costs for the new staff member. And that doesn't include the potential loss in continuity and quality in your organization, stress to the rest of the team while they cover the vacant position, and the time you spend screening and interviewing other candidates.

FIRST THINGS FIRST

What is the first thing to do when you have a vacant position? Determine whether the vacancy needs to be filled. If so, with what kind of skill set? One of the temptations that we have is to immediately start looking for someone like the person being replaced. Look at the job from a fresh point of view. This could be an opportunity to restructure, reorganize, or promote. If you need to replace the position, do you need the same type of position? In the electronic files, there is a case study example from Providence Health & Services of a workflow chart that the organization made to examine the flow of a patient through their system. Making the chart to review workflow resulted in the decision to change the assignments and add a position with a different skill set in order to more efficiently, effectively, and profitably streamline the operations.

DEFINE THE JOB

What is the purpose of the job? What is the ultimate product or service that the person in this position needs to perform? What is the relationship of this job to others in the organization?

What will this new team member do? What are the most important duties that this new team member will perform? What is the nature and scope of his or her decision making?

How will this new team member perform the job? What are the reporting relationships? What are the general working conditions? That is, what are the hours and days of the week? Where will the person report? Who are the coworkers and peers of this team member?

Are special interpersonal skills required? Does this person interact with patients frequently? What specific skills and training are needed for this new position? Is it important that this person be detail oriented? What skills are absolutely necessary?

What about physical attributes? Is physical strength required? Is size a factor? If you elect not to hire a disabled person, you must be able to show specifically how the disability prevents the person from doing the work.

I have included information about the Americans with Disabilities Act in the electronic files.

WRITE THE JOB DESCRIPTION

Define the qualifications necessary to fill the job. Include the correct duties, responsibilities, qualifications, licenses, and/or certifications. Verify the job title and salary range. Attach the rules of conduct to the job description if you've decided to include the behaviors from the rules of conduct in the job description. I believe that introducing the rules of conduct as a part of the interview and screening process is an important way to inculcate the behaviors that you want into your organization. Determine the technical, self-management, and team dimensions of the job.

INTERVIEWING GUIDELINES

By following certain guidelines, you can ensure successful hiring practices (Exhibit 15.1). Taking time to prepare prior to the interview and adhering to consistent interview practices, you can make hiring more efficient and help to promote selection of a candidate who will be qualified, perform well, and fit well with your team, your values, and your culture.

EXHIBIT 15.1	Review Resume in Light of Qualifications Necessary		
		Assess	Comment
Determine if job candidate's resume provides evidence of meeting the technical and self-management dimensions of job.			
Look for job accomplishments.			
Beware of qualifiers: "knowledge of," "assisted with," "exposed to."			
Don't excuse sloppiness (typos, errors in punctuation, and spelling).			
Look for red flags: too many jobs in recent years, unclear indication of leaving jobs.			
Remember that people often get help with their resumes; the resume may not be indicative of candidate's true communication skills.			
Note: This exhibit is available as an electronic file.*			

*Instructions to access the electronic files are available in Appendix A.

TELEPHONE INTERVIEW PREQUALIFICATION

Time is a precious commodity, so consider prescreening via a telephone interview. Exhibit 15.2 provides a sample interview process.

EXHIBIT 15.2   Telephone Interview Screening

Candidate: _____ Date: _____

Interviewer: _____

INTRODUCTION

Hello, my name is _____ from _____. I received your application for the position of _____ in the _____ Department. Are you still interested in this position? I am conducting telephone interviews, so is this a good time to discuss your skills and qualifications for this position? This interview will take about 15 minutes. If not, can we schedule a different time to discuss your background?

QUESTIONS

Why are you looking to leave your current position? What interests you in this position? What is your current salary? _____ What are your salary expectations? _____

(As the manager, it's important to note what the salary range is for this position.)

Please tell me about your previous work experience. What skills and abilities do you have that you feel qualify you for this position?

What does *excellent* customer service mean to you? Can you give me an example of a time when you provided excellent customer service in the past six months?

The work hours for the position are _____, and you are expected to be at work on time. Can you meet this job requirement?

There may be times when overtime is necessary. Are you able to meet this job requirement?

Do you have any questions about the position?

CLOSING

At this point, you should determine whether the candidate is interested, qualified, available, and willing to interview further for the position.

If the candidate's salary requirements are not within your range and budget, you can let him or her know what the salary range is and determine their level of interest. If the salary range is not acceptable, thank him or her for the interview. If there is interest by you and the candidate for an interview, briefly explain the next steps.

(Sample)

Thank you for taking the time to discuss your skills and background with me. I plan to finish telephone interviews by (date) and will then be selecting candidates for a personal interview. I will contact you directly if you are selected to participate in the next steps in this process. Is this the best number to reach you? Thank you for your time, and for your interest in

_____.

University of California, Irvine Medical Center. Used with permission.

CHOOSE THE INTERVIEW TEAM

Select who will be interviewing the candidate. Depending on the nature of the position, it may be wise to have the candidate interview with you, team members in the same department (to provide a better indication of the daily work and environment), and, if it is a supervisory position, any future staff the person would have. In higher-level positions, members of management should be included, and often the interviews should consist of several group interviews, to include different levels of staff.

It is best to meet with these groups beforehand to go over who should be asking which questions or covering certain topics and to ensure that they ask department-specific questions. Explain what is expected of the interviewing team as far as feedback after the interviews; make sure you stress documentation of the candidate's responses. Develop some core questions prepared as a basis for comparison.

Decide what kind of interview you'd like to conduct — straight questions and answers, role playing, or scenarios after which you ask the candidate how he or she would respond. Many organizations are using behavioral interviewing techniques to get to know more about the candidate, how the person will work with the other team members, treat customers, and so forth. Exhibit 15.3 lists questions to avoid during an interview.

PREPARE FOR THE INTERVIEW

Choose an appropriate environment for the interview — one where there will be privacy and no interruptions. When scheduling candidates, allow time between candidates so that you can take notes after each interview. Confirm the interview by sending an e-mail to the candidate with the following information:

- ▲ Location and time of the interview;
- ▲ Names of the interview committee, if applicable;
- ▲ Copy of the job description; and
- ▲ Copy of the rules of conduct.

CONDUCT THE INTERVIEW

Sweaty Palms is the title of a book about interviewing. Although I've never read the book, I've always liked the title because it's descriptive of almost

 **EXHIBIT 15.3   Questions to Be Avoided**

Topic	What Can't You Ask?	What Can You Ask?
Age	How old are you?	Are you over 18?
	What is your birth date?	
	What year did you graduate?	
Citizenship/ National Origin	Are you a U.S. citizen?	Are you authorized to work in the United States? [not necessary to ask this — this is verified with the I-9 at time of hire].
	Where were you born?	
	Where were your parents born?	
	What is your native language?	
		What language(s) do you read/ write fluently? (only if required by the position)
Marital/Family Status	Are you married?	Would you be able and willing to travel as needed for the job? (only if required by the position)
	Do you plan to have a family?	
	Do you have any children?	
	What are your child care arrangements?	This position requires occasional overtime (nights and/or weekends); would this present a problem? Would you be willing to relocate if necessary?
		Note: These questions should be asked of ALL applicants.
Affiliations	What clubs or social organizations do you belong to?	List any professional or trade organizations you consider relevant to the position.
Personal	How much do you weigh?	Are you able to lift a 60-lb weight, as this type of physical activity is part of the job? [when specifically required in duties of job]
	How tall are you?	
Disabilities	Do you have any disabilities?	Are you able to perform the essential functions of this job, with or without an accommodation?
	Do you have any medical conditions?	
	Do you need accommodations to perform this job?	
Arrest Record	Have you ever been arrested?	At time of offer, advise the candidate that the offer is contingent on completion of a clean criminal background check.
Military Record	If you were in the military, were you honorably discharged?	In what branch of the armed services did you serve?
		What type of training did you receive in the military?
Religion	What religious holidays do you observe?	There are no legal questions related to this subject.
	Does your religion prohibit you from working any particular days?	

every interview I've ever conducted. And I've conducted more than 4,000 interviews. Some candidates spill coffee, trip, and faint. Others do just fine. Others learn about themselves by answering reflective questions about their values, skills, and goals that they had never considered.

Create as comfortable an interview setting as you can; this should not feel like an interrogation. The more comfortable we make it for the candidates, the better chance we have of finding the best candidates for the job. We don't want to hire people who are the best at *interviewing*. We want to hire people who are high performers in the job and who will fit with the culture you are creating.

Be on time and avoid sitting behind the desk during the interview. Begin by coming out of your office to greet the candidate, introduce yourself, and shake hands. It can be very intimidating for a candidate to be led into an office where the interviewer sits waiting behind the desk. If you need to use your office, be sure that your calls are held or that your phone is forwarded to voice mail to prevent interruptions from calls. Sit close to the candidate, preferably at an angle. Be aware of glare on the candidate; avoid having the candidate facing a window. Offer the candidate a cup of coffee, water, or a cold drink.

Open the conversation with icebreakers to build rapport and make the applicant feel more at ease. Build a friendly atmosphere, show genuine interest, and listen attentively. Comment on the weather, ask about the traffic, compliment the candidate or interviewee on his or her suit, or if he or she found parking easily, and so forth. Many interviewers open with "Tell me a little about yourself," and candidates often start to ramble and get more nervous (unless they've taken interviewing courses). I recommend that you steer away from that type of question at the beginning.

Start your session with a brief overview of the position. Don't go into great detail, because that can sway their responses or limit them. The purpose of giving them a brief introduction is in case they misunderstood a major part of the job (such as required travel or occasional overtime), so that they have an opportunity to speak up before wasting your time and theirs.

TALK LITTLE, LISTEN MUCH

Approximately 75 percent of the interview should be the candidate's responses to your questions. Managers should talk only 25 percent during the interview. Many inexperienced managers make a huge mistake when they talk 75 percent of the time rather than 25 percent. They don't get to know the candidate. Interview the candidate first and then, if he or she is still qualified and interested, describe more about the organization and position. I know of many managers who describe the culture that they want and then have the candidate describe the environment they are seeking. Such interviews go like this:

Manager: "We're looking for team players, who have positive attitudes, put patients first, and go the extra mile. What environment are you looking for?"

The candidate responds: "One where I can be a team player, display my positive attitude, put patients first, and go the extra mile!"

The goal of the interview is to get to know the person, the individual's personality, behavioral characteristics, and unique competencies that will make this person the right match for the job and your organizational culture.

During the interview process, you want to discern the following information about the candidate. The best predictor of future performance is past performance. Find out the extent of the individual's experience and effectiveness of past performance as it relates to your job requirements as well as the person's:

- Level of responsibility previously held (Is it the same? Less? More?);
- Skill level and knowledge level;
- Strengths and shortcomings (Would this individual help or hurt team performance?);
- Level of stability and maturity;
- *Fit* with your organizational culture; and
- Attitude and behavior toward customers, peers, management, and workload.

Ask open-ended questions. Don't ask questions that require a "yes" or "no," or short response. Asking open-ended questions allows the applicant to respond completely and often reveals more information that will lead into additional questions. Exhibit 15.4 gives sample interview questions.

EXHIBIT 15.4   Sample Interview Questions from UCI Medical Center

Attributes	Questions	Least Desirable Answer	Most Desirable Answer	Rating
Opening Question	Please tell us about your skills, abilities (and/or education) that you feel make you qualified for this position.	States has no special skills or abilities, no education or experience States has applied for many different positions and has not been hired "I just need a job"	Describes in detail specific skills, abilities, education, and experience suitable to position. In addition, observe for: • Interpersonal skills • Team player • Strong background • Adaptability • Good communication skills	☐ Insufficient ☐ Adequate ☐ Superior
Purpose	Why are you interested in employment with us?	Provides answers such as: • To get a job • To work close to home • Good benefits • Need a change • More money	Describes specifics related to: • Great work environment • Opportunity to advance • Looking for new challenges May mention: • Good reputation • Teaching facility • Educational opportunities	☐ Insufficient ☐ Adequate ☐ Superior

(Exhibit continues)

EXHIBIT 15.4 (continued)

Sample Interview Questions from UCI Medical Center

Attributes	Questions	Least Desirable Answer	Most Desirable Answer	Rating
Department-Specific Questions (Please identify 5 questions — a scenario of a specific situation, as well as specific questions related to the exact skill set needed.) Department-Specific Questions:				☐ Insufficient ☐ Adequate ☐ Superior
Customer Service	Describe the most difficult customer you ever had to assist? *(Prompt questions)* • How did you handle? • What was the outcome? • Would you do anything differently next time?	Answers: • "Never had difficult customer" • "Informed supervisor" • Blames customer	Describes specific examples without criticism or blame. Describes appropriate behaviors and verbal responses: • Takes ownership of problem • Is not judgmental of customer • Uses "I" statements • Articulates positive outcome	☐ Insufficient ☐ Adequate ☐ Superior
Teamwork	What type of work environment do you prefer?	Unable to answer, or answers: • "Everyone does their own job" • "A boss that leaves me alone" • "No one bothers me"	Describes specific examples/behaviors such as: • Team oriented • Supportive environment • Involved • Respectful • Professional • Availability of resources/ training • Good communication	☐ Insufficient ☐ Adequate ☐ Superior

University of California, Irvine Medical Center. Used with permission.

Categories for Open-Ended Questions

Ask questions in categories such as:

▲ *Past or current positions* — What did you enjoy most about your last job? How have your previous jobs prepared you for more responsibility?

▲ *Relationships with people* — How would you describe your supervisor? How would you characterize your coworkers? What kind of people do you enjoy working with? What kind do you find difficult?

▲ *Stimulating self-assessment* — What do you consider your greatest strength professionally? In what areas would you most like to improve? Why?

▲ *Career aspirations* — What position do you expect to hold five years from now? What are you doing to achieve your career goals?

▲ *Job application* — How can you apply your skills and experience to this position?

Questions for Physicians

▲ *Commitment* — What do you like about being a physician? What do you dislike? What are your career aspirations?

▲ *Compassion* — What experiences have been most powerful in shaping your professional identity? What feedback have you been given about the first impression you make with patients and families? Describe some of the ways you establish rapport with patients and family members. Describe a conflict situation you have had to address with a patient. Describe a conflict situation you have had to address with your colleagues.

▲ *Skills* — Describe your skills as a physician. What is an example of a challenging patient and what skills did the situation require?

▲ *Charting and record-keeping* — What record-keeping methods do you prefer? How do you feel about charting and keeping records up to date?

Nonverbal Cues

Be sure to watch for nonverbal signals that the candidate is sending. Is his or her body language open, natural, and nondefensive? Is there good eye contact? Can you sense enthusiasm for the job? Does the person become tense when you ask about the reason for leaving his or her last position? If you feel that a candidate is hiding something when responding, ask the individual to elaborate in order to get more information or clarification.

DESCRIBE THE ENVIRONMENT

After you've concluded that you'd like to consider this candidate, describe the vision, mission, and values of the organization. Let the person know what behaviors you expect from members of the team. Also, include any negatives about the position because creating too rosy an image does not give the applicant a true description of the position. During the hiring process can be a good time for managers and other team members to strengthen their vision and mission statements.

CLOSE THE INTERVIEW

Although it may be tempting to offer the position during the interview, don't do it. It's important to compare notes from this candidate with information gathered during the interviews with other candidates. Give the candidate an estimated schedule for the decision-making process, and let him or her know when you'd like the successful candidate to start working at your organization.

CHECK REFERENCES

In screening the candidate's references, consider the following areas and ask relevant questions:

- ▲ Describe the organization's culture, values, and goals. Then ask, "Is this candidate aligned with these values and goals?"
- ▲ Explain the job. Then ask, "How do you think he or she would fit into the position?"
- ▲ If appropriate, ask, "When did he or she work for you? What were the job responsibilities?"
- ▲ Ask how the candidate's reference would describe the applicant's:
  - Attendance;
  - Dependability;
  - Skill level;
  - Level of discretion, confidentiality, and good judgment;

- Accuracy;
- Team skills;
- Customer service;
- Strengths; and
- Areas for improvement.
▲ "Why did the candidate leave his or her position?"
▲ "Would you rehire this individual?" Yes ___ No ___ If no, ask "Why not?"

End the conversation by thanking them for their time and cooperation.

MAKE THE DECISION

As Collins emphasizes in his book, *Good to Great*, "put the who before the what."[8] Skills can improve, but personality and motivation will not change.

I've heard many times that J.W. Marriott, the founder of Marriott International, believed we're either born with motivation or we're not. It's something you can't usually acquire along the way. One of your candidates may have better skills, but it's important to consider all factors that can affect your workplace culture and goals.

Organizations that are known for their quality and effectiveness usually have a robust process for hiring and promoting their team members. In the late 1990s, Southwest Airlines had about 200,000 applicants per year, interviewed 35,000 and hired 4,000.[9] The interviews are done not by human resource professionals, but by peers; that is, pilots hire pilots, reservations people hire people who make reservations.

Southwest has a People Department that identified 35 top pilots, then interviewed them to identify traits that the 35 had in common.[10] Team skills were identified as very important for the pilots, so Southwest now probes candidates for concrete examples of their teamwork, and listens for warning signs, such as candidates who say "I" all the time. Southwest interviewers turned down a pilot with outstanding flying credentials because he was rude to a Southwest receptionist during the recruiting process.

Herb Kelleher, former CEO of Southwest, says, "We draft great attitudes. If you don't have a good attitude, we don't want you, no matter how skilled you are. We can change skill levels through training. We can't change attitude."[11]

One big mistake I often witness in hiring is that managers tend to like and hire candidates who have personality styles similar to their own. Be aware of this, and focus on the position requirements and the skills and experience of the candidates. As tempting as it is to compare the candidate with yourself or with the incumbent, fight the urge. Every successful new hire who is a high performer, goal oriented, and fits with your culture enhances the ability to align team member performance with organizational goals.

 CHAPTER PRESCRIPTIONS

- Hiring new team members shouldn't be an opportunity to *replace* the previous employee. Think about how the new team member can fully serve the practice in the best ways possible.
- Make your vision and mission the main focus when advertising for a new position.
- Don't *just* interview a candidate, but find out whether he or she is truly a good fit for the organization. What can the new person bring to the practice that might be lacking?
- Use the hiring process to your advantage. Get to know the individual's true goals, and determine whether the candidate is a good match for the organizational goals you use to guide your practice.

CHAPTER 16

Orientation

Orientation is often dis-orientation. I wonder how many new team members are spinning at the end of the first day with their new employer.

New team members start the day excited, apprehensive, curious, enthusiastic, hopeful, confident, insecure, cautious — the emotions are all over the map. Will they like it? Will they succeed? Will they be accepted? How long will they work there? As described in Chapter 7, the first stage of any change is resistance, even for a positive change like a new job. An interesting effect of the resistance stage is that we aren't able to listen well — and one of the things we do to new hires is talk at them, sometimes for two days!

Change is a shift from the known to the unknown, and a new job means all new territory. New hires need to adjust before we can become fully productive again. The most frequent complaints about new team member orientation are that it's overwhelming, boring, or that the new team member feels all alone to sink or swim. I know many staff members who say their supervisors were on vacation when they started working at a new job; these new hires floated around aimlessly for a week until the supervisor returned. As the saying goes, "You only have one chance to make a good first impression," and many organizations miss that opportunity. The result is often a *dis-oriented* team member who is not productive, feels helpless, goal-less, and is likely to leave within the first 90 days. From my experience, more than one-fourth of staff members leave within the first 90 days, and many return to their previous employer — if that employer will take them back. This damages the new hire's self-esteem; costs the organization large amounts of money in advertising, interviewing, and orientation; plus, there are hidden costs of wear and tear on staff morale as it spends time and energy trying to get the new hire up to speed.

PURPOSES OF A GOOD ORIENTATION PROCESS

Orientation is an important component of the recruitment and retention process. It's not just a *meet and greet* activity, but a process with many benefits. Some of the benefits from creating a comprehensive, well-planned new hire orientation include:

- ▲ *Reduced anxiety.* As mentioned at the beginning of this chapter, there are many emotions involved with starting a new job. A good orientation program helps reduce the anxiety that comes from entering the unfamiliar organization, provides guidelines for standards of conduct, and shows team members how they fit into the organization. When oriented well, the team member doesn't spend a lot of time trying to second-guess the role and responsibilities that are involved in the new position.

- ▲ *Reduced start-up costs.* A proper orientation can help the team member get up to speed and fully productive more quickly. This reduces the costs involved with learning a new job.

- ▲ *Reduced turnover.* As mentioned earlier, more than 25 percent of new hires leave within the initial three months of starting a new job. A poor orientation program often causes new hires to feel that they aren't valued very highly and that they are being set up to fail. Orientation should demonstrate to staff members that they are valued and that the organization wants to provide them with tools to succeed in their new job.

- ▲ *Time saver for the manager.* The better the initial orientation, the less likely it is for the manager and team members to invest time later answering basic questions or correcting errors the new hire made because of not understanding some organization policies, procedures, or goals.

- ▲ *Realistic job expectations, positive attitudes, and job satisfaction.* It's extremely important that new team members learn as quickly as possible what the organizational goals and expectations are, what their roles and responsibilities are, how they fit into the organization, what they can expect from others in the organization, as well as the values and attitudes of the organization.

WHY ORIENTATION PROGRAMS FAIL

There are several reasons orientation programs fail. The most significant causes are:

▲ The program is poorly planned;

▲ The new team member does not receive a clear picture of his or her role and responsibilities; and

▲ The new employee does not feel welcomed by the team.

Why is it so important for the new hire to feel welcome? When new team members feel welcome and accepted, they are more willing to ask questions, problem solve, participate in making decisions, and take initiative. They become productive members of the workforce much more quickly.

A comprehensive orientation program takes time, energy, commitment, and a monetary investment. However, it can pay off tenfold in benefits for the new hire, the department, and the organization.

TIPS FOR A SUCCESSFUL ORIENTATION

Following are some tips to provide a successful orientation for new team members.

▲ *Examine your program from the viewpoint of the new team member.* Ask new team members what they want to know. Ask recent new hires what they wish they had learned at the start, plus what they liked and disliked about their orientation process. Because it will still be fresh in their minds, they can provide important input. Ask the senior management team what they want the new recruits to know about their jobs and the organization.

▲ *Start the orientation process as soon as the individual accepts the position.* Send an agenda with the offer letter that shows what time to start work, where to park, and where to present themselves on the first day. Keep in touch with the new hire from the time he or she accepts the offer until the time orientation begins.

▲ *Be ready for new team members.* Greet them; make sure a work area has been created for them on Day 1. Inform the other team members of the start date for the new hire and encourage them to reach out to him or her. Introduce the new hire to others in the office, and make them feel welcome.

▲ *Include the mission, vision, values, rules of conduct, history, and "who's who" at the orientation* to provide firm footing for new team members.

▲ *Answer the most fundamental questions of the new hire — how the work that he or she does affects the department and the organization.* Allow enough time for each new team member to understand the roles of everyone in the department, and how his or her role fits into the big picture. Define the what, when, where, and why of the new position before expecting him or her to be fully productive — but don't overwhelm this new recruit, who is trying to absorb so many things at one time.

▲ *Anticipate questions from the new hires.* Provide them with answers to frequently asked questions, a glossary of the organization acronyms and buzzwords, a phone list, and an organizational chart that shows key positions. Distribute a list of company resources that includes the name and e-mail of people who are designated to answer questions.

▲ *Provide a departmental mentor or buddy to the new recruit for at least 90 days to assist with questions during the orientation process.* The mentor can provide a departmental tour and introduce the new team member to his or her coworkers. Choose the mentor carefully — select a positive and knowledgeable team member who is a good representative of your culture. Also, ensure that the mentor is able to commit time and energy to the new hire — if a mentor is working toward a strict deadline on an important project, save that mentor for another new hire after the demanding project is finished.

▲ *Make sure the new hire does not eat alone during the first week.* The first day is a good time for the manager to take the new team member to lunch and include other team members.

▲ *Create a positive experience for new hires so they will return home at the end of the day, eager to report to their families what a great opportunity they have at this new organization.* Help them feel eager about returning on the second day!

A successful orientation happens only if your new team member decides he or she has made a wise decision to join your organization.

Getting to know the other team members is an important step for having the new team member feel valued and cared for in the job. One company has bagels every Friday for the office, and whenever there's a new hire, the bagels are served at his or her desk. Before team members can take a bagel, they must introduce themselves to the new hire. It's been a delicious way to welcome new team members on board.

Some organizations list new members in the newsletter. Others create a team member book that has pictures of each member and some information that each wants to share with the others. These can include interests, hobbies, family, favorite type of music, favorite food, favorite movie, favorite book, role with the organization, and so forth. New team members are immediately included in the team member book. Some organizations send the information via e-mail as an announcement and a welcome. Another puts the new team member's name on the marquis. I smile as I remember accepting a consulting assignment in Kentucky: As I walked into the facility, there appeared my name in lights — truly, in lights! — "Welcome, Dr. Susan Murphy." I couldn't wait to start working with them.

PHYSICIAN ORIENTATION TOPICS

A good orientation program for physicians can increase retention, morale, productivity, and loyalty, and can optimize coding and documentation. In a traditional model of physician orientation, the established physician introduces the eager, young physician to his or her nurse, points out the new physician's three exam rooms, and lets the new physician know about the established physician's upcoming two-week vacation in Europe. The hope is that when the established physician returns, the new physician will know how to find the closest emergency room, be familiar with the local specialists, and understand the peculiarities of the office staff. All this accomplished without a lot of pesky questions for the senior doc, right? Well, the problem with this orientation model is that it doesn't work. Instead, it takes much longer for a new physician to become oriented to the practice and takes longer for him or her to feel like an integral part of the practice.[12]

Dr. R. Grimshaw from the Austin Regional Clinic has developed a physician orientation program that is available for download one time for personal, noncommercial reference through the American Academy of Family Physicians at www.aafp.org/fpm/2001/0400/p.39.html. Grimshaw initially developed the program for the Austin Regional Clinic, which has 125 providers, 50 of whom are family practice physicians. According to Grimshaw, this program could easily be adopted by a practice of any size with any specialty focus.

The program establishes structure around some strategic goals for new physicians:

▲ A visit-frequency target for new physicians is set: 25 visits per day (twenty-one 15-minute visits and four 30-minute physicals) within the first seven to eight weeks;

▲ New physicians are expected to have between 30 percent and 70 percent same-day appointment availability;

▲ Physicians' coding and documentation are reviewed after one and four months of employment as part of the program; and

▲ New physicians receive guidance through a mentoring program and short vignettes about various practice management issues.

The physicians developed single-page, practice management pearls to advise new physicians and increase consistency in the clinic. They chose the topics of pearls based on which subjects prompted the most questions, problems, or complaints from new physicians in the past. The pearls include:

▲ Angry patients;

▲ Charting;

▲ Coding;

▲ Discharging patients from the clinic;

▲ Manipulative patients;

▲ Patients with lists;

▲ Phone-message management;

▲ Physicals;

▲ Physician–patient communication;

▲ Poor outcomes and unexpected deaths;

▲ Procedures;

▲ Referring patients to the after-hours clinic;

▲ Refills;

▲ Same-day appointments;

▲ Specialty phone advice;

▲ Utilization management; and

▲ Workers' compensation.

The clinic also identifies and recruits specific mentors for physicians prior to their arrival who are asked to be available by phone and to meet occasionally with new physicians in nonclinical settings, such as a lunch or dinner off site. In addition to the formal system, the department chief, clinic manager, and administrative representatives make scheduled contact with the new doctors through phone calls or drop-by visits at lunch to provide reinforcement and positive feedback.[13]

POSITIVE RESULTS

The Austin Regional Clinic has experienced positive results because of this orientation–integration program. Productivity is up "dramatically,"[14] documentation is complete, and undercoding of services has been uncovered. In addition, the practice management pearls are being shared with other specialties, and morale has significantly improved.

SUMMARY

To attract, retain, and integrate new team members into your organization, it's important that they believe they are welcomed and that they can be productive and successful. By providing a carefully planned orientation process, you can create a culture where team members and patients can thrive.

CHAPTER PRESCRIPTIONS

- Many team members believe that an orientation is overwhelming and boring. Create a positive and inclusive orientation process for your new hires.
- Make team members aware of the overall organization and their place within it. It's imperative that new hires feel as if they fit into the structure and that their presence within the organization is pivotal.
- Don't allow new team members to feel lost and unwanted. Provide a thorough and meaningful orientation. Ask the senior management team what they want the new recruits to know about their jobs and the organization. Remember that you're building an organization — each member needs to work with the others to achieve success.
- Provide effective orientation so the new recruit will feel valued and will be aware of the new position's responsibilities. When provided with such a positive environment, the team member will want to thrive and succeed.

CHAPTER 17

Developing Team Member Performance Plans

A colleague of mine, a psychologist, has spent 20 years working at one of the most prestigious medical centers in the country. When I called Marilyn to interview her for this chapter, she told me that she has never received feedback on her performance. Each year she gets surprised by a cost-of-living adjustment to her paycheck. She supposes that she's doing an okay job because no one has given her negative feedback. "It's the old 'no news is good news' scenario," she sighed.

This is not an isolated situation. From my experience, there are many medical groups, large and small, that don't have a formal performance management process. Many have job descriptions, and those descriptions include the phrase "other duties as assigned."

In many other medical groups, some of the components for performance management are present but not connected. For example, most staff have job descriptions and their managers conduct performance appraisals year after year. Staff then create performance plans, and often go to training so they can develop skills. Everyone works long, hard hours. There are activities such as planning, budgeting, perhaps even board of directors' retreats. However, all too often, these activities are done in a vacuum — without being tied directly to the mission, values, and goals of the organization.

Let's look at an example that contrasts two types of managers; one type focuses the team members on activities, and the other focuses on accomplishments and goals.

OVERALL GOAL OF PERFORMANCE MANAGEMENT

To me, the second beekeeper in this "Beekeepers and Their Bees" story models performance management at its best. He systematically developed a

THE BEEKEEPERS AND THEIR BEES[15]

Once upon a time, there were two beekeepers who each had a beehive. The beekeepers worked for a company called Bees, Inc. The company's customers loved its honey and wanted the business to produce more honey than it had the previous year. As a result, each beekeeper was told to produce more honey at the same quality. With different ideas about how to do this, the beekeepers designed different approaches to improve the performance of their hives.

The first beekeeper established a bee performance management approach that measured how many flowers each bee visited. At considerable cost to the beekeeper, an extensive measurement system was created to count the flowers each bee visited. The beekeeper provided feedback to each bee at midseason on her individual performance, but the bees were never told about the hive's goal to produce more honey so that Bees, Inc., could increase honey sales. The beekeeper created special awards for the bees who visited the most flowers.

The second beekeeper also established a bee performance management approach, but this approach communicated to each bee the goal of the hive — to produce more honey. This beekeeper measured two aspects of their performance: the amount of nectar each bee brought back to the hive and the amount of honey the hive produced. The performance of each bee and the hive's overall performance were charted and posted on the hive's bulletin board for all bees to see. The beekeeper created a few awards for the bees that gathered the most nectar, but also established a hive incentive program that rewarded each bee in the hive based on the hive's production of honey — the more honey produced, the more recognition each bee would receive.

At the end of the season, the beekeepers evaluated their approaches. The first beekeeper found that his hive had indeed increased the number of flowers visited, but the amount of honey produced by the hive had dropped. The queen bee reported that because the bees were so busy trying to visit as many flowers as possible, they limited the amount of nectar they would carry so they could fly faster. Also, because the bees believed they were competing against each other for awards (because only the top performers were recognized), they would not share valuable information with each other (like the location of the flower-filled fields they'd spotted on the way back to the hive) that could have helped improve the performance of all the bees. (After all was said and done, one of the high-performing bees told the beekeeper that if he'd been told that the real goal was to make more honey rather than to visit more flowers, he would have done his work completely differently.) As the beekeeper handed out the awards to individual bees, unhappy buzzing was heard in the background.

The second beekeeper, however, had very different results. Because each bee in the hive was focused on the hive's goal of producing more honey, the bees had concentrated their efforts on gathering more nectar to produce more honey than ever before. The bees worked together to determine the highest nectar-yielding flowers and to create quicker processes for depositing the nectar they'd gathered. They also worked together to help increase the amount of nectar gathered by the poor performers. The queen bee of this hive reported that the poor performers either improved their performance or transferred to another hive. Because the hive had reached its goal, the beekeeper awarded each bee his portion of the hive incentive payment. The beekeeper was also surprised to hear a loud, happy buzz and a jubilant flapping of wings as he rewarded the individual high-performing bees with special recognition.

Moral: Measuring and recognizing accomplishments rather than activities — and giving feedback to worker bees — often improve results of the hive.

high-performing team that produced extraordinary results, received rewards for its accomplishments, and enjoyed the ride!

The overall goal of performance management is to ensure that the whole organization and all of its subsystems, including its managers, staff, departments, processes, and systems, are working together in an optimum fashion to achieve the results desired by the organization. It links the work of each manager and team member to the mission of his or her department as well as to the overall mission of the organization. All team members play a key role in the success of your organization. Just as in the "Beekeepers and Their Bees," story, how well you manage the performance of your team members directly affects not only the performance of the individual team member, but also the performance of your entire organization.

WHAT IS PERFORMANCE MANAGEMENT?

A good performance management system focuses on achieving results by aligning the performance of all team members with the organizational goals. Performance management is a systematic approach for managing employees and involves planning, monitoring, developing, appraising, rewarding, and improving performance in support of the organizational mission, values, and goals.

Performance management works to achieve consensus, cultivate continuous improvement, support relationships, and ensure that the entire organization is focused on achieving the desired results. It encourages the team to focus on results and accomplishments, not just activities and busyness.

It's a dynamic process that cascades throughout the organization, in every department and in every individual. The ultimate goal of a performance management system is improved organizational performance. An effective performance management system achieves several outcomes, including motivation and retention of talent as well as improved profit, performance, quality, customer service, morale, and efficiency.

Performance management is the systematic continuing process of:[16]

- ▲ Planning work and setting expectations;
- ▲ Continually monitoring performance;
- ▲ Developing the capacity to perform;
- ▲ Periodically rating performance in a summary fashion; and
- ▲ Rewarding good performance.

PERFORMANCE BENEFITS FOR MANAGERS, TEAM MEMBERS, AND ORGANIZATIONS

Performance management provides the structure for managers to serve as mentors and coaches, and allows them to offer support, encouragement, and guidance in a systematic way. For staff, it provides a framework in which to operate. Most team members welcome some structure as long as it isn't too constraining. When team members are clear about what's expected of them and have the necessary support to contribute efficiently and productively, their sense of purpose, self-worth, and motivation will increase.

FIVE KEY COMPONENTS OF PERFORMANCE MANAGEMENT

Many managers have been practicing effective performance management naturally during all their supervisory lives, even without formal training in

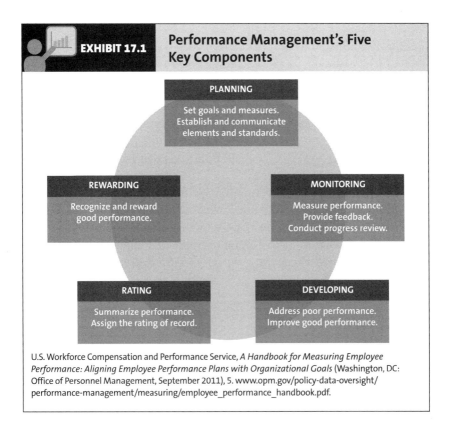

EXHIBIT 17.1

Performance Management's Five Key Components

PLANNING
Set goals and measures. Establish and communicate elements and standards.

REWARDING
Recognize and reward good performance.

MONITORING
Measure performance. Provide feedback. Conduct progress review.

RATING
Summarize performance. Assign the rating of record.

DEVELOPING
Address poor performance. Improve good performance.

U.S. Workforce Compensation and Performance Service, *A Handbook for Measuring Employee Performance: Aligning Employee Performance Plans with Organizational Goals* (Washington, DC: Office of Personnel Management, September 2011), 5. www.opm.gov/policy-data-oversight/ performance-management/measuring/employee_performance_handbook.pdf.

this important area. Others have only been doing one component of this process — that of periodically assigning ratings to the team members' performance. Compared to the other four components, rating performance is the least important part.

Let's look at these five key components[17] more carefully (these are illustrated in Exhibit 17.1).

Planning

In effective organizations, work is planned in advance. The planning process means setting performance expectations and goals for the organization, the departments, and the individuals. These goals cascade throughout the organization, and each is congruent with the vision, mission, and values of the organization. High-performing organizations get staff at all levels involved in the planning process to ensure that they understand the goals of the entire organization, how their roles and responsibilities fit in with all the organizational goals, what needs to be done, why it needs to be done, and how well it should be done. Performance standards should be SMART — specific, measurable, achievable, results-oriented, and time-bound.

Monitoring

How well the team members are performing their roles and responsibilities and handling assignments and projects are monitored continually in effective organizations. Effective managers are consistently measuring performance and providing ongoing feedback to team members on their progress toward reaching their goals. By monitoring continually, managers can identify performance that is not goal oriented and provide assistance so that the team member can get back on track before bad habits are formed. Habits become engrained after 21 days, so it's important for managers to provide monitoring and FAST (frequent, accurate, specific, timely) feedback to their team members.

Developing

In effective organizations, managers identify individuals' developmental needs. Team members receive additional training to learn new skills and handle assignments with higher levels of responsibility. Providing team members with training and developmental opportunities encourages good performance, strengthens job-related skills and competencies, and helps team members keep up with new technology and other changes in the workplace. The developing component enables team members to address poor performance and improve good performance. Team members who are Generation Xers and Millennials will stay more engaged when their managers take an interest in their professional development.

Rating

Summarizing a team member's performance helps with comparing performance over time or across a group of individuals. It is important that organizations know who their best performers are. Rating is based on work performed during an entire appraisal period, and often has a bearing for pay increases, bonuses, and promotions. With ongoing monitoring and feedback, a performance rating should never be a surprise.

Rewarding

In effective organizations, rewards are often used and are both formal and informal. Rewarding means recognizing individuals for their performance and acknowledging their contributions to the organization's mission and goals. For good managers, recognition is an ongoing, natural part of every day. Rewards can range from a sincere "thank you," a note of appreciation, time off, or a bonus. A study in *Incentive Magazine* found that 57 percent of respondents said they preferred to be recognized by an immediate supervisor, compared to only 21 percent who placed higher value on a presentation from the company president.[18]

SIGNIFICANT CONNECTION BETWEEN PERFORMANCE MANAGEMENT AND TEAM MEMBER ENGAGEMENT

In Chapter 11, I report the results of a study by researchers Marcus Buckingham and Curt Coffman of the Gallup organization. For their best-selling book, *First, Break All the Rules*,[19] they interviewed 80,000 managers in 400 organizations and found a significant connection between performance management and employee engagement. They established 12 questions that measure the core elements needed to attract, focus, and keep the most talented employees, and seven of these elements relate directly to performance management principles!

In another study of 100,000 employees from 2,500 organizations, the Gallup organization pinpointed employee attitudes that are present in highly productive work groups and that relate directly to the rate of employee turnover, customer satisfaction, and productivity. Many of these attitudes reflect effective performance management practices.[20]

Individuals in these highly productive teams report high levels of agreement with the following statements. Notice how these statements relate directly to good performance management:

- ⏶ I know what is expected of me at work. (planning)
- ⏶ At work, I have the opportunity to do what I do best every day. (planning)
- ⏶ In the last six months, someone at work has talked to me about my progress. (monitoring)
- ⏶ There is someone at work who encourages my development. (developing)
- ⏶ I have the materials and equipment I need to do my work right. (developing)

▲ This last year, I have had opportunities at work to learn and grow. (developing)

▲ In the last seven days, I have received recognition or praise for doing good work. (rewarding)

Exhibit 17.2 presents a job description and performance plan for medical assistant or nursing support in a medical practice. GE Healthcare Camden Group provided this document.

Medical Assistant/Nursing Support: Guidelines for Performance Plan

In Exhibit 17.2, the position description is shown on the first two pages and the performance plan is on the third page. The very beginning of the document shows the position summary that ties the medical assistant to the big picture.

The position summary clearly states that this team member assists the physicians with the examination and treatment of patients and performs routine tasks needed to keep the clinical office running smoothly.

The performance plan has three components:

1. Job description and summary;
2. Performance standards; and
3. Performance tracking.

Team members sign this document and acknowledge receipt of the job description and that they can fulfill all of the requirements of the position.

Checklist for Effective Performance Plan

When developing performance plans, check against these guidelines:[21]

▲ Are the critical elements truly critical?

▲ Is the range of acceptable performance clear? Are the performance expectations quantifiable, observable, and/or verifiable?

▲ Are the standards attainable? Are the expectations reasonable?

▲ Are the standards challenging?

▲ Are the standards fair? Are they comparable to expectations for other staff in similar positions?

EXHIBIT 17.2   **Sample Job Description and Performance Plan**

MEDICAL ASSISTANT/NURSING SUPPORT
POSITION DESCRIPTION AND PERFORMANCE PLAN

REPORTS TO: Back Office Supervisor

POSITION SUMMARY
Assist the physicians with the examination and treatment of patients and perform routine tasks needed to keep the clinical office running smoothly.

JOB RESPONSIBILITIES

- Greets patients and escorts them to the examination and/or procedure rooms.
- Takes vital signs (pulse, blood pressure, temperature) as well as weight and height; accurately transcribes results in patient's chart.
- Assists in completion of forms required by physician prior to examination (for example, health questionnaires, medical history, etc.).
- Removes casts, dressings, and staples as required; prepares patient for examination, test(s), or procedure(s).
- Provides instructions when appropriate; obtains signed consent forms when required.
- Sets up procedure tray(s).
- Notifies physician when patient is ready for examination.
- Assists physician with examinations and procedures as needed. Prepares and administers medication as prescribed by the physician.
- Labels and color codes blood samples, including packaging of specimens for shipment to appropriate outside labs.
- Maintains and restocks clinical supplies for back office (for example, examination and procedure rooms) in addition to inventory control and generating monthly inventory list.
- Organizes and keeps a running inventory of medications in med rooms and refrigerator (routinely disposing of expired medications as warranted).
- Cleans and scrubs down rooms and countertops per clinical policy.
- Cleans, packages, and sterilizes instruments and procedure supplies (forceps, etc.).
- Tracks all lab results (for example, calling for cultures, blood type, and lab information) and documents and initials results in chart when hard copy is not available.
- Adheres to OSHA [Occupational Safety and Health Administration] guidelines.
- Retrieves prescription calls off voice mail at least three times a day and responds within given time frames.

(Exhibit continues)

EXHIBIT 17.2 (continued)   **Sample Job Description and Performance Plan**

- ▲ Reviews charts for next-day appointments; checks for pending lab or diagnostic test results at the end of each business day; obtains said results prior to the patient's scheduled arrival.
- ▲ Initials and files all patient-related correspondence within 24 hours of receipt.
- ▲ Ensures that all charts are appropriately filed at the end of each business day.
- ▲ Maintains daily lab and procedure logs; supplies patient insurance information to lab within 24 hours of test.
- ▲ Records services rendered on fee tickets (lab, etc.) and checks for accuracy.
- ▲ Highlights physician notes for ancillary tests, surgeries, or specialist referrals ordered and scheduled as directed.
- ▲ Directs patient to checkout counter.
- ▲ Performs any other services deemed reasonable by physician or supervisor.

QUALIFICATIONS

Experience and Education. High school diploma or equivalent or completion of certificated medical assistant program preferred. A multitasked professional with at least three years of experience in performing back-office activities in a medical environment.

Knowledge. Basic medical back-office procedures and medical terminology; first aid measures; equipment, supplies, and instruments used in a medical office; simple routine clinical laboratory methods; universal blood and body fluid precautions; OSHA rules and regulations; established protocol for storing poisons, narcotics, acids, caustics, and flammable items; restrictions imposed by various managed care carriers; various forms inherent to profession; patient confidentiality regulations.

Abilities. Establish and maintain cooperative relationships with staff members and create a responsive, caring environment for patients; respond promptly to physician's direction(s); maintain medical records in a concise and accurate manner; employ correct aseptic techniques in preparation of instruments and equipment; react quickly in emergency situations and maintain current CPR [cardio pulmonary resuscitation] card; recognize and prevent possible safety hazards; ensure proper maintenance of equipment; communicate clearly and facilitate patient education when warranted; act as advocate and assist physician in meeting the physical and mental needs of patient; exercise independent judgment; perform functions that consistently fall within the legal boundaries of profession.

Note: This description indicates in general terms the type and level of work performed and responsibilities held by the employee(s). Duties described are not to be interpreted as being all-inclusive.

I acknowledge receipt of this job description and can fulfill all of the requirements of this position.

Signature: _____ Date: _____

(Exhibit continues)

	EXHIBIT 17.2 (continued)	Sample Job Description and Performance Plan

Job Description/Summary	Performance Standards*	Performance Tracking†
Assist the physicians with the examination and treatment of patients and perform routine tasks needed to keep the clinical office running smoothly.	10–15 minutes average waiting time in exam room	Patient log and feedback
	5 minutes average exam room turn-around for the next patient	Patient time log
	100% accuracy in clinical forms documentation	Chart audit
	100% compliance in inventory control and standardization	Inventory control log
	100% compliance to clinical operational protocols	Physician and peer feedback
	100% physician satisfaction	Physician feedback

* Performance Standards — expected measures of individual performance
† Performance Tracking — process activities to track achievement of performance standards

© GE Healthcare Camden Group. Used with permission.

- ▲ Are the standards applicable? Can the appraiser use the standards to appraise performance? Are they measurable?
- ▲ Will team members understand what is required?

OUTCOMES OF THE PERFORMANCE MANAGEMENT SYSTEM

The overall outcomes of the performance management system will cascade throughout the organization as each unit and individual plays its part and accomplishes his or her own goals. The effect on the entire practice structure and operation may include the following major outcomes for the practice:

- ▲ *Performance management stabilization* — creating alignment, organizational initiatives and strategy, department goals, individual performance plans;
- ▲ *Organizational performance* — productivity, adaptability, quality;

▲ *Team member satisfaction* — motivation, engagement, retention, loyalty;

▲ *Reward systems* — merit pay, variable pay (short- and long-term incentives, including effect on equity-based rewards), recognition; and/or

▲ *Development* — succession planning, training, career progression.

Performance and development planning should be conducted:

▲ Annually, at the start of each performance cycle;

▲ When a new team member is hired and needs clear goals;

▲ When a team member is transferred into a new department; and

▲ When organization or department plans are completed.

INTERNAL AND EXTERNAL INFLUENCES

Performance management does not operate in a vacuum. It's a dynamic system that is affected continually by frequent internal and external pressures that throw it off balance. In Chapter 1, I described the Weisbord Six-Box model. After examining the six boxes inside the system and how they influence one another, I explained the effect of the external influences on the system. Each system is influenced by changes in the other systems.

Internal influences can include budget shortfalls, revamping of the organizational structure, changes in business strategy, and staff and management turnover.

External influences can include changes in customer demands, legal challenges, government regulatory changes, labor market shortages, industry characteristics, resource availability, technology, competition, economics, and politics.

THE DASHBOARD OF ORGANIZATIONAL GOALS: "IF YOU CAN'T MEASURE IT, YOU CAN'T MANAGE IT"

Although dashboards were discussed in Chapter 2, they play an important part in performance management as well, because in effective organizations, the organizational goals cascade throughout every aspect of the organization.

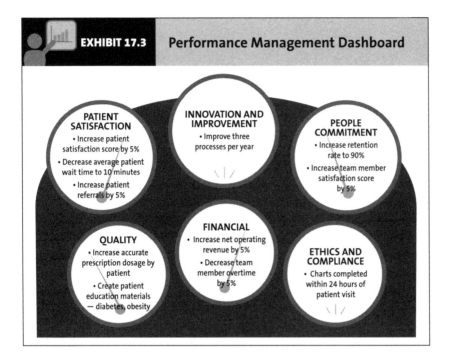

EXHIBIT 17.3 Performance Management Dashboard

PATIENT SATISFACTION
• Increase patient satisfaction score by 5%
• Decrease average patient wait time to 10 minutes
• Increase patient referrals by 5%

INNOVATION AND IMPROVEMENT
• Improve three processes per year

PEOPLE COMMITMENT
• Increase retention rate to 90%
• Increase team member satisfaction score by 5%

QUALITY
• Increase accurate prescription dosage by patient
• Create patient education materials — diabetes, obesity

FINANCIAL
• Increase net operating revenue by 5%
• Decrease team member overtime by 5%

ETHICS AND COMPLIANCE
• Charts completed within 24 hours of patient visit

Robert S. Kaplan and David P. Norton developed this concept of creating a set of measures that they refer to as a "balanced scorecard";[22] I like to call it a dashboard. These measures give managers a fast but comprehensive view of the organization's performance, like the dashboard in an airplane cockpit, with several dials and indicators. For the complex task of flying an airplane, pilots need detailed information about fuel, air speed, altitude, bearing, and other indicators that summarize the current and predicted environment. Reliance on only one instrument can be fatal.

Leading healthcare organizations are adopting these dashboards to display their goals and performance measurements. I concur with many experts who believe that if you can't measure it, you can't manage it. Exhibit 17.3 provides an example of a dashboard with short-term SMART performance goals that can be tracked. Exhibit 17.4 is a performance management self-assessment.

WHY DON'T TEAM MEMBERS PERFORM?

Leadership is the ability to accomplish goals through others, so it's up to the leaders to diagnose what gets in the way. There's not one easy answer about

EXHIBIT 17.4	How Good Are You at Performance Management?

SELF-ASSESSMENT

1.	Do you understand your organization's mission and goals?	Yes	Somewhat	No
2.	Do your department goals support the overall organizational goals?	Yes	Somewhat	No
3.	Do you have a written performance plan with clear performance goals for yourself?	Yes	Somewhat	No
4.	Do you involve your team members in setting their own written annual performance goals?	Yes	Somewhat	No
5.	Do each of your team members clearly understand how they contribute to the overall mission and goals?	Yes	Somewhat	No
6.	Do you provide FAST (frequent, accurate, specific, timely) feedback to team members about their performance?	Yes	Somewhat	No
7.	Do you meet at least quarterly with each team member to review his or her performance against goals?	Yes	Somewhat	No
8.	Do you hold annual performance reviews with each team member, providing a written appraisal and co-creating a performance/career development plan?	Yes	Somewhat	No

© 2016 Susan A. Murphy, MBA, PhD

Note: This exhibit is available as an electronic file.*

why some individuals don't perform. Following are some of the reasons team members don't perform plus some ideas about what the manager can do to get individuals on track:[23]

▲ *Team members don't know how or what they should do.* The manager can provide training, give clear directions and expectations about the goals, be approachable and encourage questions, and plan projects and assignments together.

▲ *They do not want to do the job.* The manager can talk about the importance of reaching the goals, work with the team member to make the job more stimulating (if possible), and problem solve together. Do not allow poor performance to continue unchecked.

▲ *There is no negative consequence for poor performance.* The manager can give consistent, honest feedback and appropriate raises. Set consequences, and if improvement doesn't occur, follow through and begin the disciplinary process.

---

*Instructions to access the electronic files are available in Appendix A.

▲ *The reward or consequence is for not doing what should be done.* The manager can (1) give positive feedback when goals are reached, especially on tough assignments; (2) let team members correct their own errors so they stay goal focused; and (3) talk about the goals often.

▲ *Team members think they are doing just fine.* The manager can provide FAST feedback and include self-evaluation by the individual to ensure that he or she is goal focused.

▲ *Team members think their way, not your way, is better, and it is not.* The manager can explain the benefits of doing things his or her way and include staff in the planning because they are more likely to support changes if they're personally involved in the process.

▲ *There are obstacles limiting their performance.* The manager can work to remove obstacles by adding resources, training, guidance, or, if appropriate, by seeking cooperation from other managers.

▲ *Team members fear a negative consequence.* The manager can practice self-control emotionally — no sarcasm or outbursts when errors are made, support individuals as they learn how to correct mistakes, and create an atmosphere of trust and encouragement.

▲ *Team members think something else is more important.* The manager can prioritize goals with team members and plan with them how to manage important projects.

CHAPTER PRESCRIPTIONS

■ Make your expectations clear to your team members and provide them with the necessary support to execute the goals, whether as individuals, departments, or the organization.

■ Make team members a major part of the planning process, and ensure that they understand just how important their goals as individuals are to the implementation of the organization's overriding goals.

■ Provide consistent and meaningful feedback to team members so they know what they're doing well and how they might improve on achieving set goals in other areas.

■ Look in the mirror! Don't stop at evaluating team members, but be sure to engage in self-assessment at all levels: individually, departmentally, and organizationally.

CHAPTER 18

Conducting Performance Appraisals

As the late management guru Chris Argyris said, "People have the capacity to go either way — toward growth or toward stagnation. The design of the system in which they work can significantly influence which way they go, and how far."[24]

NO SURPRISES

There should never be any surprises during a performance appraisal. Throughout the year, the effective leader has been giving frequent, accurate, specific, timely (FAST) feedback to each team member, which lets the team member know when performance is aligned with goals and when it is not.

Chapters 8 and 9 provide specific examples of how to give goal-focused feedback to team members as well as information about the *educable moment*, which is the time immediately following an action when behavior can best be reinforced.

FEEDBACK ONCE A YEAR IS NOT EFFECTIVE

Giving feedback once a year at a performance appraisal and expecting an individual's behavior to change has the same effect as dieting once a year on your birthday and expecting to lose weight. Effective leaders provide coaching all year long, so the annual performance appraisal is only one part of the entire performance management system. I believe that one of the most important effects of the performance appraisal is that team members are made aware of the significance of the contribution they are expected to make and what those expectations are. When properly and fairly conducted, the performance appraisal process can increase a team member's sense of personal investment in the organization, strengthen the relationship between the leader and team member, protect the organization legally, enhance the culture of the organization, and align the team member's performance with organizational goals. When conducted poorly, the opposite can occur and work against the leader, the team member, and the organization.

PLANNING AND PREPARATION

Performance planning begins at the initial preemployment interview when goals, expectations, and values are discussed. The annual performance appraisal is a formal continuation of those discussions.

An effective performance appraisal has four attributes:

1. It is a *formal discussion* between a team member and his or her supervisor.
2. It is a detailed examination of how the team member is *currently performing* on the job.
3. It is a means of determining how the team member can perform more effectively in *the future* and ensuring his or her *continued professional growth and development*.
4. It is a *beneficial* process for the team member, the supervisor, and the organization as a whole.

By *formal* discussion, I don't mean to imply that it's a formality. A performance appraisal requires careful planning and preparation; it cannot be handled effectively in a casual chat. It is a discussion that occurs at prescribed intervals and follows a specified form specific to your organization. It is not a cursory review. The manager and team member look at the team member's current level of performance in achieving goals and at the quality of that performance, and then determine the reasons (positive or negative) for that level. For example, if one individual is performing a task better than all the other team members, determining the reasons for that individual's success may help improve the others' performance.

It's important to remember that appraisals aren't just a review of the past but are also a guide to the future. To be effective, performance appraisals must chart a path to the future with plans to increase performance in some areas, if appropriate, as well as begin a process that assists managers in identifying talent, rewarding achievement, and encouraging professional growth. Many organizations now say, "Our employees are our most important asset." I like Michael Eisner's quote when he was the CEO of the Walt Disney Company: "My inventory goes home every night."[25] The key to achieving the benefits of a successful performance appraisal system is the linking of the team member's skills and achievements to the goals of his or her department, and ultimately to the achievement of the organization's goals and mission.

MANAGERS INITIATE PROCESS

Managers have the responsibility to initiate the performance review process and to schedule the upcoming meeting. I continue to be disappointed with many managers who are late in initiating this process. Team members usually know, to the day, when their year is up and their appraisals and raises are due. Although staff members often fear the process, they want feedback from their manager and then to receive their increase. Some team members complain to me that their managers are always late. Even though the salary increase is often retroactive to their anniversary date, the team members don't want to be the ones to initiate the conversation about the late performance review because they're concerned the manager may score them lower because they're behaving like a pest. Resentment builds and the review meeting becomes even tenser.

TEAM MEMBER UPDATES JOB DESCRIPTION AND SELF-ASSESSMENT

Invite the team member to suggest any updates to the job description roles and responsibilities and to complete a self-assessment prior to the meeting. I have always encouraged the team member to return the self-assessment to the manager before the meeting, which allows the manager to see how the person views his or her own performance. As a manager, you can gain valuable insight into what an individual is thinking and use this to craft the discussion at the performance review meeting.

MANAGERIAL PREPARATION

I recommend that you complete the evaluation form at one sitting, and then review it at a later time. Edit and then reedit. Every word is important to the team member, and I guarantee that many of your team members will read their reviews several times, especially any portion you rate less than "excellent." Review the team member's job description, performance goals, and rules of conduct, and assess his or her job performance against these criteria. Review the team member's history, including job skills, training, experience, and special or unique qualifications. Note any variances in the individual's performance that need to be discussed, and ensure that you provide specific examples for every area. The next step is to review what you have written and check for any biases or inflammatory wording. Then determine rating and merit increase.

As you are reviewing the team member's performance before the meeting, I recommend you consider the following questions from Rummler and Brache.[26] If any of the six statements can be answered "no," you may need to include that discussion in the performance review meeting. There could be some system problems that are impeding the team member's ability to excel in his or her position.

1. Do the performers understand the job goals (standards they are expected to meet)?
2. Do the performers have sufficient resources, clear signals and priorities, and a logical job design?
3. Are the performers rewarded for achieving the job goals?
4. Do the performers know if they are meeting the job goals?
5. Do the performers have the necessary knowledge or skill to achieve the job goals?
6. If the performers were in an environment in which the five questions were answered "yes," do they have the physical and mental capacity to achieve the goals?

PITFALLS TO AVOID

It's easy to succumb to pitfalls that may skew an honest assessment of the team member's job performance. For example, you may give too much weight to recent events that have occurred that don't represent the team member's behavior during the entire year. Additionally, there are some team members whom managers like better — people who have similar values, interests, and personality traits. It's important to evaluate job performance and not play favorites. Another pitfall is called the *halo or horns effect* that occurs when the manager is influenced by a recent single event involving the individual. The manager may also be tempted to be lenient and rate everyone higher than deserved in order to make it easier to get through the process, as well as make it easier for the team to like the manager. It's also tempting to rate all the team members similarly and place everyone in the middle of the scale.

Other examples of pitfalls can be a bias or prejudice that the manager holds against the team member that has nothing to do with job performance.

These prejudices could include religion, education, family background, age, or gender. Sometimes a team member may have excelled or performed poorly in one or two areas, and this may trigger the manager to give an unbalanced evaluation based on those few areas. Another pitfall to an effective performance review process is when the team member is not allowed enough time to complete the self-assessment.

THE APPRAISAL INTERVIEW

The appraisal interview is one of the manager's most important meetings with the team member for the entire year. Team members often dread this meeting and need the manager to make the meeting private and as comfortable as possible. Schedule one to one-and-a-half hours of uninterrupted time for the meeting. Following is an eight-step outline of how to best conduct the meeting so you and the individual both have the opportunity to discuss and review all that you both need and wish to.

1. **Greet the team member and establish rapport immediately.** The individual is probably apprehensive and will welcome your gesture to establish a warm climate. It's important to keep in mind that your opening remarks set the tone for the rest of the meeting.

2. **Explain the purpose and benefits of the performance review process.** Ask if the person has any questions or comments before you start.

3. **Request the team member give his or her opinion of performance since the last appraisal.** Ask where the person believes he or she is doing well and areas where he or she might improve. Seeking a team member's opinion of his or her performance shows that you, as the manager, respect his or her contribution, expertise, and knowledge. This can give you an accurate picture of how the team member is doing and may uncover some problem areas where you can help.

   Ask open-ended questions to gain information — who, what, when, where, how, why, describe, tell me. Don't talk too much during the assessment — this is the individual's time to present his or her evaluation of performance.

4. **Present your own evaluation of the team member's performance and give recognition for accomplishments since the last review.** Avoid terms such as *always* and *never*. A key to raising performance levels is motivation, and one key to motivation is recognition. By providing specific examples of performance where you believe that your team member deserves recognition, the individual will feel appreciated because he or she knows you've "caught them doing something right," as Ken Blanchard preaches.[27]

   Confirm where you agree with your team member during the performance review. Where you disagree, give your own views with specific examples. Let the team member see that you are interested in helping him or her succeed.

5. **Seek your team member's input on one or two performance areas that he or she believes could be developed.** Compare the individual's responses with your choices, then negotiate together to develop an action plan. Check his or her understanding and reaction. Psychologists indicate that when an individual is faced with more than two areas in which performance should be improved, that person becomes defensive and feels the supervisor is being critical instead of supportive. This can endanger the performance review and lead to a nonmotivational discussion.

6. **Ask your team member if there is anything that you could be doing to help him or her in being more effective at work.** This can provide the manager with some feedback of how to be more effective with the team.

7. **Review with your team member the benefits of the performance review and summarize key points to ensure understanding by both manager and staff member.** Review the overall performance, stressing the areas where the individual is excelling.

8. **End the performance review with a positive, motivating message.** By ending with upbeat, encouraging words, the team member returns to work in a positive frame of mind.

Knowing that your manager is on your side can be a powerful motivator. By conducting an honest, respectful performance appraisal that is focused on the goals of the department and the organization, you are aligning your team member's performance with the organizational goals. Exhibit 18.1 provides a performance appraisal checklist for managers.

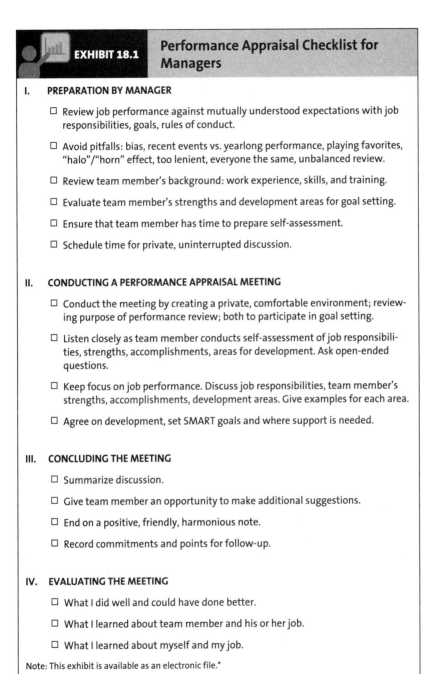

EXHIBIT 18.1 Performance Appraisal Checklist for Managers

I. PREPARATION BY MANAGER

☐ Review job performance against mutually understood expectations with job responsibilities, goals, rules of conduct.

☐ Avoid pitfalls: bias, recent events vs. yearlong performance, playing favorites, "halo"/"horn" effect, too lenient, everyone the same, unbalanced review.

☐ Review team member's background: work experience, skills, and training.

☐ Evaluate team member's strengths and development areas for goal setting.

☐ Ensure that team member has time to prepare self-assessment.

☐ Schedule time for private, uninterrupted discussion.

II. CONDUCTING A PERFORMANCE APPRAISAL MEETING

☐ Conduct the meeting by creating a private, comfortable environment; reviewing purpose of performance review; both to participate in goal setting.

☐ Listen closely as team member conducts self-assessment of job responsibilities, strengths, accomplishments, areas for development. Ask open-ended questions.

☐ Keep focus on job performance. Discuss job responsibilities, team member's strengths, accomplishments, development areas. Give examples for each area.

☐ Agree on development, set SMART goals and where support is needed.

III. CONCLUDING THE MEETING

☐ Summarize discussion.

☐ Give team member an opportunity to make additional suggestions.

☐ End on a positive, friendly, harmonious note.

☐ Record commitments and points for follow-up.

IV. EVALUATING THE MEETING

☐ What I did well and could have done better.

☐ What I learned about team member and his or her job.

☐ What I learned about myself and my job.

Note: This exhibit is available as an electronic file.*

---

*Instructions to access the electronic files are available in Appendix A.

HOW TO PROVIDE FEEDBACK DURING APPRAISAL

Some general guidelines for giving feedback include:

▲ Focus on relevant performance and behavior, not the person;

▲ Focus on specific, observable behavior, not on general impressions;

▲ Avoid loaded terms that produce an emotional reaction or cause defensiveness;

▲ Focus on areas over which the person can exercise some control or for which he or she can use the feedback to improve;

▲ When encountering defensive reactions, deal with reactions rather than try to convince, reason, or supply other information; and

▲ End on a positive note. Focus on keeping the self-esteem of both parties intact.

360-DEGREE FEEDBACK

The 360-degree feedback method is a tool that provides team members the opportunity to receive feedback from their manager, three to eight peers, direct reports, and customers. The team member also responds to a self-assessment for comparison. This format allows individuals to understand their effectiveness as employees, coworkers, and managers. I've been involved in several 360-degree assessments, and I know firsthand how critical it is that this form of feedback system be established in a careful, methodical manner that includes training and support for all involved. When implemented well, 360-degree feedback enables people in organizations to better serve customers, enhance interpersonal skills, and develop their careers. This kind of feedback can provide each individual important insight about the skills and behaviors valued in the organization to accomplish the mission, vision, and values and to align performance with the organizational goals. I recommend that the 360-degree feedback be separate from the formal performance appraisal system. When first rolled out, this form of feedback works best as a professional development tool. Sure, it can identify areas for improvement; however, I've seen it work best initially when it is not associated directly with compensation changes.

CAREER DEVELOPMENT QUESTIONS

Research indicates that more than 60 percent of staff, no matter what age, gender, or generation, want career development opportunities. During the performance review, it can be a good time to ask your team members some questions about their career goals. Some questions about career level performance goals include:

- ▲ What job or occupation would you like to have in three to five years?
- ▲ What skills, experiences, and competencies are required by the job?
- ▲ What are you planning to do to prepare yourself for that job?
- ▲ How can I support your efforts?

CHAPTER PRESCRIPTIONS

- Ensure that team members are made aware of the importance of the contribution expected of them and exactly what those expectations are.
- Remember that an effective performance appraisal process can increase a team member's sense of worth and investment within the organization, strengthen the relationship between employer and team member, enhance the culture of the organization, and align team member performance with organizational goals.
- Approach each performance appraisal as a discussion that occurs at assigned and expected intervals and follows a specific set of rules.
- Team member appraisals are useful in assessing the individual's past performance, but should also be used to set clear goals for the future. Therefore, have the team member fill out a self-assessment prior to the meeting so that the manager can address issues that are specific to each team member's needs. It's also helpful to have a sense of how the team member views his or her work performance before the meeting.
- Provide meaningful and accurate feedback for your team members — if you just tell them what they want to hear, you may be liked, but your organization is sure to suffer.
- People are always more apt to be open to criticism when they are also told what they are doing well. Be sure to hone in on what you feel the team member is bringing to the organization, and then discuss areas for improvement — use the organizational goals as a tool for aligning each team member within the practice.

ENDNOTES

1   "2014 National Scorecard on Payment Reform," Catalyst for Payment Reform, accessed Nov. 17, 2015, www.catalyzepaymentreform.org/how-we-catalyze/national-scorecard.

2   "Total Number of Medical School Graduates," The Henry J. Kaiser Family Foundation, 2014, accessed Nov. 18, 2015, http://kff.org/other/state-indicator/total-medical-school-graduates/.

3   Cejka Search and the American Medical Group Association (AMGA), *2013 Physician Retention Survey* (St. Louis, MO: Cejka Search and Alexandria VA: AMGA, 2013).

4   A. Sheldon, *Managing Doctors* (New York: Aspen, 1986).

5   J.C. Collins, *Good to Great* (New York: HarperBusiness, 2001), 41–64.

6   Medical Group Management Association, *MGMA Cost Survey: 2014 Report Based on 2013 Data* (Englewood, CO: MGMA, 2014).

7   Collins, *Good to Great*, 44.

8   Collins, *Good to Great*, 45.

9   Joan Magretta and Nan Stone, *What Management Is: How It Works and Why It's Everyone's Business* (New York: HarperCollins, 2002; London: Profile Books, 2013). Citation refers to Profile Books edition.

10   Magretta and Stone, *What Management Is* (2013).

11   Magretta and Stone, *What Management Is* (2002), 207.

12   R. Grimshaw, "Tailoring New Physicians to Fit Your Practice," *Family Practice Management* 8 (April 2001), 39–43.

13   Grimshaw, "Tailoring New Physicians to Fit Your Practice," 39–43.

14   Grimshaw, "Tailoring New Physicians to Fit Your Practice."

15   U.S. Workforce Compensation and Performance Service, *A Handbook for Measuring Employee Performance: Aligning Employee Performance Plans with Organizational Goals* (Washington, DC: Office of Personnel Management, September 2011), 13, accessed June 22, 2015, www.opm.gov/policy-data-oversight/performance-management/measuring/employee_performance_handbook.pdf.

16   U.S. Workforce Compensation and Performance Service, *A Handbook for Measuring Employee Performance*, 4.

17   U.S. Workforce Compensation and Performance Service, *A Handbook for Measuring Employee Performance*, 4–6.

18   M. Rauch, "Cash and Praise a Powerful Combo," *Incentive Magazine* (June 1, 2003).

19   M. Buckingham and C. Coffman, *First, Break All the Rules: What the World's Greatest Managers Do Differently* (New York: Simon & Schuster, 1999).

20   Buckingham and Coffman, *First, Break All the Rules*, 32.

21   U.S. Workforce Compensation and Performance Service, *A Handbook for Measuring Employee Performance*, 67.

22   R.S. Kaplan and D.P. Norton, "The Balanced Scorecard — Measures That Drive Performance," *Harvard Business Review* (January/February 1992).

23   Adapted from M. Brounstein, *Handling the Difficult Employee: Solving Performance Problems* (Menlo Park, CA: Crisp, 1993).

24   Chris Argyris, *Overcoming Organizational Defenses: Facilitating Organizational Learning* (Boston: Allyn & Bacon, 1980).

25   Ed Young, *The Creative Leader: Unleashing the Power of Your Creative Potential* (Nashville, TN: Broadman & Holman, 2006), 182.

26   G.A. Rummler and A.P. Brache, *Improving Performance: How to Manage the White Space on the Organizational Chart* (San Francisco: Jossey-Bass, 1995).

27   K.H. Blanchard and S. Johnson, *The One Minute Manager* (New York: Morrow, 1982).

PART 4

Relationship Management and the New Workforce

CHAPTER 19

Conflict Is Inevitable

"All I wanted was a pair of hands and I got the whole man!" lamented Henry Ford a century ago as he tried to form an assembly line to build automobiles.[1] It's true that along with the hands come a person's personality, communication styles, experience, personal characteristics, values, and view of the world. These differ in everyone and are root causes of conflict.

Conflict is a fact of life. It is inevitable. Conflict is the condition in which two or more people's concerns and ideas — the things they care about — appear to be incompatible. Often people mistakenly equate conflict with fighting, and this makes conflict seem dangerous and destructive. However, when we realize that conflict is simply a condition where people's concerns are incompatible, it becomes clear that fighting — arguing, name-calling, blaming — is only one way of dealing with the condition.

Why is it important for leaders to understand how to handle conflict? Because destructive, unhealthy conflict always obstructs the pathway to reaching organizational goals. Research indicates that managers spend at least 30 percent to 40 percent of their time handling conflicts.[2] They have to manage frictions and resentments between people, deal with complaints, negotiate for resources, and enforce policies. To ensure a goal-focused culture, managers must stop destructive conflict in its tracks.

The ability to reconcile differences — to handle conflicts openly and constructively — is essential for team effectiveness. To be effective as a team, all members need to have a shared vision of what they're trying to achieve, must reach agreements on goals, develop strategies for achieving the goals, and help each other accomplish their tasks despite their differences. Good leaders ensure that all members of the organization have ways of solving problems caused by disagreement before conflict becomes a major obstacle to getting work done.

Conflict management is the practice of identifying and managing conflict in a sensible, fair, smooth, and efficient manner. Conflicts occur between individuals, among groups of people, and within groups of people. Strong leaders are constantly aware of the potential for conflict as well as the need for conflict management before productivity and morale suffer.

DESTRUCTIVE CONFLICT IS EXPENSIVE IN THE WORKPLACE

How can we calculate the amount of time, resources, and energy spent on destructive, unresolved conflict in the workplace? Costs of conflict can involve productivity losses because of poor morale, gossip in the hallways and at breaks, sabotage, absenteeism, staff turnover (costing 50 percent to 150 percent of the first year's salary), stress-related medical conditions, workers' compensation, theft, violence, and lawsuits. Additionally, we'd have to include the heart-breaking costs associated with destroyed relationships and broken families. We might even include the loss of public confidence for a medical practice when it is accused of having scandals, poor quality, or poor working conditions. In reality, the costs of conflict are staggering.

Leaders are responsible for the workplace culture. A workplace culture that allows destructive conflict to permeate it can be very expensive to the medical practice and can directly affect patient care. Destructive conflict increases the amount of stress among the team members — negative energy permeates the offices. As described in Chapter 9, I often say that negative workplace environments are filled with "carbon monoxide," creating an atmosphere that is colorless, tasteless, and odorless, yet lethal. Carbon monoxide cultures are sick cultures that can hurt patient care, teamwork, and efficiency.

The direct costs from workplace conflicts can be astronomical, as reflected in statistics gathered by the Rand Corporation relative to workplace litigations:[3]

- ▲ $700,000 is the average jury award in wrongful termination;
- ▲ 15,500 sexual harassment cases are filed annually;
- ▲ 70 percent of jury trials are won by employees;
- ▲ 55 percent of claims are awarded damages; and
- ▲ $2.7 million is the average amount of punitive damages awarded in employment cases.

Conflict Between Individuals

People have differing styles of communication, working, and decision making, as well as different goals, values, views, perceptions, and cultural backgrounds; the possibility of these differences leading to conflict between individuals is always at hand. Typical signs of conflict trouble are when coworkers:

▲ Contradict, gossip, and bad-mouth one another;

▲ Stop speaking to each other or ignore each other; and

▲ Deliberately undermine, sabotage, or stop cooperating with each other, to the downfall of the team.

Conflict Between Groups of People

Whenever people form groups, they tend to emphasize what makes them *better than* or *different from* other groups, and this can sometimes transform from healthy competition to destructive conflict. Typical signs of conflict trouble between groups include:

▲ Cliques or factions meeting to discuss issues separately when they affect the whole organization;

▲ Deliberately undermining or sabotaging the other group; and

▲ Using threatening slogans or symbols to show that one group is right and the others are wrong.

CREATING PRODUCTIVE CONFLICT AND COOPERATION

Conflicts are most often caused by lack of communication, differing perceptions, opposing values, and disparate perceived outcomes. But not all conflicts are the same. There are two major categories: (1) destructive conflict and (2) productive conflict, which ends in growth and resolution. The former damages relationships and often makes it more difficult for the warring parties to move forward. A productive conflict, conversely, resolves the problem at hand while preserving relationships.

Imagine yourself approaching your colleague and saying, "I'd like to talk to you about that meeting yesterday. I have a different perspective on where I think we should be headed with this, and I'd like to discuss it with you." This is an example of using a conflict or disagreement as an alternative way to reach a goal. This sort of direct, substantive encounter can produce growth and strengthen relationships. If you talk to your colleague about the problem and resolve it, you'll feel closer to him or her because you've worked out the issue together.

To achieve healthy, productive conflict, you need to master the art of cooperation. Cooperation hinges on:

  ▲ Respecting the opposition;

  ▲ Valuing the relationship with those of the opposing viewpoint;

  ▲ Recognizing that you need the opposition to implement the desired outcome;

  ▲ Supporting your opponent's self-esteem and sense of power; and

  ▲ Supporting your own self-esteem and sense of power.

Unfortunately, this kind of productive conflict is unfamiliar territory to many of us. We may find any confrontation uncomfortable. Because we're insecure in our ability to navigate a disagreement, we'll often go to great lengths to evade it. As a leader, it's important that you practice productive conflict not only for the sake of your own relationships, but because it's important to model this behavior for your colleagues and team members. A healthy culture is an environment where there is cooperation and productive conflict.

Anger Is Often a Secondary Feeling

"I'm so angry because you didn't remind me about that important meeting to review budget allocations for next year! Why didn't you send me an e-mail about it? I'm too busy to keep track of everything!" screams Dr. Howard.

We often think of anger as a primary feeling; however, it is a secondary feeling where unmet expectations are the root cause. Some primary feelings at the root of anger are:

  ▲ Guilt;

  ▲ Hurt;

  ▲ Disappointment;

  ▲ Fear; and

  ▲ Confusion.

These primary feelings are important to recognize so that when we are working hard to manage conflict, we know where to look for the real source of the anger. Then we can strategize how to resolve it. For example, in the preceding case, it may look like Dr. Howard is having conflict with his office staff. By looking behind the anger, he might see that his anger is rooted in several other feelings, such as guilt because he forgot about the meeting, or disappointment or fear that he did a lousy job of representing his department in front of the budget decision makers.

LEADERSHIP ACTIONS FOR MANAGING CONFLICT IN A HEALTHY MANNER

When conflict arises, there are some basic actions to take in order to manage conflict productively (Exhibit 19.1). Practice these actions yourself and encourage your team to use them also. When conflict arises:

▲ *Focus on the problem, not the person.* This is a critical step in managing conflict. By looking primarily at the problem, it helps to take defensiveness and emotions out of the process. Look at the problem, jointly decide alternative solutions to solve the problem, then select the best solution and implement it.

▲ *Maintain the self-confidence and self-esteem of both the other person and yourself.* Focus on keeping the self-confidence and self-esteem of both parties intact. If either you or the other person becomes defensive during this process, then you will have two problems to deal with — the initial problem as well as the problem of the other person's defensiveness.

▲ *Maintain a positive and constructive relationship.* Focus on doing all that you can to build and maintain positive and constructive relationships.

With many of our colleagues, we will have ongoing relationships and dealings for years to come. As the old saying goes, "It's easy to win the battle and

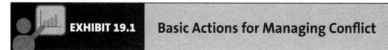

EXHIBIT 19.1   Basic Actions for Managing Conflict

If someone does something that upsets you:

▲ Do not attack the person.

▲ State the negative impact the person has caused you and others.

▲ State this for the emotion felt (anger, upset, concern, frustration) and the impact the person's action had on you or others.

▲ If appropriate, provide the person a way out by suggesting how to correct the situation.

© Willard Zangwill. Used with permission.

lose the war." Work to create win–win relationships with all the people in your life.

HOW TO DECREASE DEFENSIVENESS

Defensiveness is behavior that occurs when individuals perceive or anticipate threat. They devote considerable energy to defending their position, devising ways to be seen more favorably, winning, dominating, or escaping the perceived or anticipated attack. Defensiveness prevents listeners from accurately perceiving the intentions of the communicator. It distorts meaning. In short, defensive behavior produces defensive listening. The reverse is also in effect. That is, as defenses are reduced, listeners are better able to concentrate on the content of the communication.[4]

MANAGING YOUR OWN DEFENSIVENESS

Defensiveness — yours and the person with whom you're having a disagreement — cuts off productive discussion and underlies most conflicts. If you don't diminish the defensiveness, no matter whose it is, you may spend 90 percent of your time trying to get around it rather than dealing with the substantive issues that require resolution. So, one of the keys to managing conflict is to learn how to control our tendency toward defensiveness and the defensiveness of the person with whom we're dealing. If we can disarm the defensiveness, we may not have solved the conflict, but we'll have fundamentally changed the tone of the interaction for the better. The following six-step process will help: (1) Become aware, (2) act calm, (3) shift your focus, (4) let the individual have his or her say, (5) paraphrase, and (6) legitimize his or her feelings.[5]

Step 1: Become Aware

We all have our defense mechanisms that we use to protect ourselves in intimidating situations, and the workplace is no exception. The problem is that we are often oblivious to the ways we deal with our feelings. It's this lack of awareness that causes problems among team members and creates a hostile culture for all concerned. Our means of defense come across in various ways. Feeling physical symptoms, tuning out, dialoguing internally, plus feeling hurt, angry, or misunderstood are among the most common. The physical signs of protecting ourselves can be anything from increased heartbeat and breathing, to heightened body temperature, to dryness of mouth. The physical signs are not the only things on which we need to focus. Our interaction with others is another key element in dealing with feeling defensive.

Many people claim that when they feel challenged, they stop listening, tune out the challenger, and start thinking of their retort. An internal dialogue begins when the individual would prefer to think of a snappy comeback, rather than listening to his or her team member's point. Replacing our hurt reactions with nasty remarks such as "You don't contribute much around here, do you?" moves the dialogue to a toxic place where personal feelings, as opposed to the team's well-being, become primary.

Being aware of your and others' responses allows you to manage the conflict skillfully. Rather than honing in on personal feelings, your focus can be working through the problem successfully.

Step 2: Act Calm

Nonverbal communication is a powerful instrument, and our body language can have a strong effect on the workplace. Communication expert Albert Mehrabian suggests that only 7 percent of the emotional impact of a message comes from your words; 93 percent derives from body language and intonation.[6] We've all had the experience of a terrible day getting the best of us just when someone walks by and asks, "How are you?" Of course, our stock response is uttered, "I'm fine, thanks." But, if we apply Mehrabian's findings, our "fine" is perceived as anything but. To get the control back, try to act calm — no easy task, but deep, slow breaths can help you gain some strength. Relax your facial muscles; much of our stress is held through clenching our jaw or pursing our lips. Open up your body. If your arms or legs are crossed, uncross them. If your fists are clenched, unlock that grasp. Finally, make a concerted effort to regulate your speech to sound like your normal speaking voice. You don't want a high or cracking voice to show others you are feeling defensive.

Step 3: Shift Your Focus

A conflict takes at least two people, and defensiveness causes you to focus solely on you, as opposed to thinking about and listening to the other person involved. By allowing yourself to shift your focus to the other person's ideas and mannerisms, you are working toward conflict resolution, instead of engaging in defensive behavior. Make a deliberate effort to engage in what the other person is saying and truly listen to his or her concerns. An anagram for listen is "silent"; silence your self-talk to hear the other person. Only through genuine human interaction can the conflict be dealt with fully. This isn't to say that listening and processing the information will be easy, because our natural inclination is to explain our side of the story. Instead of defending yourself, look at the situation from the other person's perspective, and you'll be amazed at how much more positivity comes from this approach. In short, hearing and listening are key elements to effective conflict resolution.

Step 4: Let the Individual Have His or Her Say

As just stated, listening is one of the crucial elements to valuable conflict resolution — something easier said than done. Listening, without providing interruptions, is your goal here. If someone is pouring out his or her thoughts about the situation in question, you need to give that person due respect. If you don't let the person finish, the individual will assume you haven't been paying attention and will need to start all over again with Point A — this time speaking slower and louder. Keep in mind that you'll get your chance to speak as soon as your team member has finished.

Step 5: Paraphrase

Your next step is to paraphrase the other person's perspective. Paraphrasing is your way of proving to Joe that you've heard what he said. If your response to his complaint is a dismissive or patronizing statement such as, "I know, I know," or "It can't be all that bad, can it?" Joe won't trust that you really grasp the depths of his problem. When you paraphrase, you prove that you've listened and that you understand.

Step 6: Legitimize His or Her Feelings

It's important to make the distinction between sympathizing and empathizing when dealing with your team member in a conflict situation. Let the individual know that you'd probably feel the same way. Being able to understand and empathize with why the situation has escalated to this point is pivotal. Remember, you aren't giving anything up; you're creating open lines of discussion.

ACCEPTING CRITICISM

Criticism provokes defensiveness, and being able to listen to someone pointing out our weaknesses is never an easy task. Try to determine whether the criticism you've received is reasonable or not. If it is constructive, reframe it in your mind as an opportunity for professional growth (although I know this can be difficult at first). Conversely, it is also your prerogative to defend yourself when you feel you're being condemned unfairly. This situation can be complicated. Following are some suggestions to help you control your feelings of defensiveness when you believe you are being criticized:[7]

▲ *Ask for a specific example of what is being criticized.*

▲ *Decide for yourself whether the criticism is fair.* Is it true? Is the situation something you are able or willing to correct?

▲ *If the criticism is fair, don't make excuses.* Instead, think of how you can rectify the situation. Ask, "What can I do to correct this problem?"

▲ *If the criticism is unfair, use "I" statements such as "I feel misunderstood," or "I don't think I can meet your goals."* Don't use "you" statements that accuse or insult such as, "You've completely misread the situation," or "You're being unreasonable," or "How dare you bring this up! You have no clue what you're talking about."

▲ *Criticism may trigger an angry response in you.* Temper that impulse. If you feel as if you're going to lose control, take a break. Reschedule the conversation for a time when you're composed and can process the information with more objectivity.

▲ *Thank your critic.* If the person has a conflict with you in the future, he or she will be much more likely to bring it to you with the hope that it will get resolved. Whether or not the criticism is valid, you are more likely to sustain a healthy working environment when your team members feel they can calmly discuss their differences with you.

▲ *When receiving criticism, make sure you stand or sit with an upright and open posture.* If you believe the criticism is unwarranted, this communicates nonverbally that you feel unshakable. If you feel the criticism is valid, this communicates that you are not going to lash out defensively at your critic.

▲ *Say "You may be right."* When my friend, Pat Heim, PhD, was on her honeymoon many years ago, a man who was celebrating his 50th anniversary told her "the secret to a happy marriage can be found in four words 'You may be right.'" I have found the phrase to be magical in its ability to defuse a conflict at work as well as home. Arguments dissipate. Recently, a married male friend admitted, "I'd rather be happy than right."

▲ *If you are verbally attacked while presenting at a meeting, walk with an open posture toward the attacker.* That almost always shuts down the confrontation because you're essentially saying, "This isn't getting to me, and I am empowered." This may be the opposite of what you feel like doing, which may be turning tail and running out of the room, but it can be effective in halting an attack.

HOW TO PREVENT OTHERS FROM BECOMING DEFENSIVE

You may find yourself in a situation where you evoke defensiveness in someone else. You may need to talk with Nicole about a problem you're having with the work she's doing on a joint project.

Nicole's nonverbal signals will help you recognize whether she is becoming defensive. She may physically pull away, turn sideways, or cross her arms or legs. She may break eye contact. She may actively defend herself, saying things such as, "You don't understand ..."; "I was going to do that but ..."; "Why didn't you call me to tell me?"

When you recognize that your coworker is becoming defensive, it's wise to stop your discussion and make an effort to lessen his or her tension. Because your basic strategy is to disarm defensiveness, anything you do to make the conversation easier is critical in conflict resolution. The following 10 techniques[8] will help you communicate with a defensive team member.

Technique 1: Describe Rather Than Evaluate His or Her Behavior

Be aware of the personal attack. A person will become defensive when the individual feels he or she is being judged harshly. When examining a team member's behavior, focus on his or her actions rather than on the individual team member. For example, instead of telling a team member, "You are condescending," you might restate it more specifically as, "The way in which you talked down to Mr. Brown yesterday when he didn't understand the procedure he was going to have really made him feel embarrassed. It's our goal to be sure that all of our patients feel comfortable asking questions."

Notice that in drawing from an actual experience, the person is able to place his or her behavior in context and see it in action. If you don't do this, the team member could easily fall into defensive behavior, making the evaluation a problem of yours, not his or hers.

Technique 2: Look for Win–Win Solutions

An effective way to deal with conflict situations is to think about the win–win model. As a whole, women are more apt to be comfortable with this pattern because they are reared to make sure most people in a given situation feel cared for. Men, conversely, are brought up in a win–lose paradigm, and that competitive paradigm can be problematic when you're all on the same team. Losers have long and strong memories, and defensive feelings can come out and show themselves under the guise of revenge — a lose–lose situation for any team.

Technique 3: Use "I" Statements

When discussing a conflict situation, avoid making the other person the persecutor. Phrases such as "You never listen to me," or "You take credit for all of the positive changes around here" can immediately set that individual on the defensive. These phrases are also dangerous because you really don't know what the other person is thinking, and you can't speak for that individual. Use "I" statements to express your reality, for example, "I feel..." and "I believe..." Statements such as, "I feel like my ideas aren't being heard," or "I feel like I'm not getting recognized for all of my hard work around here" can function much more effectively in deemphasizing who's to blame and place focus on the issue at hand.

Technique 4: Avoid the Words *Always* and *Never*

Avoid words that can back you into a corner. No issue is an all-or-nothing venture, and to do so belies its complexity. Keep away from words like *always* and *never*, which illustrate your inability to concede various portions of the conflict.

Technique 5: Say "Help Me Understand" Instead of "Why?"

The word *why* can be inflammatory and cause defensiveness as the other person feels compelled to respond immediately with excuses: "Because ..." This is especially true when you're dealing with those who prefer to use an indirect communication style. Indirect communicators politely hint and ask questions about issues rather than "call it like they see it" or say what they mean as direct communicators do. I've found that using the three words "help me understand" is an excellent way to decrease defensiveness and move forward to problem solving.

Technique 6: "I've Noticed ... and I'm Wondering ..."

A more indirect, less confrontational way of opening a discussion about a hot topic can be to start with "I've noticed ... and I'm wondering ..." Examples include "I've noticed that when I greet you in the morning, you don't respond, and I'm wondering if I've offended you in some way or if there is something negative going on between us." Or "I've noticed that when I ask you for feedback about my performance in my new role, you change the subject, and I'm wondering how you believe I'm handling my new responsibilities that you've given me."

Technique 7: Avoid Piling It On

When dealing with a conflict, avoid bringing in any other issues than the present one. It's easy to find ourselves frustrated, and when we feel that way, we have a tendency to pull in all sorts of past experiences. If you truly want to resolve the dispute, don't deal with anything but the one at hand. It may be tempting to add, "And another thing that you've done ..." However, this will only serve to irritate and exasperate the other person. Keep focused, and resolve one topic before you move on to the next.

Technique 8: Use Humor

One of the best tools you can use to alleviate the stress and frustration that comes with conflict is humor. As long as the laughter is not at the expense of someone else, lightening the mood can work wonders in helping people let their guard down. I use humor frequently. Consider using a little self-deprecating humor — it can diffuse the heat of battle. Once I arrived at a conflict meeting wearing a t-shirt that had a bull's eye on the front and fake bullet holes. The whole atmosphere changed as all the meeting participants burst into laughter.

Technique 9: Watch Your Nonverbal Cues

We all have to deal with stress, and most of us use gestures, or comfort cues, to pacify ourselves during taxing times. These gestures are self-soothing; for example, some women may twirl their hair, and men oftentimes twist their mustaches or fidget with the change in their pocket.

Being aware of comfort cues while you're engaged in a conflict with someone can be pivotal in dealing with the conflict appropriately. You can use the information to determine whether the individual is troubled and liable to strike out defensively. Likewise, being personally aware of your own use of the cues is equally important. Keep yourself in check and use the calming techniques discussed in the preceding section, "Step 2: Act Calm."

Be conscious of pointing your index finger. Pointing out of enthusiasm or excitement when you're talking about a fabulous vacation does not offend. It's the accusatory, shaming tone of your conversation coupled with the gesture that's considered to be a power move in our culture.

Eye rolling, frowning, scowling, and the other facial expressions will only deepen the negativity between those involved in conflict. Conversely, friendly facial expressions can alleviate the tension caused by the conflict.

Empathetic eyes joined with a thoughtful smile can help build unity among team members.

Technique 10: Focus on the Future

Earlier I mentioned the importance of staying on topic and not "piling it on." It's just as important not to revisit old business when in a conflict situation. If you're the one being criticized for past abuses, shift the conversation to the present circumstances and how those circumstances should be dealt with in the future. If, for example, you didn't get Penny the correct information that she needed and she keeps telling you how much you've embarrassed her, you could reply by saying, "The CEO gave me some critical work at the last minute that needed to be done immediately, and I had to drop yours to second on my list. But, I'd like to commit to you that if something like that happens again, I promise to call you at once so that we can organize a strategic move we're both happy with." Dealing with the conflict in this manner demonstrates a great deal of respect for your team member, as well as illustrates your empathy and desire to work out a practical solution.

CREATING A SAFETY ZONE FOR PRODUCTIVE CONFLICT

To handle conflicts in a healthy and productive manner, you need to prevent defensiveness in both yourself and your colleagues. By creating a safe environment where you know what to look for and how to deal with defensiveness, you lessen the chances of conflicts swelling to dangerous proportions.

Similarly, equipping your team members with the tools to deal with conflict will help create a healthy, trusting team culture. Essential elements necessary for resolving conflict constructively include taking a time-out, maintaining privacy, and never putting a conflict into writing.

Take a Time-Out

There are many times when immediate action is not the best choice. Taking a moment and counting to 10 can be one of the best strategies for you in the long run. Whether you just need to calm down or the situation needs to wait while you address a more pressing issue, keep in mind that you must choose a time when the conflict will be tackled.

So, whether you want to wait until you find a more private venue, or you need to just gather your thoughts, set a specific time and location with your colleague in order to emphasize how seriously you are taking the matter. For example, you might say, "Michael, can we meet in my office at two o'clock to discuss this issue? That way we'll have more time to dedicate to really getting to the heart of the matter." Be sure that you keep your appointment; otherwise it can be perceived as a power move.

Maintain Privacy

Note that the preceding example has you inviting Michael to meet in your office for a one-on-one meeting. Discussing grievances and/or conflicts in a private place provides a nondisruptive setting for the rest of the office. If the criticism was dealt with out in the open, the dynamic shifts to one where the individuals become concerned with saving face, rather than focusing on a resolution. If you start to feel that a disagreement is getting heated, take the initiative to move it to a private location where others won't be your audience. Look for a room with a door but without an internal window. It's important to conduct an emotion-laden conversation without turning it into a spectator sport.

Never Put Conflict in Writing

Written communication lacks the nuance of verbal or visual communication. Without subtle signals of tone or facial expression, it's easy to misread a person's true intent. It is therefore imperative to avoid conducting your conflict in writing — and that includes high-tech forms of written communication such as e-mail. Similarly, if someone sends you an e-mail that pushes your buttons or hits you the wrong way, do not dash off a stinging reply. If you feel the need to address the issue, pick up the phone or walk to the office of the person who sent you the e-mail. You might say something such as "It sounds as if you're angry about the situation. Is that what you meant? And if so, let's talk about it."

GUIDELINES FOR CONFLICT MANAGEMENT

Exhibit 19.2 is a procedure that was developed in order to create honest, open, productive conflict management.

 **EXHIBIT 19.2** **Sample Conflict Resolution Guidelines**

Conflicts are a reality we would all like to avoid. To support our organization's open communication environment, all conflicts need to be resolved immediately. We prefer that they be solved informally and confidentially with only the individuals who are involved. No one should criticize or complain to someone who cannot do anything about it. Anyone receiving such a complaint should redirect that person to individuals who can do something about the situation. If team members decide not to confront a conflict, then they should understand the reason they are withholding their feelings. The more we all cooperate and follow this rule of thumb, the fewer the problems that will become enhanced.

The following are our organization's guidelines for resolving conflict:

1. **Anyone experiencing a conflict should go directly to that individual to discuss the problem.** This conversation should take place in a private location. Not giving that individual the opportunity to discuss concerns is justly unfair. Frequently, conflicts are a misunderstanding, which once discussed become easily resolved.

2. **If the initial discussion does not solve the problem, wait a day and try again.** It is very likely that the reason the initial discussion did not go well is because the coworker may be under a great deal of pressure (for example, having a bad day), which may be the reason for the conflict in the first place. Always try to give your coworker the benefit of the doubt. Waiting one day may be time he or she really needs.

3. **If after the second attempt, the conflict is still not resolved, go to either your supervisor, the director of human resources, or to another manager with expertise in conflict resolution to discuss the problem.**

(Exhibit continues)

EXHIBIT 19.2 *(continued)* **Sample Conflict Resolution Guidelines**

The role of this person is to:

    a. Listen and advise as to how to approach the coworker once again; or

    b. Meet with the two individuals in conflict to discuss the problem. Frequently, an objective listener can bring light to the situation. Also, having someone else present will often result in better listening all around.

4. After the final discussion has taken place and the conflict seems resolved, always answer the following three questions together:

    a. Why did the conflict occur?

    b. What could we do differently next time to discourage the conflict?

    c. What did we learn about each other that we didn't know before?

In providing *service excellence* to each other, we need to accept the responsibility for our actions and provide for our coworkers a supportive environment in which we can all work and communicate.

CHECKING BEHAVIOR EFFECTIVENESS AND ACTIVE LISTENING

It is important during your conflict resolution discussion to constantly check that your words are matching your behaviors (verbal and nonverbal); otherwise the other individual will question your sincerity. Areas to focus on are:

Verbal

▲ **Tone of voice.** Try not to raise your voice. Keep it low. If the individual feels he or she is being attacked, the natural instinct is to be defensive.

▲ **Maintain self-esteem and confidence of the other person.** Stay focused on the problem, not the person.

▲ **Occasionally repeat back what you think you heard.** This makes the person believe that you are listening.

Nonverbal (body language)

▲ **Try not to cross arms or lean back in your chair.** Keep an open posture, trying to lean forward at times.

▲ **Maintain good eye contact.**

ACTION STEPS

    1. Explain the problem as you see it.

    2. Describe the effect the problem is having on you.

    3. Ask for the other person's views.

    4. Agree on the problem that needs to be solved.

    5. Explore and discuss potential solutions.

    6. Agree on what each person will do to resolve the problem, and set a follow-up date.

(Exhibit continues)

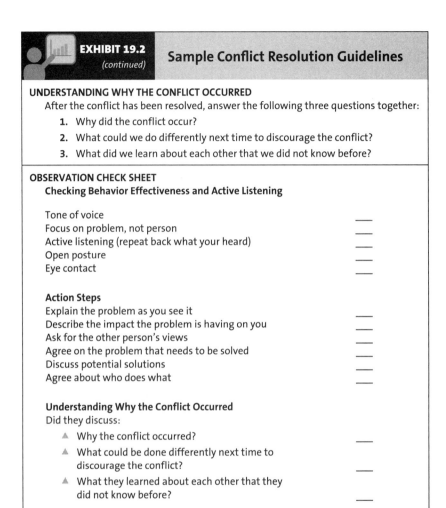

EXHIBIT 19.2 (continued) **Sample Conflict Resolution Guidelines**

UNDERSTANDING WHY THE CONFLICT OCCURRED
After the conflict has been resolved, answer the following three questions together:
1. Why did the conflict occur?
2. What could we do differently next time to discourage the conflict?
3. What did we learn about each other that we did not know before?

OBSERVATION CHECK SHEET
Checking Behavior Effectiveness and Active Listening

Tone of voice ____
Focus on problem, not person ____
Active listening (repeat back what your heard) ____
Open posture ____
Eye contact ____

Action Steps
Explain the problem as you see it ____
Describe the impact the problem is having on you ____
Ask for the other person's views ____
Agree on the problem that needs to be solved ____
Discuss potential solutions ____
Agree about who does what ____

Understanding Why the Conflict Occurred
Did they discuss:
⚊ Why the conflict occurred? ____
⚊ What could be done differently next time to discourage the conflict? ____
⚊ What they learned about each other that they did not know before? ____

© 2016 Susan A. Murphy, MBA, PhD

Note: This exhibit is available as an electronic file.*

ELIMINATING MAJOR CAUSES OF WORKPLACE CONFLICT

In most instances, eliminating the major causes of workplace conflict is simply a matter of knowing what they are and then correcting or avoiding them in your organization. The 10 major causes of workplace conflict are described in the following paragraphs, along with examples of each and their solutions.

---

*Instructions to access the electronic files are available in Appendix A.

Conflict 1: Rules — Wrongly Established or Inconsistently Enforced

Example: Heather is often late returning from lunch, but the manager avoids talking with her directly and instead establishes a sign-in/sign-out rule. Coworkers become angry with both the manager and Heather.

Solution: The manager needs to talk to Heather; no sign-in/sign-out rule is necessary. "Inconsistently enforced" refers to situations when some have to obey rules and others do not. There will always be conflict in these types of cases, so ensure that you behave consistently.

Conflict 2: Overlapping Responsibilities

Example: Everyone answers the phone when the receptionist goes to lunch.

Solution: Assign schedules so people can be held accountable. On Mondays, Wednesdays, and Fridays, Jack covers the phone; on Tuesdays and Thursdays, Martha covers it. Establish a backup plan too.

Conflict 3: Resource Competition

Example: Only one computer is purchased and is given to Ted in scheduling. Other team members are upset that Ted gets the computer.

Solution: Explain why Ted got the computer. Others still may not like it, but they'll understand why, which reduces or eliminates conflict.

Conflict 4: Promotion Competition

Example: Two people within the department apply for a management position. When one is selected, the other will be upset.

Solution: Talk with the person who was not selected and state specifically why he or she was not chosen. Although he or she may not agree, he or she will understand why. If he or she is still upset, it will be with you, not with the other person.

Conflict 5: Interdependence

Example: Jim cannot get started on the billing until he receives the information from Cheryl about patient procedures. Cheryl is often tardy; therefore, Jim ends up working overtime several days a month.

Solution: The manager is responsible for workflow, so the manager should get involved and find out why Cheryl gives Jim late information. Set standards to keep this from happening in the future. (See Part 1 for procedures for setting goals and ensuring that goals are met.)

Conflict 6: Quality vs. Quantity

Example: Coworkers disagree about which is most important.

Solution: Set expectations and standards; then monitor and enforce both quality and quantity.

Conflict 7: Working Quarters That Are Too Close

Example: People working in cramped quarters have conflict.

Solution: Tell them that no additional space is possible at present. Then let them design their own space — tell them anything they want to do is okay. Even if they do not rearrange the furniture, they will be happier because they now know that nothing else is possible.

Conflict 8: Differing Work Habits

Example: Two team members who hold the same position work at different speeds and there is always conflict.

Solution: Set standards that apply to everyone. Recognize and praise when there is good performance, and develop a team member who may be slow.

Conflict 9: Unresolved Conflicts

Example: Two team members are conducting conflict openly, causing other team members to get involved and take sides.

Solution: The manager *must* call in the involved workers and mediate an agreement that produces work output. Unresolved conflict does not go away and destroys teamwork and quality patient care.

Conflict 10: Personality Clashes

Example: Two team members have a personality conflict. One is very extraverted and talks much more than the other.

Solution: It's the boss's responsibility to resolve conflict when it affects the work. If this personality clash begins to have an unacceptable effect on work, talk about it with the two team members, do problem solving, and establish consequences if needed. The manager is responsible for creating a positive culture.

CHAPTER PRESCRIPTIONS

- Focus on creating a healthy culture — an environment where there is cooperation and productive conflict.
- Try to keep in mind that conflict is simply an occurrence when people's concerns are incompatible. Fighting is not (and should not) be the way in which to deal with conflict.
- Remember that destructive conflict always gets in the way of achieving organizational goals and success.
- Productive conflict is essential to creating a strong and unified team — always avoid a carbon monoxide culture!
- Work through conflict together because this brings team members closer.
- Strong leaders are constantly aware of the potential for conflict as well as the need for conflict management before productivity and morale suffer. Stay alert for signs of conflict.
- To achieve healthy, productive conflict, you need to master the art of cooperation.
- Use good communication skills, such as active listening, paraphrasing, and validation of your colleague's feelings. Remember that "Why did you ...?" can be much less effective than "Help me understand ..."
- Keep a close eye on your colleagues' facial expressions and tone of voice when there is disagreement. Keep in mind that a calm and caring nature is key.
- Keep your sense of humor. Take your job responsibilities very seriously and yourself half as seriously!
- When disagreements have been resolved, leave them in the past and move on to the next challenge — together.
- When conflict arises:
  - Focus on the problem, not the person;
  - Maintain the self-confidence and self-esteem of both the other person and yourself; and
  - Maintain a positive and constructive relationship.

CHAPTER 20

Managing Conflict

I'm often amazed that some managers believe that a conflict only affects the two people having it. Please, don't believe for a nanosecond that the only people affected by a conflict are those who are participating. Everyone working with the conflicting team members is affected by the stress of the conflict — this can include patients and vendors. People feel like they're walking on eggshells when antagonists are around. In some cases, team members feel like they need to take sides. This can certainly distract your team from aligning their performance with the goals! The conflict can take on a life of its own.

WHAT DO YOU DO WHEN TEAM MEMBERS HAVE CONFLICT?

When should the manager get involved? If disagreements and turf wars escalate into interpersonal conflict among team members, you must intervene quickly. The manager is responsible for creating a healthy, values-based, goal-focused culture where your team can thrive. Many managers believe that if they avoid conflict, it will go away. Trust me, it won't. Even if it seems to have gone away for a while, it's often festering beneath the surface. Unresolved conflicts will often reappear with a vengeance once stress or a new disagreement occurs. And it seems to reappear at the worst possible time.

HOW DO YOU MANAGE THE CONFLICT WHEN IT'S TIME TO DO SO?

My preference is to separately meet with each of the conflicting parties first, and I've had many successful outcomes doing it this way. Some consultants recommend starting with a meeting with both of them together.

When I meet with each separately, I use open-ended questions and ensure that each recounts the facts, not personal attacks on the other party. After the team member finishes, I ask, "Is there anything else you'd like to say?" Ninety-five percent of the time, there's at least one more item that has been festering — my goal is to get everything on the table. Before my one-on-one meeting ends, I ask the individual to name three positive characteristics about the other party. Additionally, I usually let them know that at the joint meeting I will be asking each of them for their point of view and for three or four suggestions that they'd like the other party to take that would resolve differences.

After I've met with both parties separately, I have at least three viewpoints. One viewpoint is mine.

The next step is the meeting with the antagonists together. At the beginning of the meeting, I set ground rules and either post them or provide them in a handout for each person. Ground rules include:

- ▲ Take turns speaking; listen attentively without interrupting;
- ▲ Focus on the issue and behavior, not the person;
- ▲ No cussing, sarcasm, blaming, or personal attacks;
- ▲ Say "I feel" vs. "You";
- ▲ Avoid using *always* and *never*;
- ▲ Focus on the future;
- ▲ Be specific with examples; and
- ▲ Be respectful.

I start the meeting by asking for agreement on the ground rules. Then I tell them the three positive characteristics they said about each other when they met with me. Next, I let each briefly summarize their viewpoint, without comments by the other. This is a short, facts-based discussion so that all parties are on the same page about the issues and areas of disagreement. The manager must intervene if either team member criticizes the other. Remind them of the ground rules.

Then ask each party to describe specific actions he or she would like the other party to take that would resolve their differences (from their homework assignment). Examples would be "I would like Joe to speak in a lower volume during phone calls so that I'm not distracted from my work." "I would like Jennifer to send the report to me by the 27th of each month so I can finish my departmental report that is due the last day of each month."

As the manager, there may be times that you need to offer ownership for some of the responsibilities. There may be something in the work situation that is driving the conflict (see "Eliminating Major Causes of Workplace Conflict" in Chapter 19). All parties discuss issues and commit to making changes needed to resolve the conflict. Take notes and discuss what each is going to stop, start, or continue doing in order to resolve the conflict. Set a follow-up meeting date to review their progress, to ensure that each is keeping their end of the agreements, and to check on how the work and their relationship are going. End on a positive note by assuring both parties that you believe in them and their ability to act as professional adults. If appropriate, encourage them to shake hands and get back to work.

DIFFICULT CONVERSATIONS

At work, at home, in friendships, and in the community, we're faced with tough conversations — and we dread them because there's often a lot at stake. How do you prepare yourself? How do you open the discussion without causing defensiveness? How do you handle the discussion?

First, you must ask yourself some questions: What's the purpose for having this conversation? What are you hoping to accomplish? What's the ideal outcome? What assumptions are you making about the other person and his or her intentions? You may feel disrespected, intimidated, or ignored — don't assume that was his or her intention. Could it be that you're feeling more emotional than the situation warrants?

What's your attitude toward the conversation? If you believe it's going to be difficult, it probably will be, so adjust your attitude for maximum effectiveness.

Now let's consider who is your opponent and what might this individual be thinking about this situation? Is the person aware there's a problem? If so, how do you think the person perceives the problem? What are this individual's needs and fears? What solution would this person suggest? Begin to reframe your opponent as a partner. Are there common concerns? How have each of you contributed to the problem?

The following are some suggestions for starting a conversation:
   ▲ "I have something I'd like to discuss with you that I think will help us work together more effectively."

- ▲ "I think we have different perceptions about_____. I'd like to hear your thoughts about this."

- ▲ I need your help with what just happened. Do you have a few moments to talk?"

- ▲ "I'd like to talk with you about_____. I think we may have different ideas on how to deal with it."

- ▲ "I'd like to talk about _____ with you, and I'd really like to get your point of view."

- ▲ "I'd like to see if we might reach a better understanding about _____. I really want to hear your feelings about this and to share my perspective as well."

In the book *Difficult Conversations: How to Discuss What Matters Most*, coauthor Sheila Heen adds, "If there's one underlying skill, it's the ability to see the conflict clearly from our own perspective, clearly from the other person's perspective, and from the point of view of a third party." With this in mind, four steps for holding a difficult conversation include:[9]

- ▲ **Step 1: Inquiry.** Cultivate an attitude of discovery and try to learn as much as possible about your opponent's point of view. Let your opponent talk until he or she is finished without interrupting him or her.

- ▲ **Step 2: Acknowledgment.** Paraphrase what you heard your opponent say. This is not agreement; this is just restating to let him or her know that you understand where he or she stands.

- ▲ **Step 3: Advocacy.** Now it's your turn. Clarify your position without minimizing his or hers. For example, "I can see how you came to the conclusion that I'm not supportive of you. I do support you and believe you're very talented. When I bring up reasons why I don't think your approach is the best, I'm not trying to criticize you, though perhaps it sounds that way. I'm looking long term and saw that your idea would be over budget and take three months too long. Maybe we can talk about how to address these issues so it doesn't feel personal and we can get to the finish line on time and on budget."

- ▲ **Step 4: Problem solving.** Ask your opponent for his or her solutions and build on something he or she says. Build sustainable solutions together. If the conversation becomes adversarial, return to Step 1.

Tips for a successful, although difficult, conversation include:[10]

- Stay clear about your purpose;
- Don't take verbal attacks personally;
- Don't assume others can see things from your point of view;
- Consider practicing the conversation with a confidant;
- Visualize various scenarios and handling the conversation well; and
- Realize that difficult conversations are a part of life and that by practicing them, they can become easier and more constructive.

CONTENT CONFLICT VS. RELATIONSHIP CONFLICT

One of the most common reasons that disagreements evolve into conflict is because we confuse conflicts over actual content — a real issue — with those having to do with the relationship between the two disagreeing people.

A content conflict involves a disagreement about something tangible — a specific and measurable fact such as the distance from one city to another, the number of ounces in a pound, or the percentage increase in a phone bill. A relationship conflict centers around what's occurring between two people on an interpersonal level — their feelings, emotions, and percep- tions. Relationship conflicts occur when someone believes they're being sabotaged, taken advantage of, or disregarded by another.

The following conversation is an example of a content conflict being inter- preted as a relationship conflict. This occurs in a staff meeting where a deci- sion is being made about which vendor to choose for a piece of equipment.

Melody says, "I like the Brand A electrocardiograph machine and believe we should order three additional ones."

John responds, "I believe we should go with Brand B because they're having a special sale this month."

Melody counters, "John, I thought you were my friend."

What happened here to cause this miscommunication and conflict? John presented Melody with a content conflict — a disagreement about some- thing tangible — the price of the equipment. Melody responded to John with a relationship conflict response — questioning his friendship.

This confusion between content conflict and relationship conflict often plays havoc in workplace communication as well as at home. Some men and more than 60 percent of women prefer to rely on feelings, harmony, and human values when making decisions rather than on logic and principles.[11] This causes many colleagues to hear that a conflict involves a relationship issue when in reality what was intended was a content discussion. And when they do so, they end up feeling sabotaged, undermined, and insulted. If we interpret a content conflict to be about the relationship, it's only natural that we would feel personally hurt.

Because workplace disagreements most often have to do with content issues, such as conflicting goals, limited resources, and differing viewpoints about quality rather than revolving around relationships, it's critical to first determine the subject of a conflict in working to resolve the problem properly.

Two colleagues caught in a content vs. relationship conflict will have difficulty turning their discussion into productive problem solving until they start communicating on the same level, that is, until they're both dealing with either the content or the relationship. To do this, at least one of them must grasp the nature of the confusion.

In the scenario about Melody and John, when John recognizes Melody has reacted to him from a relational point of view rather than the content perspective that she intended, John can back up and say, "Hang on a minute. I'm your friend and I value our friendship. I'm talking about the cost of the machine. You're so good at shopping for deals that I thought that would appeal to you!" In this way, John reassures Melody that all is well in the relationship, thus defusing some of Melody's defensiveness.

When a conflict revolves around content for one colleague and relationship for another, it's best to deal with the relationship issue first. Otherwise any solutions that arise won't be optimal, because one party may remain hurt, distrustful, or resentful. If you're both familiar with content–relationship-type conflicts, one of you can say, "Hold it. Are we disagreeing over something that's between us or an actual issue that's on the table?" If you've been discussing a content issue and discover that it's really a relationship issue, then deal with the relationship at that point.[12]

Exhibit 20.1 is a worksheet for determining how you approach conflicts.

EXHIBIT 20.1   How You Approach Conflicts Worksheet

It's important for you to understand how you instinctively view conflicts. If a problem arises, do you automatically look for a relational issue as its source or a concrete issue? Take a look at the following situations. In each scenario, Response A reflects a relationship point of view and Response B reflects a content point of view. Which thought pattern are you more likely to choose?

1. A coworker tells you that she believes your suggestion about holding an elaborate office party will be too expensive and distracting during this crunch time of flu season when balancing high patient volume with high patient satisfaction is critical. You:

    a. Wonder why she would say something like that. You don't understand why she's so thoughtless of everyone's need for a little rest and relaxation during this tough time.

    b. Take her words as input and rethink your suggestion to see if her ideas have merit.

2. A friend working at another organization is supposed to meet you for lunch at noon today. It's 12:20 and he hasn't arrived. You:

    a. Are upset that he would treat you like this. You thought he would have the decency to show up on time or call.

    b. Decide to call his office to ensure that the date and time are correct. Once confirmed, you have a cup of coffee and plan to order lunch for yourself if he hasn't arrived by 12:30. He obviously has been detained in traffic or something else came up that is out of his control and his phone isn't working. You hope he's okay.

3. Your team member informs you that he believes patients may feel intimidated when you stand during your discussions with them vs. sitting down next to them. You:

    a. Are furious. How dare he speak to you like this, after all the times you've supported him when others criticized his management abilities?

    b. Realize that he has always tried to serve as a mentor to you. Perhaps he has a point.

4. You received some critical feedback from your boss today. She said your work hasn't been up to par lately. You:

    a. Wonder if the comment you made the other day about her son offended her.

    b. Take a critical look at your performance to see if her comment has any merit.

5. Greg keeps resisting your recommendation. When you ask what's behind his balkiness, his responses don't make sense to you.

    a. You begin to wonder if you've done something to offend him.

    b. You take a hard look at the facts and your assessment of the situation.

(Exhibit continues)

EXHIBIT 20.1
(continued)   **How You Approach Conflicts Worksheet**

6. You depend on Jeremy to provide data for your weekly reports. Lately you have had to repeatedly ask for the information, and it is slow in coming. You:

   a. Ask him if there is something wrong between you.

   b. Ask if he is having problems getting his work done.

If you've chosen A in the majority of these scenarios, then it's likely that you view conflicts from a relational rather than a content vantage point. If you've chosen B most often, you see conflicts through the lens of content. Whichever choices you made, however, be careful not to misread a conflict just because you're accustomed to approaching it from a habitual vantage point.

© P. Heim, S. Murphy, with S. Golant, *In the Company of Women: Indirect Aggression Among Women: Why We Hurt Each Other and How to Stop* (New York: Tarcher/Putnam, 2003). Used with permission.

HANDLING CONFLICT WITH STYLE

One of the greatest contributions to the field of organization development is from Kenneth W. Thomas, professor of management at the Naval Postgraduate School in Monterey, Calif., and Ralph H. Kilmann, professor of organization and management at the University of Pittsburgh in Pennsylvania. In the early 1970s, they identified five style categories for dealing with conflict: collaborating, competing, compromising, accommodating, and avoiding. Thomas and Kilmann found that we conduct our conflicts using a favorite style, one with which we feel comfortable, based on our temperament, social skills, and personal predisposition. Some of us want to win all of our conflicts, so we are competitive. Some want each party to win and are more collaborative. Others cave in and withdraw when faced with disagreement. By gaining an awareness of the conflict mode that dominates our behavior as well as the conflict mode of those who work with us, we can begin to identify the experiences that trigger destructive conflict behaviors, and we can personally intervene before the conflict cycles out of control.[13]

Our instinctive conflict-handling mode can either help us or hurt us in resolving conflicts. Each of these five styles of approaching conflict has its usefulness as well as limitations. The style you use with your manager or coworker might be collaborating or cooperative, while the one you use with a vendor may be competitive or compromising. A style appropriate for resolving a conflict with your spouse or child might not be as productive when you're at odds with a team member at work. We're all capable of using different styles, and to be an effective leader, we need to be able to change our approach as the situation demands. For example, you would want to work with physicians in a collaborative way with regard to incentive plans, but in a competitive way when demanding payment from insurers.

Once you understand your own style preferences as well as those of your team members, and the times these styles would be most effective, your relationships and leadership effectiveness will improve with your colleagues, your staff, and your customers.

According to Thomas and Kilmann, the five conflict-handling styles are described in terms of two underlying dimensions: cooperativeness and assertiveness. Cooperativeness is the degree to which you try to satisfy the *other person's* concerns. Assertiveness is the degree to which you try to satisfy *your own* concerns.

Thomas and Kilmann describe the five styles as:

1. Collaborating: cooperative and assertive;
2. Competing: assertive and uncooperative;
3. Compromising: intermediate in assertiveness and cooperativeness;
4. Accommodating: cooperative and unassertive; and
5. Avoiding: uncooperative and unassertive.

Collaborating

A collaborative approach to conflict is both assertive and cooperative. Collaborating is the opposite of avoiding. It involves an attempt to work toward a win–win solution with the other party to find a solution that fully satisfies the concerns of both parties. Collaboration can be useful in such situations as resolving a condition where both parties are competing for resources, exploring a disagreement to learn from each other's insights, or finding creative solutions to interpersonal problems. Collaborating would work well when reviewing vendor contracts with the physicians and the controller in your medical practice. Physicians compare and contrast the quality of medical supplies from different vendors, while the controller shows the effect of supply decisions on the bottom line. With a win–win outcome in mind, the medical practice team can reach good decisions about which vendors to use and the duration of contracts.[14]

Use collaboration only on important issues because it takes time and energy. Reaching high-quality decisions is a benefit of collaborating because there is synergy and input from both parties, greater communication from openly exchanging information, and usually more commitment for the decision. Collaboration preserves and strengthens the self-esteem, trust, and relationship of the involved parties, which can help create goodwill should future conflicts arise. Women often use a collaborative style when making decisions, problem solving, and approaching conflicts.

Collaborating can be useful:

▲ For finding solutions when concerns are too important to the medical practice to be compromised or ignored;

▲ When exploring different ways of looking at issues;

▲ For gaining commitment of both parties; and

▲ For fostering relationships by understanding the views of others or working through core problems in the relationship.

Collaboration has its downside, however, especially if it's your only way of dealing with conflicts. Digging through issues can require lots of time and energy, and you may find yourself discussing issues in depth that do not deserve such attention. Trivial problems don't require optimal solutions; involving everyone in a decision can bog down the process.

If you frequently use a collaborative style, check to see if you are overanalyzing problems or shying away from taking risks. If you rarely use the collaborating style, ask yourself whether you have a pessimistic view that could be keeping you from employing this style. Ensure that your team members feel their concerns are being incorporated into the decision-making and problem-solving processes.

For collaborating to be effective, both parties have to choose the same style — you can't collaborate with someone who wants only to compete with or avoid you. When you insist on collaboration, you may miss cues indicating defensiveness, strong feelings, impatience, competitiveness, or conflicting interests.

Competing

Competing is an assertive and uncooperative conflict management style. This is a power-oriented mode in which you tend to stand up for your rights, defend a position that you believe is correct, or simply try to win and have your own way. The competing individual pursues his or her own concerns at the expense of another by sometimes using force, pulling rank, exerting coercive power, or arguing. When you're competing, you're unwilling to relinquish your goals for any reason.[15]

There are times when competing is appropriate because there are times a win–win resolution is impossible. A competing conflict management style may enable a medical practice manager to see to it that his or her ideas are implemented for the sake of attaining a team goal and making a project the best it can be. It may be the style of choice when decisive action is called for to make an unpopular decision to attain a goal of decreasing costs — make a change in vendors, cut back on staff, and other bottom-line situations. A competing style would be appropriate when the government changes regulations about how your practice should bill diagnosis-related groups — no amount of discussion makes a difference in the outcome. If you're going after a great job, an incentive-linked bonus, or the last available seat on an airplane, you may have no choice but to compete. And if you're dealing with someone who predominantly uses this style, you might need to adopt a competitive style to protect yourself and your team.

Men often choose a competitive approach when making decisions and approaching conflict, which I discuss at length in Chapter 22.

Competing can be useful:

▲ When quick, decisive action is vital, such as during emergencies or when making tight deadlines is critical;

▲ Regarding important issues in which unpopular actions, such as cost cutting, layoffs, discipline, or enforcing rules, are required. It is rare for a person affected by these actions to support them;

▲ When you know you are right about issues vital to you or your medical practice's welfare; and

▲ To protect yourself and your team against people who take advantage of noncompetitive behavior and you need to defend yourself.

There are many drawbacks to using competing as your dominant conflict management style. You may not have good working relationships with your colleagues; they may be withholding important information from you. Additionally, your team may be less inspired to reach goals when decisions made about their jobs are made without their input.

If you are competitive, ask yourself whether you are surrounded by "yes" men and women. Perhaps they are compliant because they've learned it's unwise to disagree with you, and they've simply given up trying to influence you. Unfortunately, this can insulate you from receiving vital information and alternative viewpoints. Your team members may also fear admitting ignorance, and this could hurt the entire practice.

This was the case for my client, Joseph, who became concerned when the other managers began excluding him from meetings and stopped responding to his requests for reports. His conflict management style (on the Thomas–Kilmann instrument) reflected his strong preference for the competing style. Once I explained the negative effect on team relationships of always being competitive, Joseph began employing collaboration and compromise. As he did so, the other managers began responding more positively to him.

Conversely, if you rarely behave in a competitive manner, you may be restricting your influence and effectiveness. You may be delaying decisions that need to be made because of failing to take a firm stand on issues when you need to do so.

Compromising

Compromising falls between competing and accommodating, and is intermediate in both assertiveness and cooperativeness. Your objective in compromising is to explore the difficulties and desires on each side and then work together to find an acceptable solution that partially satisfies both parties. It's a form of sharing or "horse-trading" that can split the difference and seek middle ground. You've each made your positions known. In a medical practice conflict, you might compromise if two departments want one new full-time-equivalent (FTE) member. In compromising, each department might gain one-half FTE member.[16]

Compromising helps to foster trust and maintain open lines of communication. It also helps you to stay focused on *big-picture* goals because you are attuned to both sides' needs. Compared to collaboration, compromising can be more expedient. There is a feeling of fairness because each party shares equal gains and losses.

Compromising can be useful:

- ▲ When goals are somewhat important, yet not worth the effort of more assertive styles;
- ▲ When two parties with equal power are strongly committed to mutually exclusive goals as in real estate buyer–seller negotiations;

▲ To achieve temporary solutions to complex issues; and

▲ As a backup style when collaborating and competing fail.

As with the other conflict management styles, there are disadvantages to emphasizing compromise over other conflict approaches. For example, you will need to be aware of your limits and of exactly how much you're willing to give up. If not, you may come away from a compromise feeling as if you've gotten a raw deal, and therefore become resentful. I often think of compromise as $2 + 2 = 3$. Each party gives up something it wants. One danger of using the compromising style too frequently in teams is that neither party may be enthusiastic about making a watered-down solution work or reaching a compromised goal.

One of my clients, Jennifer, took the Thomas–Kilmann instrument and discovered that her preferred conflict management style is compromising and that she rarely uses collaboration, which produces a win–win outcome. Now during negotiations, Jennifer feels more effective knowing about all five styles in her conflict styles tool kit, and she makes a conscious effort to use other styles when conflict situations arise.

If you find that you rarely compromise, it is helpful to understand why. Could it be that you find it difficult to make concessions when dealing with others? Compromising can be an effective tool for physicians and other team members as they work on teams to accomplish goals.

Accommodating

Accommodating is the opposite of competing. It is unassertive and cooperative. When you are accommodating, you may neglect your own concerns to satisfy those of the person with whom you are in conflict. The accommodating style incorporates an element of self-sacrifice, of yielding to a viewpoint in opposition to your own. A physician in the medical practice might choose to use the accommodating style when she offers to attend the evening medical staff meetings at the hospital so that a colleague can attend his child's school play.[17]

When you are accommodating on minor issues, you enhance goodwill by building social capital through helping, doing favors, and apologizing when necessary. You can support other people and help them meet their needs. Admitting you're wrong and conceding a point gives others permission to do so as well, which can help build your team.

Accommodating can be useful:

▲ When you realize you are wrong or are outmatched and losing. This can show you are reasonable;

▲ When the issue is more important to the person with whom you are disagreeing. Accommodating can build relationships by satisfying the other person's needs;

▲ To build up credit that can be used in the future when other issues may be more important to you; and

▲ When preserving harmony and avoiding disruption are especially important.

I was raised in Atlanta, where women were encouraged to use the accommodating style; that is, to "be nice" at all costs. During my career, I've learned about the other four styles and find that I am not only more effective as a leader, but happier and feel more authentic as well.

The downside to accommodating can be that your ideas and concerns become overshadowed, and they don't get the focus they deserve. Continually deferring to others' interests can deprive you of influence and recognition. It also robs the medical practice of your good ideas. If you are constantly helping others reach their goals at the expense of your own, you could be seen as a martyr. You could lose your boundaries and encourage exploitation by others.

As a leader, being overly accommodating can lead to lax discipline because of deferring too much to the concerns of others. Policies and procedures are crucial for you and your medical group practice.

Conversely, if you find that you rarely act in an accommodating style, you may want to explore how you impact others. Others may see you as someone who believes you are never wrong and someone who isn't a team player.

Avoiding

Avoiding is the opposite of collaborating. It is unassertive and uncooperative. Avoiding conflict means you neither pursue your own concerns nor those of the person with whom you are in conflict. Avoiders understand that resolving conflict takes time and can be stressful. It can be quite useful if a relationship is vital but the conflict is trivial. For example, if there is disagreement in the office about the color to paint the staff lounge, you may choose to use the avoiding conflict management style in favor of using the services of a licensed decorator and spending your time on something of more value to you and the practice.

Another benefit to using an avoiding conflict management style is that you may reduce your stress, at least in the short run, by being able to avoid unpleasant topics and people, as well as saving time and energy by not focusing on low-priority issues.[18]

Avoiding can be useful:

- ▲ When an issue is trivial and not worth the team's time;
- ▲ When you're wasting your time because you perceive no chance of satisfying your concerns. For example, you may be frustrated by situations where you have little power to change, such as national policies or someone's personality;
- ▲ When the potential damage of dealing with an issue outweighs the benefits of resolving it;
- ▲ To give people a chance to cool down and regain perspective and composure;
- ▲ When you want to gather more information about the issue; and
- ▲ When others can resolve the conflict more effectively.

If avoiding is your dominant conflict management style, you may find that small issues grow into big problems and end up taking more of your time and attention. Other team members may not know what you need or where you stand on an issue. This can affect your ability to maximize your team's performance.

Discovering your preferred conflict management style can be important in strengthening leadership skills. Larry, a young manager, learned that he prefers to compete or avoid. His staff and colleagues had difficulty building trust with him because he seemed to approach issues in an all-or-nothing fashion. After coaching sessions, Larry now uses other conflict management styles and is a more effective manager. He attends more meetings, volunteers information on issues under discussion, and is working on developing his sense of humor.

However, if you rarely avoid conflict, there may be times when you should. You may feel overwhelmed by the sheer volume of issues and unfinished business that keeps piling up. In that case, you'll need to devote more time toward setting priorities and using delegation skills.

CHAPTER PRESCRIPTIONS

- Remember that conflict affects everyone within the organization, not solely those engaged in the conflict.
- Be sure to first determine the subject of a conflict to enable you to resolve the problem properly.
- Be prepared to intervene if disagreements and turf wars escalate into interpersonal conflict among team members.
- Do not think that avoided conflict goes away — it won't. It will continue to fester and has the potential to grow into a major problem if not dealt with.
- Get everything on the table so that the conflict can be addressed and remedied.
- Discuss issues and commit to making changes needed to resolve the conflict.
- Be specific as you take notes and discuss what each member involved in the conflict is going to stop, start, or continue doing in order to resolve the conflict.
- Understand the intricacies involved with relationship conflicts, which occur when someone believes another is sabotaging, taking advantage of, or disregarding him or her.
- The confusion between content conflict and relationship conflict often diminishes communication in the workplace. Decipher between content and relationship conflicts, and respond on the appropriate level.
- When dealing with both a content and a relationship conflict, deal with the relationship issue first.
- Remember that there are five conflict management styles: collaborating, competing, compromising, accommodating, and avoiding. Each style can be useful, depending on the situation.
- A collaborative approach to conflict is both assertive and cooperative. Use collaboration when you want to find a win–win solution that fully satisfies both parties.
- Be aware that when you avoid conflict, you neither pursue your own concerns nor those of the person with whom you are in conflict. You neither address nor resolve the conflict.

CHAPTER 21

Conflict Management and Teambuilding

Throughout this book, we cover important skills that leaders need in order to align performance with practice goals. If you are the team's leader, you are responsible for creating a healthy, positive workplace culture and flushing the carbon monoxide that negative attitudes can generate from your workplace. I frequently offer oxygen masks to clients as desktop gifts in order to remind them to provide their teams with sufficient oxygen. You pump in fresh air by engaging in productive conflict; by relying on Situational Leadership, SMART (specific, measurable, achievable, results-oriented, and time-bound) goals, and FAST (frequent, accurate, specific, and timely) feedback; by respecting your team members and maintaining nurturing relationships with them; and by good communication and attentive listening.

Teambuilding is another key component in creating a dynamic and winning team. Understanding how to handle conflict in an open and healthy manner is essential to the success of an effective team. High-performing teams do not come about miraculously; they evolve and strengthen with the help of each member understanding his or her role in a step-by-step process. Learning about these steps gives you insight into how to create the most valuable team experience. The initial part of this discussion focuses on defining the four stages of team development, and the latter explains the leadership actions needed at each stage to align the team member's performance with the practice goals.

HOW A GROUP BECOMES A TEAM — HEALTHY CONFLICT MANAGEMENT IS A KEY TO SUCCESS

Being thrust into a team environment has much in common with our everyday interactions with people about whom we are unsure. Just as we are cautious and protective of ourselves when we meet and mingle with new folks, we ought to examine work environments in a similar fashion. Individuals want to determine who is with and/or against them or who may sabotage or betray them. Because of these feelings, people step into the team a bit warily, progressing along two major axes:[19] (1) task focus, which concerns the logistics of what needs to be done and who will do it; and (2) process focus, which deals with the interpersonal relationships among the team members. In other words, how the members interact with each other becomes incremental to the overall team performance and its reflection on the practice.

In examining the task and process axes, it is vital that the two develop simultaneously for the teams' goals to be achieved. If one axis progresses more rapidly than the other, achievement of the goal is impeded.

I witnessed a good example of this when I worked with the CEO of a cardboard box manufacturer. The CEO asked me to help him develop a strategic plan for his organization. His most significant goal focused on the task of increasing productivity and profits. As I consulted with the company, I learned that the lack of productiveness and profit stemmed from the staff members' behaviors. Because they didn't like one another, the team members were sabotaging each other by hoarding supplies, harming their equipment, and the like. They were undermining one another, resulting in their failure to complete their tasks and inevitably in the company's lack of profit. Be aware that the staff members were not the only ones contributing to this problem; the CEO was also to blame. His absolute focus on productivity (the task) to the exclusion of interpersonal relationships (process) was destructive and ultimately hampered performance and undermined revenue.

As the preceding example illustrates, the danger of focusing solely on the task or concentrating exclusively on the process can be equally as damaging. In another case on which I consulted, the management team at a psychiatric facility was constantly concerned with how everyone was feeling (process). Although this attitude made for a positive work environment and the CEO, a psychiatrist, was appreciated by his staff, the team failed to market the facility effectively. Patients' bills were consistently not sent out to them for payment (task), so by the time I was called in, the facility was already in bankruptcy.

Although these two examples are rather extreme, it's clear that group members must focus on the task to be performed as well as the interpersonal relationships among them as the group grows into a team.

THE FOUR PHASES OF TEAM DEVELOPMENT

How does a group develop into a high-performing team? Through a lot of very hard work and focus, a group can progress through four stages of development. I humorously describe the four stages as: mob, crowd, group, and then after a miracle has occurred, team. The textbook titles for the four stages are: forming, storming, norming, and performing. Let's take a closer look at them in the following subsections.[20]

Forming Phase

The forming phase is the time when the group members physically come together to meet one another, set goals, and create a sense of team identity. At this stage, it's important to have a strong leader at the helm, someone whom the team members can depend on to protect, guide, and direct them. Just as we need to protect ourselves when we are thrust into new social environments, the leader needs to protect the team from other teams or groups who may tread on their sales territory, patient lists, or the like. Because the team is still quite new at this stage, the need for guidance is indispensable, and the members need to feel that their leader is encouraging them from the outset. Connie Gersick, professor of human resources and organizational behavior at the University of California, Los Angeles, found that the tone set in the first few minutes of a project team's initial meeting is the tone the team has to live with for the rest of its history.[21] Now that's a powerful few minutes! Just think of the positive atmosphere you could create in just those first few moments.

The forming stage focuses on stability, rather than on challenging the practice's customary behaviors. Little listening appears at this stage; therefore, it is difficult for new changes to come about just yet. People will typically put their hands up to be called on, and they'll approach topics in a more general manner so as not to interact directly on a topic. Members are still feeling one another out, and they are generally talking *at* each other in order to avoid direct interaction. Weaknesses are also disguised, and personal objectives are unclear. It is at this stage that most people are worried about themselves individually, rather than themselves as part of the team.

Because of the team members' concern with figuring out their place on the team at this stage, very little is actually accomplished. That doesn't mean, however, that the forming stage is pointless. The most important thing to keep in mind is that forming is a step in the greater process. As long as the members don't get stuck in forming, they will move to the next step, storming, which deals with conflict issues.

Storming Phase

As we discussed in the previous stage, forming can be equated to the beginning of a new relationship, where everyone is cautious, yet optimistic. In other words, people oftentimes find themselves on their best behavior. The second phase, storming, is when people become fed up with always being nice. The honeymoon is now over, and work needs to become the priority. As is the case with any group, conflicts will occur, and strange as it may sound, they need to occur. Team members will disagree with how to accomplish the task. Be happy when these conflicts arise; people who are willing to listen and discuss the various ways to achieve a goal can ultimately come up with the best decisions possible. In fact, an important part of my consulting practice is working with teams to increase their ability to have healthy conflict and disagreements.

Because the storming phase breeds conflict, both content and relationship problems are brought up. Many of the work issues can easily become personal between team members, and factions may begin to form. Feelings of defensiveness, competitiveness, polarization, and focus on who is right rather than what is right for the organization can drive the team members. This fragmented behavior disallows the task to be the focus, and it often leads to increased tension and decreased productivity.

Think of storming as teenage angst in one's life span. Group members may act like troubled adolescents who are resisting the adult behavior. Members test their roles, defying each other, especially those in leadership positions. They may say things like, "Are you planning on just deciding everything for us? Don't we get to voice our concerns? You know, we aren't children!" It may be difficult to hear these concerns when the members' behavior is childlike, but a good understanding of the storming phase reminds you that you need to be able to move beyond this point. Be sure that leadership is strong during this period, because strong-willed members may try to steamroll the others, which may inhibit them from becoming participative.

All teams have disagreements as to how to achieve their goals, even when the members agree on the goals to be met. The key to creating a cohesive team is learning how to manage and resolve such conflicts in a productive, healthy way.

Because of the potential for hurtful conflict, storming can be a particularly treacherous time for healthcare teams. Patient care can suffer because the conflicts in the office can be consuming and distracting. Competitiveness and polarization may create situations that are permanently damaging and debilitating to a team.

I've found that when team members understand the dynamics of team development, they're more likely to see storming as group growth rather than dysfunction or personal attack. After their first blowup, informed team members have actually asked with glee, "Is this storming? Did we finally get there?" They embrace it rather than push it away. It's quite common for groups to get stuck either just before the storming phase because they shy away from conflict or during storming because they're deeply engaged in unproductive, destructive conflict.

Norming Phase

The norming stage follows the tumultuous storming phase. Just as animals need to sniff out those about whom they're unsure, people act out similar behavior. During norming, group members become more accepting of their and others' roles within the group. Acceptance of differing mannerisms and actions begins to surface. The purpose of this stage is to grab onto this group feeling and use it to the group's and the organization's advantage. Begin to create group norms and standards. Norms are the group's written and unwritten rules of conduct and expectations. They can be informal, such as, "No one comes to a meeting more than five minutes late," or they can be formal, written rules of conduct for the whole team, such as, "Be honest and dependable," "Deliver what you promise," or "Stand behind and support team decisions." (In Chapter 2, I included several examples of codes of conduct that help groups reach the norming phase of team development.)

There is more probing on the interpersonal levels and about team dynamics during the norming phase. Members may ask others why they haven't been contributing, whether the environment is one in which they feel comfortable. For example, someone may say, "I notice that you don't seem to say much at the meetings, but when we talk one on one, you have amazing insight into what's happening. Don't you feel comfortable verbalizing your ideas to the team?" People feel more at ease with addressing their colleagues at this stage, and the norms and expectations that were devised in the previous stage help to create the standards. The mission statement also becomes real now because team members hold each other responsible for it. "We say our team members are our number one asset, but what you're talking about doing here doesn't sound like we value our team members at all!" More listening occurs, and the team develops an esprit de corps.

Frequently I'm called in to work with groups to increase their listening skills, and I find that they know how to listen, but they just don't want to! Coaches of successful teams serve as role models for listening and insist that team members listen to one another. It's one of the hallmarks of a high-performing team.

Conflict still occurs during norming, but it centers on how the team is going to solve a problem rather than who's right and who's wrong.

Performing Phase

The final stage of performing is difficult to reach. At this stage, the team is working at optimum potential, focusing on diagnoses of problems and making expedient, appropriate decisions. The goals and mission that were created early on are always in focus, guaranteeing that the choices made reflect the organization. At this point, open and productive debate is another area of benefit, and the team is able to deal with issues in a flexible and valuable manner. It is at this stage that the leader steps back a bit and basks in the strong, functioning team that has evolved. In addition, the leader tends to behave more like another team member because less guidance is needed. The effects of reaching this complex stage are superb. The group tends to have insight into the interpersonal process, and members are highly productive and reach their goals.

I witnessed a high-performing team in action when I was a board member for a large, nonprofit organization dedicated to a medical issue. Several of the members were physicians and had served on the board for nearly 20 years.

Our organization had been invited to present our issues before a congressional committee in Washington, and the team was facing the delicate situation of choosing whom from the board we would send as our representative. If this team had been in the forming phase, the physician with the most seniority on the board would have been a shoe-in for this plum assignment. If this team had been in the storming stage, there would probably have been conflict among several factions as each jockeyed for the position to have its favorite crony selected. Because the team was in the performing stage, it had an eloquent discussion about who would be the most persuasive and articulate person to promote their goal of increased visibility and funding. We selected the newest member, a bright, young physician who had been a board member for only three months.[22]

As mentioned earlier, the performing stage allows the leader to step into a role that is more equal to the team members. The team begins to work more collaboratively, and the leader facilitates, rather than directs, discussions. The team really becomes a *team* at this stage, and individuality takes a backseat to the whole. Teammates enjoy sharing the positive attention with one another, and they are much more apt to celebrate one another as well.

Interdependence is another benefit of this stage, and those common norms, expectations, and goals drive the team.

LEADERSHIP ACTIONS CRUCIAL TO TEAMBUILDING

No matter which stage of development your team is in, there are key principles that will help you move your group to the next level. Following are the strategies for each stage.[23]

Phase 1 — Forming Strategy: *Exhibit Strength*

Being a good leader is tricky. It's not easy balancing the organization's needs along with your need to gain the team's respect. Acting with authority during the forming stage can be awkward, but it's necessary to outline structure, assurance, and direction for the team. Without these authoritative directions, the team can become a messy and uncoordinated group. As the new group gets out of the starting gate, it's vital that you give focus toward the SMART team goals and be aware of the four-part group process we just discussed. Without such leadership, the groups' wheels will never get moving.

Phase 2 — Storming Strategy: *Embrace Conflict*

Conflict is not something we strive to get ourselves into. To build a strong team, however, you'll need to make it a priority. Involving team members in conflict is a realistic and necessary part of their job. No team functions as a Pollyanna entity, in which everyone agrees with each other, and it really shouldn't. Hearing others' points of views and perspectives allows for an open and fruitful discussion. If a trustworthy environment is created, teammates will begin opening up and taking risks. They'll feel invested in the process when their ideas aren't shut down but are listened to and taken into consideration.

Gender can also play a role in the storming phase because men and women vie for position in different ways. For a more in-depth discussion on this issue, see Chapter 22.

By using productive conflict resolution and leadership techniques, your team can push through this difficult phase. Allow for differences; focus on the problem, not the person; and discuss underlying values and beliefs. Use the collaborative conflict management style when appropriate by bringing the factions together, and discuss how the team can best reach its goals. You're directly attacking the problem rather than allowing it to fester in a covert way, and this can enhance the trust within the group.

Phase 3 — Norming Strategy: *Cultivate Trust*

This stage is more satisfying for all team members than the forming and storming phases. As the environment becomes more trustful, members of the team have an easier time confronting other team members when they see them violating a norm.

The basis for teamwork and the binding element in all high-performing teams is trust. To develop a team that cultivates trust among its members, you must practice and insist on the following characteristics:[24]

> ▲ *Honesty,* which is the avoidance of lies or exaggerations;
>
> ▲ *Openness,* which is a willingness to share information and ideas, to disclose your own feelings, and to listen to others;
>
> ▲ *Consistency,* which is the ability to do what you say and say what you do and to make your behavior predictable;
>
> ▲ *Respect,* which is the capacity to treat all team members with dignity and fairness. This includes your ability to allow workers to make mistakes and learn from them;
>
> ▲ *Supportiveness,* which is the capacity to reinforce others when they offer ideas and opinions; and
>
> ▲ *Competence,* which is the willingness to prepare adequately and to exhibit excellence in results.

Trust often grows through open communication. Listening is a key ingredient in developing trust. Listening is not waiting for your turn to talk! It means giving your full attention to another team member and wanting to know what he or she means by his or her words.

Finally, ensure that competition among team members is not among the group norms you've established. When building a team, emphasize that competition is with other external organizations, not with the other team members.

Phase 4 — Performing Strategy: *Continue to Pay Attention*

It's difficult to get to the performing stage, but once you're there, you must keep working on teambuilding to sustain peak output. Teams can regress if attention is diverted from their development and functioning. I know of an organization that had been holding quarterly teambuilding sessions for several years. The company's financial situation became so positive that it was able to go public and soon it began acquiring businesses around the world.

There was a downside to their explosive growth, however. Because the acquisition process took so much time and energy, the company suspended the teambuilding sessions for a year, and everything began falling apart: Teammates had destructive conflicts; they withheld information; they stopped supporting each other. Because of the erosion of trust, manufacturing problems developed that hurt the bottom line.

A high-functioning team will suffer from inattention. This was a tough lesson for this company to learn, but the president quickly made necessary adjustments. He has now elevated quarterly teambuilding to one of the organization's highest organizational priorities.

Teams are not static; they evolve over time. If conscientious teambuilding is abandoned, a high-performing team can revert to earlier, more turbulent, less productive phases. With constant attention, a high-performing team will continue to reach its goals, flourish, and exceed expectations.

Great leaders ensure that goals are reached and team members are rewarded. They encourage team members to celebrate their achievements and savor their victories. Celebrations can actually build team confidence, which leads to greater ability to take risks, and thus more winning.

SUMMARY OF TEAM DEVELOPMENT

Throughout each phase of team development — forming, storming, norming, and performing — it is critical that leaders understand their leadership role and always work to align team performance with organizational goals (Exhibit 21.1).

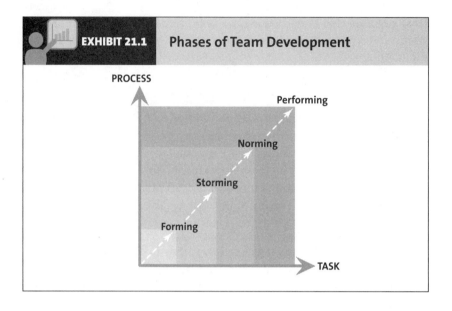

EXHIBIT 21.1   Phases of Team Development

PROCESS

Performing

Norming

Storming

Forming

TASK

GROUPTHINK

Have you ever wanted to speak up in a meeting and decided against it because you did not want to appear like you weren't a team player? Or have you ever sensed that your team members were reluctant to express their own opinions? If so, you have probably been a victim of groupthink. Whenever I work with groups, I always cover the concept of groupthink because it is so easy for groupthink to impair decision making. I'm sure that groupthink has been around since the beginning of time, although it wasn't named until the 20th century.

What exactly is groupthink? Groupthink is a type of thought exhibited by group members who are trying to minimize or avoid conflict. They want to reach consensus without critically testing, analyzing, and evaluating ideas. Group members often employ groupthink because they don't want to disagree with other group members for fear of embarrassing or angering them. The result of groupthink is that cohesive groups often make hasty, irrational decisions where doubts are set aside because members don't want to rock the boat. The higher the esprit de corps is among the group members, the greater the danger that independent critical thinking will be replaced by groupthink.

The term *groupthink* was first coined in 1952 by William H. Whyte in *Fortune*.[25] Irving Janis, who did extensive work on the subject in the early 1970s, defined groupthink as a "psychological phenomenon in which people strive for consensus within a group. In many cases, people will set aside their own personal beliefs or adopt the opinion of the rest of the group."[26]

Causes of Groupthink

I've found there to be three situations when groupthink becomes problematic:

1. In highly cohesive groups;
2. When no outside experts are used; and
3. With strong leaders of groups in the forming phase.

Highly cohesive groups, such as in a medical practice where physicians have worked together amicably for several years, are much more likely to engage in groupthink. The closer the members are, the less likely they are to raise questions to disrupt the cohesion. Many physicians are conflict averse and can easily drift into groupthink.

Often, groups don't think about including outside experts, especially well-educated groups like physicians. Additionally, groups often have blind spots where they don't know what they don't know. Sometimes intentionally, sometimes because of a blind spot, the group isolates itself from outside experts. To make a well-informed decision, the group needs to invite qualified experts to help weigh the possible risks.

When there is a strong, outspoken, opinionated leader, groupthink becomes a decision-making style. The leader is more likely to promote his or her solution. This is especially true in groups that are still in the forming phase, when the group is dependent on the leader and expecting the leader to make all the decisions.

Symptoms of Groupthink[27]

Janis found that groupthink occurs when:

- ▲ *Illusions of invulnerability* lead members of the group to be overly optimistic and engage in risk-taking;
- ▲ *Unquestioned beliefs* lead members to ignore possible moral problems and ignore consequences of individual and group actions;
- ▲ *Rationalizing* prevents members from reconsidering their beliefs and causes them to ignore warning signs;

▲ *Stereotyping* leads members of the in-group to ignore or even demonize out-group members who may oppose or challenge the group ideas;

▲ *Self-censorship* causes people who might have doubts to hide their fears or misgivings;

▲ *"Mindguards"* act as self-appointed censors to hide problematic information from the group;

▲ *Illusions of unanimity* lead members to believe that everyone is in agreement and feels the same way; and

▲ *Direct pressure to conform* is often placed on members who pose questions, and those who question the group are often seen as disloyal or traitorous.

Two Classic Cases of Groupthink

The space shuttle *Challenger* disaster is a classic case of groupthink and is frequently cited during discussions about groupthink. I often show the video of this disaster to my clients. The *Challenger* exploded shortly after liftoff on Jan. 28, 1986. The National Aeronautics and Space Administration (NASA) scientists and engineers had been eager to get the mission under way, because the launch was already six days late because of several problems.[28]

On January 27, an engineer brought up a concern about the O-rings in the booster rockets. Several conference calls were held to discuss this O-ring problem, and then the group decided to go ahead with the launch.

In hindsight, the decision to launch the *Challenger* despite the knowledge of a potential mechanical problem met several of the symptoms of groupthink. The decision makers ignored warnings that contradicted the group's goal to launch the space shuttle as soon as possible. The group also suffered from a feeling of invulnerability. They failed to completely examine the risks of their decision; they played it off as if it were nothing important. Additionally, the group had suppressed the few engineers who were speaking up about concerns because there was pressure not to delay the launch. At this time, Congress was seeking to earmark large funding to NASA given the large amount of publicity on the Teacher in Space program. These misjudgments led to the tragic loss of several astronauts, and damage to NASA's near-perfect safety record.

The housing bubble and financial crisis illustrated failure by groupthink as described by Stan Sorscher in a 2010 article in the *Huffington Post*.[29] He describes the conceptual convention at that time was that housing prices would always go up. Within that convention, smart and experienced people could not process observations that contradicted the prevailing wisdom. He noted that groupthink can have an "eyes open" presentation, using the example of a bank officer or executive who may have been perceptive enough to recognize the herd behavior and see that the herd is heading to disaster. However, if the banker had taken defensive action too soon, it would have cost his or her bank money. In other words, if his or her competitor's bank stayed in the bubble an extra six or nine months and realized additional (unsustainable) gains, then the bank that dropped out too soon would have been punished by its shareholders for poor performance. No bank could have "afforded" to break ranks with the herd.

PREVENTING GROUPTHINK

According to Irving Janis, decision-making groups are not necessarily doomed to groupthink. Janis devised seven ways of preventing groupthink:[30]

1. Leaders should assign each member the role of "critical evaluator." This allows each member to freely air objections and doubts.
2. Higher-ups should not express an opinion when assigning a task to a group.
3. The organization should set up several independent groups, all working on the same problem.
4. All effective alternatives should be examined.
5. Each member should discuss the group's ideas with trusted people outside of the group.
6. The group should invite outside experts into meetings. Group members should be allowed to discuss with and question the outside experts.
7. At least one group member should be assigned the role of devil's advocate. This should be a different person for each meeting.

Preventing Groupthink Today in Organizations

A few years ago when the Wrigley family was a major landowner on Santa Catalina Island, 26 miles off the Southern California coast, they implemented practices to prevent groupthink. At city council meetings, when decisions needed to be made, the family waited until everyone else had given their opinions before announcing theirs. The family understood the

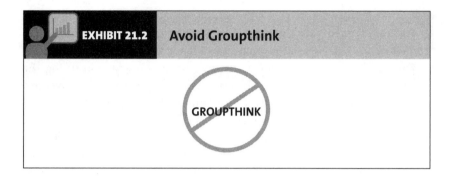

EXHIBIT 21.2   **Avoid Groupthink**

power and influence they wielded and did not want to influence the opinions of others. When making decisions in your organization, be sure to keep groupthink in mind. Some of my clients have framed the "avoid groupthink" symbol and hung it in their board rooms (Exhibit 21.2).

From my experience of consulting with groups in many industries, I've found that most people find disagreement and conflict very uncomfortable and unmanageable. When groups do not deal well with conflict and are not focused on teamwork, there is stagnation. When there is open disagreement and the members are not focused on teamwork, chaos is rampant. When there is a focus on healthy, open disagreement and teamwork and cohesion, there is an optimal state for a high-performing team to develop. When there is a focus on teamwork and cohesion, but disagreement and healthy conflicts are discouraged, the group is ripe for groupthink (Exhibit 21.3).

CONFLICT WITH DIFFICULT COLLEAGUES AND TEAM MEMBERS

Oliver Wendell Holmes Sr. wrote, "Every person's feelings have a front door and a side door by which they may be entered."[31] This implies that as we're dealing with highly emotional issues, we may not want to always approach the issue frontally. We may have to come at the issue from a fresh perspective. Innovation in building relationships can be a tremendous asset for an effective leader.

Difficult people can frequently distract you and your team from reaching your goals. Difficult people can serve as decoys that veer us off target as they, often shamelessly, burn up time, energy, and resources.

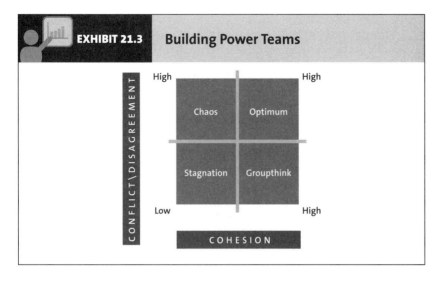

In your leadership role, there will be times when you must deal with persons that Robert Bramson appropriately named many years ago in his best-selling book, *Coping with Difficult People*.[32] Bramson describes the difficult person as one who acts in a chronically difficult manner. Use the following four questions as a litmus test to determine if someone falls into that category. If your answer to all four questions is "no," then you are probably dealing with a difficult person:

1. Has the person in question usually acted differently in three similar situations?
2. Am I reacting out of proportion to what the situation warrants?
3. Was there a particular incident that triggered the troublesome behavior?
4. Will direct, open discussion relieve the situation?

Even if you have mastered the appropriate use of conflict management styles, are familiar with conflict resolution guidelines, and have a virtual toolbox full of conflict management tools, trust me, you will encounter some people — perhaps even a team member — who are difficult people, those who only use one style of conflict management. For example, a bully may use only a competitive style, and a gossip may use avoiding by telling everyone except the person with whom she's having a conflict.

You may encounter bullies, gossips, snipers, and clams. By recognizing their tactics and hidden conflict management styles, you can identify and better manage the situation you must contend with. Bear in mind that in each case, there is some kind of payoff for the person who engages in being a difficult person. Don't label the person; label the behavior. The way to deal with difficult people is to find their payoff and deny them from getting it.

The Bully

Bullies use a competitive conflict management style. Although bullies usually have low self-esteem and self-doubt, they try to fool others into thinking they are powerful. They control through put-downs, putting others on the defensive by asking questions such as, "How could you ever get an idea like that?" They are quick to anger and have a predictable fast attack.[33] This type of difficult person is like a bull trying to gouge you. If you acquiesce, complain, or try to appease, the bully sees you as weak. Often with a bully you might be talking about something like a new TV show you recently saw or a trip you took, and the bully suddenly attacks with, "Why didn't you...?" and you immediately get defensive! This is very effective behavior for this sort of person because you're never sure what's going to set this individual off. Bullies enjoy watching people walk on eggshells and feeling in control.

How Do You Neutralize the Bully?

So what do you do? It's important to understand that you aren't going to fight with bullies; you're going to stand up to them. Instead of saying, "John, you're wrong!" You say, "John, I have a different perspective." You don't want to fight with bullies. These people are world-class fighters and have been behaving this way for a long time, and you are an amateur. Even if you win this battle, you'll lose the war with the bullies. If they explode, do not intervene in the middle of the explosion. Let them wind down. During a bullfight, the matador stands in one place and lets the bull wear himself out. With bullies, act like they're not getting to you. "Never let him see you sweat" is good advice here. Hold yourself erect and don't back away. Maintain eye contact. This isn't easy and takes practice. Massage the bully's ego by only speaking the truth. "Oh, Bill, what a fantastic plan! I've never thought of that strategy before."

When bullies are threatened, they can be vicious. It's hard to remember that they have small egos because they behave as if their egos are tremendous. In reality, their egos are very fragile. Try to get the bully to listen; you have to often get a bully's attention in one of several ways. You can say the bully's name repeatedly: "John, John, John, John, John ..." or physically move. If you're standing up, sit down. If you're sitting, stand up (slowly). I know a woman who purposely drops something on the floor, like a pen or a notebook. If there's movement, people tend to think, "My gosh, what's going on?" Disagree in a tactful way and with facts; do your research. Use phrases such as "in my judgment" and "in my opinion." And then be ready to be friendly, because often, bullies will start to respect you for standing up to them.

The Gossip

A gossip is a person who habitually spreads intimate or private rumors or facts. The destructive gossips attack behind your back and then will innocently act as if they have done nothing. They talk negatively about you to other team members, but then behave as if they're your good friend. There could be many reasons for gossiping behaviors. Some gossips carry a grudge and try to undermine anyone who interferes with their plans. Some gossip for attention. Others gossip because of low self-esteem and the feeling of power they get by tearing someone else down. The gossip's payoff is that he or she doesn't have to confront you directly.[34]

How Do You Muffle the Gossip?

When faced with dealing with a gossip, many people will say, "I'm just not going to honor such remarks with my time and energy. I'll take the high road. It's untrue, so why should I address him or her?" Unfortunately, this allows the gossip to continue doing damage. In dealing with a gossip, it's best to confront this behavior. In a nonthreatening manner, meet privately with the gossip and ask if there's a problem. The gossip's mission is to do damage while remaining hidden and yours is to eliminate this payoff. You want to stop the attacks, not to get even or escalate the conflict.

Ask the gossip if it's possibly true that he or she said these things about you behind your back. Be sure to pose this as a tentative question — as in "possibly true" — not with a statement such as, "I have 20 witnesses." Giving the gossip an out with the word "possibly" will help to defuse his or her defensiveness. Still, you can anticipate denial. The person is almost sure to say, "Oh no, I'd never say that about you."

Thank the individual with a statement such as, "I'm so glad, because I would hope that if you had a problem like this, you would come to me and speak with me directly."

Don't expect this to instantly solve the problem. Before long, you will probably hear that the gossip has been talking behind your back. Again, you must get in the individual's face with the same strategies. Expect the cycle to repeat several times. Over the long haul, however, gossips will learn that if they talk about you, it will get back to you and you will confront them. This is exactly what the gossips want to avoid, and it will help extinguish this behavior over time.

If You're the Manager[35]

Gossips must be stopped or they will damage your team culture. Meet with the gossip in private and let the person know what you've heard. Ask the individual if this could possibly be true. Your staff member will probably deny it. Thank the person and remind the individual that if he or she ever has a legitimate business concern, you encourage bringing it to you directly. You won't tolerate offensive comments made behind your or others' backs. The healthy workplace environment is too important to be jeopardized by gossip.

The Sniper

Snipers are similar to bullies because they want to show their power at your cost.[36] The sniper can hide in a crowd and maintain cover while skillfully getting others to laugh at you by using indirect hostile aggression. I often describe a sniper as someone who will stab you in the back and then turn you into authorities for having a concealed weapon!

If you're giving a presentation about a new product idea, a sniper might make a thumbs-down gesture or could say sarcastically, "Ha, ha, ha. What a novel idea. I think I've read about it in a book... it was Chapter 11!" You know this is a dig, so you respond, "So, Jay, you don't like what I'm recommending?"

"I didn't say that. I said I thought it was novel." The sniper is trying to discredit you and get the rest of the group to laugh at you. Snipers are masters at using nonverbal cues, such as rolling eyes, snickering, winking, and elbow jabs. Part of this strategy is to encourage the group to go along with the ridicule. The sniper's payoff is that he or she gets to damage you without having to confront you directly.

How Do You Disarm the Sniper?

The basic action to take with snipers is to smoke them out; take away their camouflage. Take control of the situation and bring the attack to the surface. Enlist the aid of the group. If the sniper ambushes you during a meeting, you could say, "Sandy, Mike seems to have a problem with what I'm recommending. What's your opinion? How about you, Barb?" When you get individual feedback from others, the sniper is no longer able to hide out among the crowd and you've skillfully denied the sniper the payoff he or she seeks.

Asking questions of the sniper instead of making assertions can be effective in keeping the conflict from escalating. For example, to respond to the thumbs-down gesture, you can ask pointedly, "What did you mean by your thumbs-down signal?" Addressing the sniper's behavior will most likely curtail future sniping.

The Clam

Clams are difficult people who become unresponsive when you need an answer or want some conversation.[37] Dealing with clams can be very frustrating because you aren't sure what the silence means. There are varieties of clams. One type is silent because the clam is hoping you will leave him or her alone. Another type uses silence as indirect aggression and enjoys watching you become frustrated and upset.

Often the clams' facial expressions are inconsistent with their words. The clam says everything is fine when the person doesn't seem fine at all. A typical exchange could be:

> "Is your new job going okay?"
> "It's fine."
> "Are you finding everything you need?"
> "Sure."
> "Are you happy here?"
> "Sure."

The clam's reward is feeling in control by not sharing information with you.

How Do You Get a Clam to Open Up?

The goal is to get the clam to talk. Start by conveying that you care about the clam. Meet with the clam privately, perhaps over breakfast or lunch. Food often facilitates conversations, plus it's difficult to remain quiet for an hour as you sit facing each other. Ask reporter-type, open-ended questions: What? Where? When? How? Who?

- ▲ "What do you like about working here?"
- ▲ "What are some of your professional goals?"

▲ "What can I do to support your career goals?"

▲ "What suggestions do you have for making our department better?"

When soliciting this input, use a friendly, silent stare. If the clam doesn't respond right away, don't rescue him or her. There is power in your silence. From my experience, it may take from 15 to 20 seconds for the clam to respond. Continue your stare with expectant silence — your eyes wide open and lips slightly parted. If the conversation remains strained, talk about this. "It seems like something is not being said here, and I don't know what it is. I think we need to talk about this. Have I offended you in some way?"

Sometimes, despite valiant efforts on your part, a clam will continue to be silent. Don't give up. "I believe there's something amiss between us. Was it my feedback about your report? Are you upset about Mary's promotion?" If the clam will not talk with you and remains unresponsive, you may need to let it go for now. Close with "I feel I've done all I can today to encourage you to talk. I value our relationship, so whenever you're ready to talk with me, I'm available." Don't end on a polite cliché, such as "Have a great weekend."

If the clam starts to open up, be attentive when the person speaks. Listen carefully to him or her with open body language. Don't fidget or keep glancing at your watch.

SUCCEEDING WITH MANAGING DIFFICULT PEOPLE

When dealing with the difficult people in your life, keep in mind the five steps described in the following subsections.

Step 1: Get a Grip

The best way to change someone else's behavior is to change your own. It's up to you to change how you behave when you are with your difficult person. Get your own emotions and self-talk under control, so that you can think strategically. If you are toying with the idea of doing nothing, remember that doing nothing is actually doing something.

Step 2: Identify the Behavior Type of Your Difficult Person and the Payoff This Individual Wants

Is your difficult person a bully, sniper, gossip, or clam? If so, what is the payoff the person desires?

Step 3: Formulate Your Plan

It is important to preplan. For example, if you're dealing with a gossip, decide when you will meet privately with this person and what exactly you will say when you do. You may need to write it out and even rehearse your script with a confidante.

Step 4: Implement Your Plan Consistently

Choose the right time for following through with your plan. Ensure that you have the time and energy to devote to your confrontation and the challenges that may come after the encounter.

Step 5: Be Strong and Consistent

Once you've decided that you want to change your relationship with the difficult person, you must be steadfast in denying the payoff. In fact, a difficult person may act worse for a while, thinking that you will revert to your previous behavior. For example, a bully may attack more ferociously and the sniper may become more caustic. It will be tempting to slack off. Don't! You've already come this far!

FIND YOUR SENSE OF HUMOR

When studying how to manage conflict, one tactic often omitted is humor. Most people, difficult and not, can be disarmed by humor that is delivered without malice. We often forget to find the humor in situations and in ourselves, especially when we're feeling uncomfortable during a conflict situation. I believe that human behavior is pretty hilarious. It's very important to take our jobs seriously, but let's not take ourselves so seriously. Some of the people who are the best at managing conflict often have a great sense of humor.

CHAPTER PRESCRIPTIONS

- Take responsibility for creating a healthy and positive workplace culture, free of negative attitudes.
- Learn to handle conflict openly and healthfully, because this is a key component to the establishment of a constructive workplace.
- Focus on both task (the coordination of activities to do the job) as well as process (the interpersonal relationships among team members).
- Whether you see them as mob, crowd, group, and team, or forming, storming, norming, and performing, it is crucial for the overall success of your team to understand these phases of team development.
- Beware of groupthink within your organization; team members won't want to disagree with other group members for fear of embarrassing or angering them. Try to emphasize the importance and necessity of expressing ideas freely and in a comfortable environment.
- Remember that a dangerous result of groupthink is that unified groups often make hasty decisions because members don't want to upset the group.
- Don't let groupthink take over strong, independent, critical thinking — remember why you hired individuals in the first place.
- Make individuals aware of their (intentional or unintentional) tactics when it comes to dealing with coworkers.
- After you identify the tactics, you are better equipped to manage difficult team members. Usually, there is some kind of payoff for the person who engages in being a difficult person. Find the payoff for difficult people and deny them from getting it.

CHAPTER 22

Gender Differences

"Why can't a woman be more like a man?" pleaded Henry Higgins in *My Fair Lady*. Why is it important to include a chapter on gender differences in a book about aligning team performance with organizational goals? Because not understanding some of the major differences in gender thinking, communication, and behavior can spell doom for your organization as it works to build a high-performing team as well as achieve high patient satisfaction scores. Many experts believe that gender difference is the largest cultural gap in organizations today and is at the root of conflicts and misunderstandings, and is one of the main reasons for veering off target from goals.

Until recent years, not only were most physicians male, but most research on diseases as well as customer service was conducted on males. The male model of an established hierarchy where the guys at the top possessed all the power seemed to work just fine in the past; it was expected that the women who worked in the office, as well as the women patients, did what they were told to do by the male physicians.

A sea change is occurring. Today, almost half of medical school graduates are women (47 percent)[38] and many medical group practice managers are women. When women are in positions of power, they often create a flatter, less hierarchical structure, so the leadership and communication style in organizations is changing as women take on these powerful roles. Additionally, new research is showing that women use physician services significantly more often than men, and the woman is usually the decision maker when it comes to choosing physicians for the family. Many women are demanding a different communication style with their physicians — they want conversation, collaboration, and rapport. Women won't tolerate a command-and-control type of relationship, and will change physicians if necessary to find one with whom they can connect. The emerging science that studies gender differences is relevant and essential to healthcare organizations for two reasons: (1) to create an organizational culture where both genders can thrive as they align performance with the organizational goals;

and (2) to educate physicians and their teams about how to achieve high patient satisfaction for male and female patients. Once men and women are exposed to the differences in gender, they understand what is behind many of the clashes and frustrations that they have in dealing with each other.

Pat Heim, PhD, introduced me to the world of gender differences many years ago, and she continues to mentor me as well as conduct research with me about this fascinating field. Pat wrote *Hardball for Women*[39] in 1992 (with Susan Golant) and is an international expert in gender differences. She and I coauthored *In the Company of Women*[40] and are currently writing another book about couples. I thank Pat for much of the content in this chapter.

This chapter is divided into three sections. In the first section, I describe some of the latest research findings about male and female biology (some of the differences in male and female brains and hormones), sociology, and genetics. The second section covers some general areas for gender differences that affect lessons learned about *appropriate* leadership, teamwork, communication, problem solving, and conflict management. I provide strategies for each gender on how to *flex* their approach so they can be effective in dealing with the other gender. Finally, there is a section on women working with women that explores the "golden triangle,"[41] the female dynamic of balancing relationship, power, and self-esteem. By understanding the golden triangle and the "power dead-even rule,"[42] you will develop insights into how to create a culture where women can work productively together — even when there is differentiated power.

GENDER ISSUES WHEN COMMUNICATING, INFLUENCING, AND SELLING IDEAS

During presentations about gender differences, I usually ask the groups both what they like and what drives them crazy about working with the other gender. Consistently, men and women report the information outlined in Exhibit 22.1 when asked what drives them crazy about the other gender. Men and women tell me that these behaviors cause them to become frustrated and angry, lose influence, and negatively affect their decision making and ability to focus on the goals.

Not Good or Bad, Nor Right or Wrong

Both men and women behave in ways that make sense to them, and each is working hard to achieve organizational goals — based on the rules of their

EXHIBIT 22.1 **How Men and Women May Describe Work Experiences with the Opposite Sex**

Women often view men as:	Men often view women as:
"Pushy, aggressive, insensitive"	"Don't get to point quickly"
"Intimidating, overbearing"	"Take things too personally"
"Devious"	"Overly emotional"
"Don't give time to think through reaction"	"Difficult to tease"
"Lack sincerity and honesty"	
"Act superior, condescending"	

gender culture. None of these gender behaviors is good or bad, or right or wrong. They are just different. When we understand where the behaviors are coming from, we can train ourselves to flex our behavior so that we can communicate more effectively with one another (see Exhibit 22.1).

The Bell Curve of Research

Throughout this chapter, there will be times when readers will be thinking, "That's not my experience." The information presented is based on research, and research is plotted on a bell curve. So, I'll be describing what most men and women are like, but there are always exceptions, especially when describing gender behavior. My intent is to communicate about generalities for men and women, not to stereotype or pigeonhole. Generalizations serve as guidelines and a means to understand others. They provide insights that can lead to awareness, empathy, and new approaches. Many times you may find yourself on the tail of the bell curve. In fact, because I've spent many years working in predominately male environments, my behavior frequently can be found on the tail of the female bell curve when I'm around men. I've learned to *flex* my behavior, so that I can function effectively with men as well as women.

Invisible Differences

Men and women see the world differently — and the differences are often invisible. It's easy to expect differences from those who are raised on different continents, such as Asia or Africa, and have a different native tongue. However, when it comes to the men and women in our lives, we may know that we're frustrated, but we usually don't realize it's because of gender differences getting in the way.

Because of physiology, sociology, and genetics, men and women have learned different lessons about *appropriate* teamwork, problem solving, leadership, communication, and conflict management. For example, most men see the world as a hierarchy where power is differentiated; most women see the world as *flatter* where power is shared. Women often strive for power in order to have influence and change things for the better, whereas men often want power in order to be at the top of a hierarchy.

Another difference is that relationships are central in the female culture but not so important in the male culture. More than 80 percent of women want to work on a team with others, whereas 80 percent of men are fine working alone.[43] Many more men would rather telecommute than women. My doctoral thesis was titled "A Study of Career Values by Generation and Gender." The most significant difference between men and women in my study was that women want close relationships and interactions with others at work.

Why Focus on Differences Instead of Similarities?

Oftentimes, people ask me why I focus on the differences between men and women; isn't that just looking for trouble? There are many ways that men and women are similar — the similarities aren't what get in the way of working well together. It's the differences that can cause the most heartburn. The number one ingredient for a healthy view of gender differences is a good sense of humor — the ability to laugh lightheartedly and respectfully at the wonderful differences between men and women.

Male and Female Differences: Biology, Sociology, Genetics

The following subsections discuss the differences in male and female biology, sociology, and genetics.

Male and Female Brains

Only recently have we discovered that male and female brains are quite different, and that men and women think differently. In *Brain Sex*, Anne Moir and David Jessel report that the embryonic brain is shaped as either a male or female at about six weeks, when the male fetus begins producing hormones that organize its brain's neural networks into a male pattern; in their absence, the brain will be female.[44] These differences make men more aggressive, competitive, and better at skills that require spatial ability and mathematical reasoning. Women are more sensitive and adept at judging character and developing relationships. Women seem to be more people oriented than men, who are often more interested in "things."

Through the use of positron emission tomography scans, scientists have found that the female brain is not as neatly organized as the male brain. Centers that control language and emotional responses can be found on both sides of the female brain. The corpus callosum, the connecting tissue between hemispheres, is 25 percent thicker among women than men,[45] causing women to experience more communication and cooperation between the two hemispheres. The more intricately wired female brain allows for more information to be exchanged between both sides: Emotions are better integrated with verbal abilities, making women more fluent at expressing feelings to others.

Perhaps this is also why a man will tend to find it more challenging to talk about how he feels than a woman does.[46]

Men tend to have brains that are 10 percent larger than women and are more left-brained (linear), while women have greater access to both sides of their brains, which makes them more holistic thinkers. Women's brains have 15 percent more blood flow and a higher blood flow to four lobes for intimacy and complex thought.[47] Whereas men often prefer to focus on one thing at a time, women like to multitask and simultaneously focus on several things. These differences can affect teamwork among colleagues where women are more comfortable speaking about their feelings than are men.

Men may be more comfortable doing one thing at a time, which may seem like tunnel vision to women, whereas women may appear scattered to men as they multitask easily. Women patients may want more expressiveness from male physicians, and male patients may expect women physicians to remain more distant.

Women also bring in and process information differently from men. Women see, smell, sense danger more readily, and have broader peripheral vision. Split-second reactions differ by gender. In women, this function is linked to a verbal response — women call out to allies for help — whereas in men, it is linked to physical action — fighting or fleeing.

Women are better at picking up social cues and important nuances of meaning from tone of voice and facial expression; and because women are typically better than men at reading emotions, they sometimes refer to what they consider this uncanny ability as "women's intuition."[48]

Male and Female Hormones

After many years of research, scientists now believe that hormones affect our behavior. Although the action of many hormones is similar in men and women, there are different levels of some of them, including testosterone and oxytocin. Both men and women secrete testosterone, although men have as much as 20 times more testosterone than women.

Testosterone enhances libido, energy, muscle mass, and strength, and when there are elevated levels of testosterone, aggression often increases as well. In the workplace, men are often thought to be more aggressive and competitive than women.

Women have a higher level of oxytocin, a hormone that is produced at childbirth and causes the uterus to contract during labor as well as triggers milk ejection when breastfeeding. According to evolutionary biologist Sarah Blaffer Hardy and biologist C. Sue Carter, oxytocin is believed to play an important role in creating the mother–infant bond.[49] Oxytocin is also released in men and women during sex and has been called the "love hormone"[50] because it has intimacy-enhancing properties. The effects of oxytocin are controlled by estrogen, a primarily female hormone.[51]

Oxytocin makes people feel better about those around them and it increases their desire to be near to and connected with others. Researchers have found that people with higher oxytocin levels tend to be calmer, more relaxed and social, and less anxious — women have much higher levels than men.

Oxytocin plays an additional role in females. Whereas men experience the fight-or-flight response when threatened, women may more naturally exhibit oxytocin-induced protective and caring behaviors during those times.[52] Shelly Taylor, a professor at the University of California, Los Angeles, has called this uniquely female phenomenon the impulse to "tend and befriend."[53]

Oxytocin, with its calming properties, may chemically induce a female to engage in tending behaviors; that is, quieting and caring for offspring and reaching out to connect with supportive females around her. Oxytocin levels in women is a major gender difference and drives women to behave in supportive, caring, protective, and intimate ways. This can be very beneficial for women in a medical practice as women are often able to deal with patients, physicians, nurses, and insurers effectively because of their ability to develop meaningful professional relationships with them.

Team Sports: The Hierarchical Culture of Men

In every world culture, the games children play are not random. Children are taught how to be appropriate adults through the games they play. When American boys grow up, they play baseball, basketball, football, cops and robbers, and war — all of which are hierarchical team sports.

Boys learn how to compete, be aggressive, play to win, and mask emotions. Playing their position in the hierarchy, boys learn to obey the coach unquestioningly, champion team loyalty, and interact with children they don't like. Gaining power is important, and power is differentiated in the hierarchy. Boys learn how to win and lose without becoming emotionally involved with the fate of their competitors. Boys typically play in a crowd of people with whom they aren't emotionally connected. They focus on reaching the goal and not necessarily on their relationships with one another.[54]

Playing with Dolls: The Flat Culture of Women

Most girls play with people they like (usually one on one, often with their best friend). Girls often play doll games, where there are no winners or losers, and learn several cultural lessons: how to get along and be nice (code for "don't get into conflict"), how to protect friendships by negotiating differences and seeking win–win situations, and how to focus on what's fair for all. As a result, girls (unlike boys) learn to *flatten* hierarchal relationships, in effect saying, "We're all in this together." There aren't firm goals and goal lines as there are in the male culture. The main goal is to preserve the friendships and relationships that are central in the female culture.

An underlying hidden rule in the female culture is that power in relationships is always shared and that it is kept dead even. As my friend Pat Heim frequently says, "There is never a boss doll player," and should one girl presume to take this role, she will be ostracized by her friends and called "bossy" or worse. In the "Women Working with Women" section of this chapter, I address the unique relationship that women have with one another, where power is expected to be kept dead even.

Hierarchy and Male Progeny

We can learn about human behavior from observing our nearest living relative, the chimpanzee. Chimp genes overlap human genes by 99 percent; our DNA is almost identical.[55] Both males and females want progeny — to get their genes into the gene pool — in other words, to procreate. All males have the same agenda, and they vie for access to the females. This creates conflict. Males of many species fight with other males for the opportunity to continue their line; some will even eat the young of their rivals in an attempt to ensure their own genetic dominance.[56]

This innate need to compete for a powerful position seems cruel, yet it may have a purpose beyond that of reproduction. Many anthropologists believe it has led to the creation of hierarchical social structures (an alpha male on top and the other lesser males below him in a sort of pyramidal arrangement). An advantage of this type of dominance hierarchy is that it eventually engenders security and peacefulness. Every male knows his place and keeps to it until and unless he feels ready to challenge the leader. Although male physicians aren't about to eat the young of their competition, I have noticed that many male physicians and male medical group managers see their work world as a hierarchy and are often more focused on climbing to the top than are many women. From my experience, more women physicians than men are interested in working part time and sharing jobs than male physicians.

Females Help One Another

Unlike males, female chimps don't need to use conflict to establish a hierarchy to guarantee the continuation of their genes. Rather than competing, females tend to rely on help from their same-gender friends to ensure their offspring's survival. Females don't fight over access to power. Their quarrels usually revolve around access to resources — food, protection of the young, males, promotions, and coveted assignments. Raising a baby is a time-and-energy-intensive activity, for both humans and lower-order mammals.[57]

Nature or Nurture?

Are we the way we are because of our biology and genetics or because of the way we've been raised — is it nature or nurture? I believe it's both. Our biology supports the way we are raised.

We treat our male and female infants quite differently from the moment we wrap them in their little blue or pink receiving blankets right after delivery. Research has shown that the amount of time parents spend touching and gazing at their infants (and the babies' return gaze) is influenced by the parents' and child's gender. Fathers touch their sons more than their daughters. In turn, boy infants gaze at their fathers more than their mothers. Mothers talk more to their daughters during their first two years than to their sons.

Fathers hold baby girls more carefully with both hands, caress them closer to the chest, and cuddle them more than boys. Boys are roughhoused and tickled more often. Fathers and mothers speak more loudly to sons during their first few years of life. We allow boys to cry longer before we pick them up, while we often attend to girls as soon as they make the first whimper. This may teach girls at a young age that someone will pay attention, soothe their pain, and meet their needs — whereas boys are taught to tough it out.[58]

Indeed, social psychologists studying sex role development have found that because of thousands of minute interactions like these throughout childhood, American girls are taught to be fragile, dependent, compliant, cooperative, and nurturing. It becomes clear to females from day one that nurturing, close, and emotional relationships are expected to be a central part of their lives. American boys are taught to be independent, tough, aggressive, competitive, and unemotional.[59]

HOW PHYSIOLOGY, SOCIOLOGY, AND GENETICS AFFECT GENDER BEHAVIOR, COMMUNICATIONS, AND THINKING

This section focuses on several gender differences that can cause misunderstandings, frustrations, conflicts, and breakdowns in communication at work as well as at home. Teams can become distracted from reaching goals when the relationships among members break down. As discussed in Chapter 21 about the necessity of conflict in building high-performing teams, there are two dimensions to building teams: the focus on the goal to be achieved and the relationships among the team members.

These gender differences can impede good communication between physicians and patients as well. When a male physician wants to be seen as the powerful figure at the top of the hierarchy while the female patient is looking for collaboration about her care plan, the situation is ripe for conflict. When a male patient is seeking an authority figure in his physician, and the female physician wants to collaborate and involve him in his care plan, the male patient may discount the medical expertise of the female physician. If the female patient is telling the male physician about her health problems and he interrupts her, she may stop talking and never come back. Some male physicians have complained to me that they don't like it when patients (either male or female) call them by their first name. I tell them that it's a compliment that patients want to see them as a colleague in their care — of course, I'm responding from a female point of view!

Hierarchical vs. Flat Structure

As discussed previously, men live in hierarchical structures. Power is differentiated and power cascades throughout the hierarchy with the men at the top having the most power. Male institutions, such as the armed forces, government departments, and major corporations, reflect this hierarchical structure. Men compete, are aggressive, play to win, and mask their emotions. Women prefer flatter structures, which promote better communication, understanding, and friendship. Women usually attempt to share power equally and flatten the hierarchy. As a result, women often negotiate differences, seeking win–win solutions, focusing on what is fair for all instead of winning. One of the problems with the power dead-even rule, however, is that work is usually played by the hierarchical rules of team sports, and what seems fair might not always be the best way to run a business. These ideas are further developed at the end of this chapter. (See also Exhibit 22.2.)

Leadership

Good leaders are those who are able to flex their style based on the needs of the follower. Unfortunately, both men and women often end up on *automatic pilot* using the style that is most comfortable or familiar rather than what will be most effective with each follower.

Command and Control vs. Involvement

In a hierarchy, the leadership style that works most effectively is command and control. Control of the game is given to a *coach* who defines a problem and then issues a command to *kill* the problem. Questioning the male coach's motives or tactics is often considered an act of insubordination. The coach's job is to keep the team focused on the goal line and to conquer problems rather than discuss them. Many years ago, my friend Pat Heim enlightened me that the command and control works most effectively in emergencies, when there is no alternative (that is, federal law), and in time-bound situations.[60] The downside of command and control is that team members are taught to accept commands they don't necessarily like and to

EXHIBIT 22.2 Hierarchical vs. Flat Structure Tools for Men and Women

WHEN COMMUNICATING WITH AND INFLUENCING MEN

Remember the hierarchy!

▲ Men don't like to ask questions and lower their position.
  • "What did I leave out that you'd like to know?"
  • "What did I not explain clearly enough?"

▲ Use a confident tone of voice.

▲ Let men know credentials. Don't minimize accomplishments.

▲ Be knowledgeable and concise.

▲ Don't use self-deprecating humor.

▲ Negotiating is a game. Start HIGH!

WHEN COMMUNICATING WITH AND INFLUENCING WOMEN

Remember the flat structure!

▲ Women want to be taken seriously — a primary concern.

▲ Introduce yourself, shake hands, look in her eyes; convey that you believe she's professional, intelligent, and respectable.

▲ Don't pressure or appear pushy — let her "set the pace."

▲ Understand that asking questions is not a sign of "weakness."

▲ Don't give orders. Say, "Let's sit down and talk."

▲ Maintain facial contact. Look at entire face — eyes, nose, mouth.

▲ Don't interrupt. Don't finish sentences.

© P. Heim, S. Murphy, with S. Golant, *In the Company of Women: Indirect Aggression Among Women: Why We Hurt Each Other and How to Stop* (New York: Tarcher/Putnam, 2003). Used with permission.

obey them without question; interpersonal relationships are relegated to the sidelines.

In a flat structure, the leadership style at work is involvement. Female managers are more likely to *share* power with others, involving them in the problem-solving and decision-making processes. Pat stresses that leadership by involvement works when you need creativity, psychological buy-in, or the team to make it work.[61] On the plus side, involvement promotes creativity and provides psychological buy-in when it takes other people to get the job done. The downside, however, is that women who lead through involvement might be viewed as weak and ineffectual by male counterparts and team members who are more accustomed to taking orders from above.

Process vs. Goal Focus

When problem solving, men often sort through options internally before offering a solution. To verbalize his thoughts and uncertainty before he has reached a solution could jeopardize a man's position in the hierarchy. Men tend to focus on the goal and want to quickly fix problems.

Women, conversely, often process issues externally by gathering input from team members, friends, or family before reaching a solution. A woman who is used to a flat structure does not think she will lose anything by soliciting input from outside sources. Goal achievement is just as important to women, but how women get there is different (Exhibit 22.3).[62]

Linear vs. Multiple Focus

As discussed previously in the male and female brains subsection, the corpus callosum in women is larger — and this affects focus. Men often lead linear lives: They get out of school, go to work, and retire after 30 years. Women tend to *live more lives* with multiple areas of focus. They graduate from school, go to work, pull out and have children, go back to work, get involved in the community, join the parent–teacher association, and so forth — all of these activities are simultaneously important. As a greater number of women become physicians, more work part time when raising families, and this affects medical practices.

Unlike women who are often juggling many things at one time, men seem to perform better when they tackle one task at a time and often judge women who are multitask oriented as unfocused. Men who perform tasks in a linear or sequential manner may be deemed not as effective by their female managers. For men, there is often a beginning, middle, and end.

This difference can cause frustration, conflict, and misunderstandings about efficiency and effectiveness.[63]

Talking It Over vs. Giving the Answer

Women most often talk through the thought process behind their decisions before giving their bottom-line answer. Men, who are not interested in the process, accuse women of being overly talkative. Men prefer to give the bottom-line answer and will backfill the process leading to the decision if they are asked.

EXHIBIT 22.3 Goal vs. Process Focus Tools for Men and Women

WHEN COMMUNICATING WITH AND INFLUENCING MEN

▲ Get to the "bottom line." Answer: "Who? What? When? How? Where"... then enumerate as necessary. Backfill later if needed.

▲ Speak quantitatively: facts, sizes, shapes, radii, square feet, revolutions per minute, torque, dollars. Talk about "things."

▲ Number items in discussion: "I've got three items: 1..., 2..., 3..."

▲ Men often do one thing at a time — get their attention.

▲ Okay to use humor to build rapport (not self-deprecating humor).

▲ Don't discuss personal things at work.

WHEN COMMUNICATING WITH AND INFLUENCING WOMEN

▲ Women are comfortable with multitasking — don't be insulted if several things are occurring during your meeting.

▲ A woman's goal is to understand and be understood.

▲ Women want to "connect."

▲ Don't give advice or "fix it" unless asked.

▲ Ask more, tell less.

▲ Politeness and manners are important:
   • "Would you mind telling me ...?"
   • "Would you like coffee while we talk?"

▲ Don't pressure. Ask for a timetable — when she plans to decide.

© P. Heim, S. Murphy, with S. Golant, *In the Company of Women: Indirect Aggression Among Women: Why We Hurt Each Other and How to Stop* (New York: Tarcher/Putnam, 2003). Used with permission.

Being a Team Player

The importance of being a team player is something I have talked about at great length in this book. It's interesting to note that when asked whether one is a team player, men and women come from two very different perspectives as they consider their responses. For most men, being a team player means knowing your place on the totem pole and playing your hierarchical position successfully. Conversely, women view their role in terms of flattening and evening out the playing field. Men tend to focus on the vertical, whereas women are more inclined to see things from a horizontal perspective. Because of these varying approaches, men have a tendency to see women tackling tasks manipulatively and women have the inclination

EXHIBIT 22.4   Team-Building Tools for Men and Women

WHEN COMMUNICATING WITH AND INFLUENCING OTHER TEAM MEMBERS

▲ Don't let others interrupt you without your permission.

▲ Questions from women may be signaling that there's a problem.

▲ If you offend a woman, the "game may never be over."

▲ If a coworker offends you, let him or her know and don't let anger fester.

▲ If you have major disagreement with a coworker, maintain professionalism, don't hold a grudge. Even go to "lunch with the enemy" if necessary.

▲ Men enjoy talking about sports, business, and money.

▲ Women enjoy talking about people, feelings, and relationships.

▲ Negotiating is a game for men. Women need to start high.

© P. Heim, S. Murphy, with S. Golant, *In the Company of Women: Indirect Aggression Among Women: Why We Hurt Each Other and How to Stop* (New York: Tarcher/Putnam, 2003). Used with permission.

to view men's dealings as mindless. Exhibit 22.4 presents teambuilding tools for men and women.[64]

Friendliness vs. Friendship

To gain a better understanding how men and women interact with one another in the workplace, it's interesting to consider their approach to relationships. From a women's perspective, friendships are friendships, no matter the time and place. Men see work as a time for competition and getting the job done. Therefore, men are more apt to treat colleagues in a friendly manner, without going so far as thinking of someone as a friend. Men keep that distance between each other so that they can comfortably speak their mind and achieve the task at hand. Conversely, women may struggle to voice sincere opinions for fear of betraying a friendship. Or, if those opinions are voiced, women may be treated differently by other women. The one who speaks out may be seen as untrustworthy and calculating.

Meetings Etiquette

Etiquette in business meetings can be a major problem area for men and women. A man who strongly believes in his ideas is likely to speak at length and dominate meetings by discussing those ideas. He tends to use a declamatory voice, making statements such as, "Obviously, the best way to do this is ...," and he will also be more likely to interrupt another speaker. The

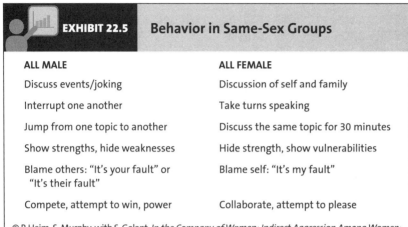

EXHIBIT 22.5   Behavior in Same-Sex Groups

ALL MALE	ALL FEMALE
Discuss events/joking	Discussion of self and family
Interrupt one another	Take turns speaking
Jump from one topic to another	Discuss the same topic for 30 minutes
Show strengths, hide weaknesses	Hide strength, show vulnerabilities
Blame others: "It's your fault" or "It's their fault"	Blame self: "It's my fault"
Compete, attempt to win, power	Collaborate, attempt to please

© P. Heim, S. Murphy, with S. Golant, *In the Company of Women: Indirect Aggression Among Women: Why We Hurt Each Other and How to Stop* (New York: Tarcher/Putnam, 2003). Used with permission.

number one complaint women have about men regarding communication is interruptions. Conversely, women often speak briefly, wait their turn, and share the floor. Women are also apt to phrase their ideas as questions: "Don't you think it would be a good idea if ...?"

As was mentioned in the previous section, men see work as a place to hunker down and get the job done, and they are constantly working toward that goal. For example, if a man has a meeting in a week, he will use that week to line up as much as he can beforehand, doing as much pre-meeting work as possible so as not to *pounce* on the other members during the actual meeting. Conversely, women view the actual meeting time as the place to talk about the issues and make decisions. If a woman brings up a new subject, a man may view it as her trying to blindside him. Women also tend to smile more often during public interactions, which can be mistakenly taken as being easy to influence. This preconception can work disadvantageously for women because others may think that she is willing to accept things she truly isn't (Exhibits 22.5 and 22.6).[65]

The Different Rules of Talk

Men and women have different rules of talk. Women typically use a language of involvement, whereas men tend to engage in verbal bantering or teasing. In addition, men and women vastly differ in their perception of nonverbal cues.

EXHIBIT 22.6	Meetings Etiquette Tools for Men and Women

WHEN COMMUNICATING WITH AND INFLUENCING MEN

- ▲ Don't let people interrupt you; speak over them. If necessary, increase volume.
- ▲ Don't ask whether you can ask a question, just ask it!
- ▲ Line up your ducks in a row before the meeting.
- ▲ Raise volume of voice if needed.
- ▲ Smile appropriately.

WHEN COMMUNICATING WITH AND INFLUENCING WOMEN

- ▲ Don't interrupt women. Interrupting is the number-one complaint women have about male conversations.
- ▲ Ask a quiet woman if there's something she'd like to add.
- ▲ Don't presume that smiles or nods are symbols of consent.
- ▲ Don't assume that asking questions are signs of weakness. This is how many women bring up issues.
- ▲ Understand that she does not know about lining up ducks before the meeting.
- ▲ Women are taught to share time with others. Even if she cares about her ideas, she may give up the floor.

© P. Heim, S. Murphy, with S. Golant, *In the Company of Women: Indirect Aggression Among Women: Why We Hurt Each Other and How to Stop* (New York: Tarcher/Putnam, 2003). Used with permission.

The Language of Involvement

When looking at the ways in which men and women interact with each other, it's also interesting to investigate the language that they use.

Linguistically, women are known to use hedges, disclaimers, and tag questions, which can oftentimes be misinterpreted for weakness. *Hedges* are words and phrases that create a noncommittal feel to a woman's language. Words like *maybe, perhaps,* and *somewhat* are good examples of the way in which women hedge or beat around the bush as a way to bring everyone into the conversation without squashing anyone's feelings.

Likewise, the use of *disclaimers* like "I may be wrong, but …" or "This may not work, however …" work to weaken the woman's emphasis on her idea(s) being the strong choice. *Tag questions* are called such because they are tagged onto the end of sentences. They work similarly to hedges and disclaimers in that the woman's ideas are not asserted as strongly; in other words, she is looking to find agreement among the other people. Examples of tag questions are, "I think we should compile a list of new equipment we want to research for next year's budget, don't you?" The "don't you" tag leads men to feel that the woman is looking for others' approval, as if she isn't confident with her ideas. However, the tag works more positively with other women who feel that the speaker is looking for input.

If we reflect back on our discussion of men viewing interrelationships as hierarchical and women viewing them as flattening, reactions to these linguistic devices are varied. Men may view a woman who uses these mechanisms as unsure or insecure about herself because she isn't being emphatic. Whereas women who encounter the use of these language structures may think the woman is attempting to involve others in the discussion — other women appreciate the use, whereas men find it weak.

Verbal Bantering

Just as women use linguistic devices, such as hedges, disclaimers, and tag questions, to make others feel accepted and safe, men use their own set of linguistic tools to make others feel part of the group. Unlike women's use of soft language to lessen their position of power, men rely on engaging in verbal bantering or teasing. Whether in the form of insult, nonverbal language, or practical jokes, men want to get across that, even though they may be competing for the same hierarchical position, they still like their colleagues.

Remember that the goal with men isn't to make friends, but to establish a friendly atmosphere. Therefore, joking with one another is an excellent way to achieve that. Comments like, "Hey, you look horrible today. Did you sleep at your desk?" can be used to break the ice between the two men and create a comfort level where joking is acceptable. Unfortunately, women do not function in the same way in their relationships. If a woman were to make a similar comment to a female colleague, she would definitely be insulted and offended at such criticism — women just don't joke in that manner, and a friend certainly wouldn't suggest that you look awful. Being aware of these linguistic differences allows you to work with them, rather than them working against you.

One outrageous example of verbal bantering involves my husband's brother, "TL." When I asked what TL stood for, thinking it was an abbreviation for Thomas Lawrence or something similar, I was informed that it stood for "Total Loss." My husband gave his brother that nickname when he was 12 years old, and it stuck! Exhibit 22.7 lists tools for communicating with and influencing men and women.

| EXHIBIT 22.7 | Language Tools for Communicating with and Influencing Men and Women |

WHEN COMMUNICATING WITH AND INFLUENCING MEN

- ▲ Be aware that disclaimers, hedges, and tag questions make you appear less confident and unsure to men (men value confidence!).
- ▲ Don't ask whether you can ask a question, just ask it!
- ▲ Don't be offended by sarcastic comments or practical jokes, which are forms of male bonding.
- ▲ Lower the pitch of your voice. High-pitched voices sound childlike and less credible.
- ▲ Use "It is," "We will," "There are," instead of "I feel" and "I hope."
- ▲ Don't say "I'm sorry," just to be polite.
- ▲ Slow down in speech. Don't talk quickly. Every sound you make is important.
- ▲ Take a presentation skills class.

WHEN COMMUNICATING WITH AND INFLUENCING WOMEN

- ▲ Bantering may not work with women.
- ▲ Teasing may not be appreciated.
- ▲ A female colleague may use disclaimers, hedges, and tag questions and may sound like she's unsure when that isn't case.
- ▲ Don't call women "girls" or "gals."

© P. Heim, S. Murphy, with S. Golant, *In the Company of Women: Indirect Aggression Among Women: Why We Hurt Each Other and How to Stop* (New York: Tarcher/Putnam, 2003). Used with permission.

What Men and Women Don't Say: Nonverbal Language

We've talked about the different ways in which men and women verbally communicate with one another, but what about nonverbal language? There is an immense difference between the way men and women use and deal with nonverbal cues and language. Men, for example, are less likely to hone in on the subtle facial expressions women may give to express how they feel. In a work environment, there are many unspoken cues that are misinterpreted between genders. Women, for example, prefer head-on interaction, which may be misconstrued as overly aggressive behavior by men who face one another when they want to *face off* and show their power. While having relaxed, nonconfrontational interactions, men prefer to stand shoulder to shoulder rather than facing one another.

EXHIBIT 22.8 Nonverbal Tools for Men and Women

WHEN COMMUNICATING WITH AND INFLUENCING MEN

- ▲ Watch body orientation — stand and sit shoulder to shoulder.
- ▲ Larger, sweeping gestures convey more confidence.
- ▲ Don't tilt your head when speaking.
- ▲ In business meetings, take up space, spread out more.
- ▲ When presenting in front of room, move around. Don't stay in one place.
- ▲ Nod head in agreement.

WHEN COMMUNICATING WITH AND INFLUENCING WOMEN

- ▲ Use more facial expressions; smile more frequently.
- ▲ Nod head more to show that you're listening.
- ▲ Watch body orientation — stand and sit face to face.
- ▲ Make frequent eye contact.

© P. Heim, S. Murphy, with S. Golant, *In the Company of Women: Indirect Aggression Among Women: Why We Hurt Each Other and How to Stop* (New York: Tarcher/Putnam, 2003). Used with permission.

Understanding these differences can work to your advantage; knowledge of the nonverbal cues can lessen unintended frustration and misinterpretation. For example, something as minute as a head nod could cause problems between men and women because women, in order to flatten the environment, tend to nod while others are talking in order to show their interest and understanding of the speaker; whereas men assume a nod means "I agree with what you're saying." These interpretations can certainly have different results, so equip yourself with the knowledge and use it to your advantage (Exhibit 22.8).

WOMEN WORKING WITH WOMEN[66]

This section describes the power dead-even rule, which forms the framework for the book, *In the Company of Women*, which Pat Heim, Susan Golant, and I wrote. We wrote the book to find why women frequently sabotage other women at work — one study found that 95 percent of women are sabotaged by another woman at work at least once during her career. The subtitle of our book is *Indirect Aggression Among Women, Why We Hurt Each Other and How to Stop.*

Women Make Great Leaders

The good news is that women make great leaders. Study after study finds that women outscore men in most leadership categories. In a 1996 investigation of 6,400 managers, of which nearly 2,000 were female, Michael R. Perrault and Janet K. Irwin found that women did better than men in 28 of 30 management skill areas, including problem solving, planning, controlling, managing relationships, leading, and communicating.[67] In another study of 676 male and 383 female managers at 211 organizations using 360-degree feedback to examine 15 management characteristics, women did better on all measures, including planning, decision making, coaching, evaluating, approachability, fostering teamwork, and empowering employees.[68]

The Root of Female Conflict: Breaches of the Power Dead-Even Rule

From our extensive research, we discovered the *golden triangle* that affects all female relationships. Take a look at Exhibit 22.9, which depicts the golden triangle. Relationships, power, and self-esteem are the three key elements essential to women's overall happiness. There is a complex interplay among these elements — how much or little a woman has of one can affect how much she has of the others.

Relationships are connections to other people: friends, family members, and colleagues. They are crucial to a woman's sense of well-being; they actually help her define who she is. *Power* refers to the external force one wields in

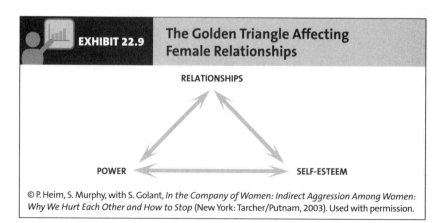

EXHIBIT 22.9 The Golden Triangle Affecting Female Relationships

RELATIONSHIPS

POWER

SELF-ESTEEM

© P. Heim, S. Murphy, with S. Golant, *In the Company of Women: Indirect Aggression Among Women: Why We Hurt Each Other and How to Stop* (New York: Tarcher/Putnam, 2003). Used with permission.

the world: position or title at work, relationship to the boss, attractiveness, net worth, a boyfriend's or husband's status, clothes, and so forth. These are real or perceived observable factors. *Self-esteem* represents internal power — the feeling of inner strength and self-worth. Generally, strength or weakness in this element is far more hidden from the world and may not match external power. (Someone like Princess Diana, for example, had enormous external power but low self-esteem.)

Research has shown a positive correlation between high self-esteem and high achievement, which can lead to the accrual of power. Conversely, a diminishment of self-esteem could affect one's perception of one's own external power.

The Power Dead-Even Rule: Power and Self-Esteem

When there is a breakdown in the balance in the golden triangle, this creates a violation of the invisible law we call the *power dead-even rule*, which operates behind the scenes and helps shape women's reactions to other women.

For a positive relationship to be possible between two women, the self-esteem and power of one must be similar in weight to the self-esteem and power of the other — dead even. (Exceptions might include situations where one woman is older and more experienced than the other or mentoring relationships.)

Women are somewhat more comfortable with a powerful woman who plays down her importance than with one who does not. When a woman has more power, behaves as if she has more power, or is perceived as trying to obtain more power, the environment is ripe for conflict. Catfights result when the power and self-esteem among women are not kept in balance — a violation of the power dead-even rule.

In Exhibit 22.10, the large outer circles represent the women's power — the tangible external force they wield. The inner circle represents their self-esteem — their sense of inner power and hidden feelings of personal strength and self-worth.

In the exhibit, Rose's and Amy's power and self-esteem are alike; thus the relationship is balanced. A good, professional friendship can occur within this kind of interpersonal equilibrium.

If Rose gets promoted to a new position and Amy suddenly becomes her employee, at the very least, Rose vastly increases her external power while

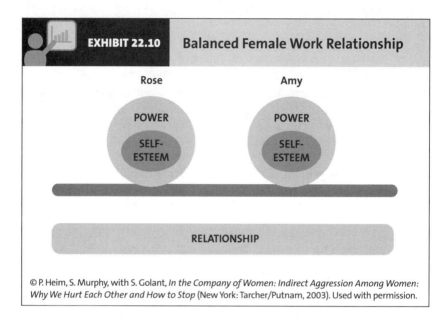

EXHIBIT 22.10   Balanced Female Work Relationship

Rose

Amy

POWER

POWER

SELF-
ESTEEM

SELF-
ESTEEM

RELATIONSHIP

© P. Heim, S. Murphy, with S. Golant, *In the Company of Women: Indirect Aggression Among Women: Why We Hurt Each Other and How to Stop* (New York: Tarcher/Putnam, 2003). Used with permission.

Amy's stays the same. (Remember, it is possible for a woman to experience an increase in power without a concomitant boost in self-esteem.) But whatever Rose's internal state, the relationship is no longer balanced (Exhibit 22.11).

This situation is ripe for conflict. When Rose, in her new management position, starts giving orders to Amy, friction escalates. Not only does the new title increase Rose's power, but also Amy, a former peer but now a subordinate, experiences a decrease in her power. When Rose orders her around, she may perceive that her new boss is trying to belittle her, thus decreasing her self-esteem as well.

Balancing the Equation

To keep a relationship with another woman in balance so as to avoid woman-to-woman conflict, one can deliberately build up her self-esteem by giving sincere compliments and offering empathy and support. Even if they know nothing of the power dead-even rule, many women seem to sense instinctively how to keep the self-esteem balanced in their work relationships with other women. Imagine this simple scenario: Melissa has noticed that Crystal is wearing a great new suit. "Crystal, that's a fabulous outfit," she may say. "Is it new?"

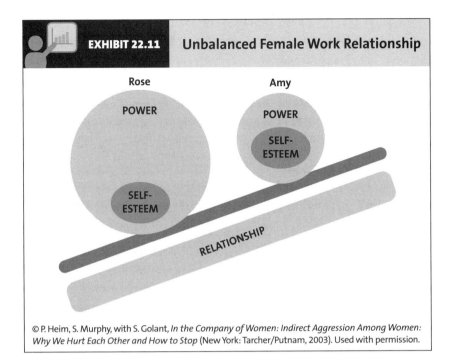

EXHIBIT 22.11   Unbalanced Female Work Relationship

Rose

Amy

POWER

POWER

SELF-
ESTEEM

SELF-
ESTEEM

RELATIONSHIP

© P. Heim, S. Murphy, with S. Golant, *In the Company of Women: Indirect Aggression Among Women: Why We Hurt Each Other and How to Stop* (New York: Tarcher/Putnam, 2003). Used with permission.

To which Crystal might quickly reply, "Oh, this old thing? I got it on sale." Or, "I was just admiring your lovely shoes." These responses either downplay Crystal's power or enhance Melissa's.

Ironically, men observing these conversations often conclude that the women have low self-esteem. "Why are they putting themselves down?" they wonder. "Why can't they just take a compliment?" But many women intuitively know otherwise. Rather than lowering their self-esteem, they actually maintain it by protecting and preserving their relationships.

Aggression: Direct vs. Indirect

When one woman in a female-to-female friendship ignores or subverts the tenets of the power dead-even rule, the other woman may become angry and look for ways to fight back. Even as she seeks to rebalance the power in the relationship, what does she do with her anger? As girls grow into adulthood, they are trained to preserve relationships at all costs, avoid conflict, and *be nice*. Rarely are they afforded the opportunity to practice conflict resolution or to depersonalize an attack. How are adult women supposed to express frustration and sense of betrayal when someone has hurt them or otherwise violated the power dead-even rule? What are they to do with their naturally occurring anger?

Feelings of anger tend to be expressed through aggressive behavior, which can be conveyed directly, overtly, and physically such as in bickering, yelling, swearing, stealing, slapping, punching, kicking, chasing, pushing, tripping, or by other more violent and deadly means. Aggression is not anger, but it is the behavior most closely associated with and arising from the emotion of anger. Aggression is behaving with the intent to physically or emotionally hurt someone.

But females in our culture are strongly discouraged from releasing anger in a physical manner. They've been trained to be nice. Indeed, we look on female aggression as evidence of pathology. So how do offender women sometimes behave? They are tempted to use indirect and covert aggressive behavior: They tell lies and spread rumors behind another's back, stomp off and sulk, snub, plant damaging information or make insinuations, take revenge by sabotage and property destruction, shun or ostracize a target person from a social group, refuse to make eye contact or otherwise pretend that person doesn't exist, make faces or derogatory gestures to others about her — all behaviors we've defined as the hallmarks of catfights. But by understanding the golden triangle of female relationships, the power dead-even rule, and how indirect aggression works, it's possible to navigate the sometimes rough seas of relationships more securely.

Summary[69]

The following subsections review the important points about women working with women.

Flatten Interactions

Being savvy about female interpersonal dynamics can work to a woman's advantage. She wants credit for her accomplishments but hates the power dead-even grief that can accompany them. Sometimes for the sake of her peace of mind, it's useful to play down her power with other women who most likely have an expectation of shared power. Consciously adopting power-balancing strategies can be helpful. When a woman knows that her self-esteem or power is greater than a female coworker's whose relationship she values, her interactions should include compassion, empathy, and reassurance. This comes from a genuine concern for how the other woman feels as well as a desire to help her. She might:

▲ *Decrease her own power in the other woman's eyes:* "Yeah, they gave me this new title, but I didn't get a pay increase."

▲ *Increase the other woman's self-esteem:* "I think you're an outstanding team member."

▲ *Increase the other woman's power:* If in a position to do so, give the other woman a coveted assignment that would provide her with an opportunity to visibly succeed.

Female managers often believe that because they're in charge, their staff members have to do what they say. But we've found that somehow, some way, someday, unless one flattens the interactions, female staff will always even the score in the end.

It Isn't Always This Way

Although the power dead-even rule applies in many female-to-female inter-actions, it is not a universal rule. Relations with mothers, older women, and female mentors are often exempt. Moreover, some enlightened women already understand that the structure of the business world is hierarchical, so they accept female bosses. Indeed, there are women managers who also recognize the problems they face when supervising other women and read-ily engage in the relationship work necessary to avoid indirect aggression. For example, they know that "Have these on my desk by Friday!" will be greeted with much more hostility than "Hi, how was your weekend? How are your kids doing? Oh, if you have a chance, could you possibly get this to me by Friday?" The latter flattens the interaction.

How Can I Make This Problem Go Away in My Organization?

Introduce the language of the power dead-even rule and talk about it in fun situations so that when the need arises during a time of potential conflict, the language is already in place and accepted as a positive strategy to diffuse conflict.

Female Alliances Keep Females Free

When a group of women leave behind destructive ways of relating, when they band together as a force of change and self-protection, they can become a powerful source for social transformation.

CHAPTER PRESCRIPTIONS

- When studying gender differences, remember that differences can make our teams stronger; always keep humor as an emphasis when dealing with gender differences.
- Most men see the world as a hierarchy, where power is differentiated; most women see the world as flatter, where power is shared.
- Relationships are central in the female culture. They are not so important in the male culture.
- More than 80 percent of women want to work on a team with others, whereas 80 percent of men are fine working alone.
- Women seem to be more people oriented, whereas men are often more interested in things.
- Boys learn how to compete, be aggressive, and play to win, which translates into their behaviors later in life.
- Boys learn how to win and lose without becoming emotionally involved with the fate of their competitors.
- Girls learn that the main goal is to preserve the friendships and relationships that are central in the female culture.
- Business is a *game* to many men. When negotiating, men start with high demands and position themselves with room to bargain.
- At a young age, girls often learn that someone will pay attention, soothe their pain, and meet their needs, whereas boys are taught to tough it out.
- To make the most out of your practice, focus on the goal to be achieved and the relationships among the team members.
- Remember that women often negotiate differences, seeking win–win solutions and focusing on what is fair for all instead of winning. Men are reared to function in the hierarchical structure, where they are working to show high placement among their peers.
- Language structures are very functional in the female culture: They flatten the hierarchy and emphasize involvement. Men tend to engage in bantering or teasing (verbal or otherwise) in order to demonstrate their hierarchical position.
- Facial expressions and other nonblatant expressions are major wedges dividing men and women within the work environment.
- Good leaders are those who are able to flex their style based on the needs of the follower.
- Remember the significance of the golden triangle. Relationships, power, and self-esteem are the three key elements essential to women's overall happiness.
- For a positive relationship to be possible between two women, the self-esteem and power of one must be similar in weight to the self-esteem and power of the other — dead even; hence, the power dead-even rule.
- Just as boys are taught to function within a hierarchical structure, girls grow into adulthood being trained to preserve relationships at all costs, to avoid conflict, and to *be nice.*

CHAPTER 23

Generational Differences

"People resemble their times more than they do their parents," according to an Arab proverb. Genes play a big role in how we look, our temperament, and many of our idiosyncrasies. However, what we value, what motivates and de-motivates us, and how we perceive life comes from many other arenas. What we value frequently dictates our attitudes, beliefs, and behaviors.

From birth to approximately age 18, we are forming our values, perceptions, sense of humor, and priorities. What we grow up without becomes critically important to us in our adulthood.

Effective leaders today are those who understand the motivators and de-motivators of the people who work with them, as well as the customers who use their products and services, and they realize that these values often differ among generations. Leaders who understand important generational differences can attract and retain high-performing team members as well as create and deliver products and services in such a way that their customers will remain loyal and enthusiastic. Recruitment and replacement costs for physicians can average $250,000 to $350,000.[70] Turnover costs for registered nurses, nurse practitioners, and physician assistants can exceed $80,000.[71]

There are several other areas of diversity in addition to generations, and they include gender differences, ethnicity, race, sexual orientation, country of origin, and physical qualities (Exhibit 23.1). Gender differences are discussed in Chapter 22.

I've found that generational and gender differences are absolutely fascinating. My dissertation was titled "A Study of Career Values by Generation and Gender," so I've been doing intensive research on these subjects for many years. Claire Raines, author and expert in generational differences, has provided me with much of the knowledge presented in this chapter, and I appreciate it.

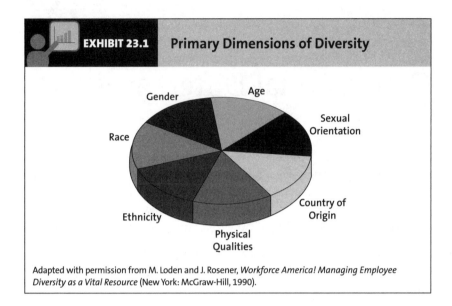

EXHIBIT 23.1   Primary Dimensions of Diversity

Gender

Age

Sexual Orientation

Race

Ethnicity

Physical Qualities

Country of Origin

Adapted with permission from M. Loden and J. Rosener, *Workforce America! Managing Employee Diversity as a Vital Resource* (New York: McGraw-Hill, 1990).

This chapter is divided into three sections. The first covers business reasons for studying intergenerational dynamics. The second discusses the origin of unique characteristics and values of each generation, and the preferences each generation has for leadership styles, communication styles, and rewards and incentives. The third includes the recruitment and retention needs of each generation and how to successfully mix and manage the generations in your organization.

BUSINESS REASONS FOR STUDYING INTERGENERATIONAL DYNAMICS

Why is it more important now than ever before to understand intergenerational dynamics? For the first time in recent history, there are four generations in the workplace. This is because of the rising age of retirement for members of the Baby Boomer and World War II generations; most Baby Boomers are saying they'd like to work at least another decade or two. In addition, there is a shortage of skilled workers available to fill open positions. Key positions are open in 6 of 10 organizations. So there is a current need to actively attract and retain all qualified workers or else these organizations will be in jeopardy.

It used to be pretty easy to discern who controlled the power and held the management positions in medical practices. Age was the key factor, and the older physicians were the leaders who ran the practice. With the flattening of organizations and the arrival of the information age, organizational structures are rapidly changing. Baby Boomers are no longer the majority and have slipped to 37 percent of the workforce, while Generation X (Gen X) represents 45 percent[72] and is now the majority wielding its influence over policies, procedures, and other key decisions. The landscape of medical practices is in the midst of tremendous change.

There are four main business reasons why the study of intergenerational dynamics is crucial in the new millennium:

1. Competition is increasing for skilled workers in the United States;
2. The trend for four generations to be working side by side will continue;
3. There's a practical need for leaders to create an inclusive workplace where staff members are actively engaged; and
4. Patients and family members are customers who come from many generations.

Increased Competition

Competition is increasing for skilled workers in the United States, and this has hit the healthcare industry hard. Currently, there are shortages in healthcare disciplines; that is, the United States has 125,000 vacant nursing positions, making it the third most difficult discipline to recruit — behind sales representatives and engineers. By 2020, it's estimated that the United States will be short by 800,000 nurses.[73] The physician shortage will continue to worsen and could be 90,000 short by 2025.[74] The U.S. population has grown 33 percent since 1980, but the number of physicians entering the workforce annually has remained static — 15,000 to 16,000 — according to the Association of American Medical Colleges.[75] The high cost of medical school, the desire by many physicians to have more flexible schedules, and the push for better work–life balance is affecting physician recruitment and retention.[76]

Over the next decade nearly 3.5 million manufacturing jobs likely need to be filled. The skills gap is expected to result in 2 million of those jobs going unfilled.[77]

Four Generations Working Together

The trend for four generations to be working side by side will continue. There are several reasons for this trend. The first reason is that members of the Baby Boomers and World War II generation need to work — healthcare costs are rising, and one-third of workers 45 to 70 years of age are caring for a spouse, parent, grandchild, or others.[78] The savings and retirement income of these generations will simply not cover their expenses. Additionally, more than two-thirds of those who are 50 years of age and older want to work.[79] Working keeps them mentally and physically active, helps them feel useful, fulfills their affiliation needs of being around others, and often provides more fun in their lives. Nearly 70 percent of all retirees plan to keep working at least part-time in their retirement years or to never retire at all. By 2014 it's estimated that one-third of the U.S. workforce will be older than 50 years of age.[80]

Inclusive Workplaces

There's a practical need for leaders to create an inclusive workplace where staff members are actively engaged. The Gallup Poll in 2006 found some startling information about employee engagement. While only 33 percent of the U.S. workforce is actively engaged, 15 percent of the workforce is actively disengaged and costs $328 billion per year in quality and productivity losses.[81] A Developmental Dimensions International study[82] of 3,800 employees in seven organizations and a variety of industries found that when leaders were actively engaged as leaders, there was a 14 percent higher engagement of employees and 19 percent higher retention rate. Highly engaged employees are 33 percent less likely to leave organizations within the next year.

Team members in all four generations want to feel respected and valuable, and an inclusive culture encourages these outcomes. Currently, there is intergenerational conflict reported in 60 percent of organizations, and conflict can lead to low morale, low productivity, low quality, and increased staff turnover. Patients will seek care elsewhere if their healthcare needs are not met by their current provider. Therefore, although a mix of generations has the propensity to lead to a culture of destructive conflict, a diversity-aware leader can turn these conflicts into opportunities for open discussions of different perspectives and create high-performing teams of talented people from all backgrounds.

Customers from Many Generations

Patients and family members are customers who come from many generations. Customers respond best when they feel understood, important, and can develop rapport with those serving them. In healthcare, patients and family members come from all generations. Even in the department of pediatrics, the main patient may be a child, but the parents and grandparents are customers too. When patients are senior citizens, other family members of all ages are often included in conferences and decision making. It's important to learn what customers of all ages consider to be quality care and exceptional service.

Recently having a meal at a restaurant, I noticed with interest that my waitress interacted differently with her customers. When she took my order, she was pleasant, polite, and stood a few feet away from the table as she took my order. The table adjacent to mine was filled with five young adults in their twenties. Before she took their orders, she pulled up a chair, sat down, and leaned forward as she asked some introductory questions of them. At the end of the meal, I asked her if she purposely behaved differently depending on the age and gender of her customers. She smiled, replying, "Yes, I do. And ever since I've started adapting to the differences of my customers, my tips have skyrocketed!"

Cohort Experiences Influence How We See the World

The term *cohort* is used by social demographers (students studying the effect of population on society) to refer to people born in the same general time span (Exhibit 23.2). People born in the same time span share key life experiences, from starting school together and reaching puberty at the same time to entering the workforce or university or marriage or middle age at the same time. A generation is also defined by common tastes, attitudes, and experiences, and encompasses what is occurring economically, socially, sociologically, and demographically. A cohort is affected by a generation's defining moments — events that capture the attention and emotions of millions of individuals at a formative stage in their lives — like D-Day, the assassination of President Kennedy, the *Challenger* explosion, and the attacks on September 11.

Generational commonalities cut across racial, ethnic, and economic differences. Each generation shares what was in the air around them: news events, music, national catastrophes, heroes, and heroic events. Equally powerful in shaping the views and values of a generation are the first, sometimes

EXHIBIT 23.2	Generation Demographics in the Workplace		
Generation	**Birth Date**	**Age**	**Percent and Number in Workforce**
World War II generation	Born before 1940	75 plus	1%, 1 million
Baby Boomer generation	Born 1940–1960	55–74	21%, 32 million
Generation X	Born 1960–1980	35–54	43%, 64 million
Millennial generation	Born 1980–2000	15–34	35%, 50 million

U.S. Bureau of Labor Statistics, 2015, www.bls.gov/emp/.

traumatic days in the labor market. For example, a cohort that joins the workforce when jobs are scarce feels very differently about life and work than one who joins the workforce when jobs are plentiful.[83] These formative experiences shared with one's cohorts are the filter through which one interprets all subsequent experiences. Researchers call the events that define a generation *markers*. They describe markers as the key set of collective experiences that shape a generation's values and attitudes and set the tone for that generation.

WHAT PLANET EARTH WAS LIKE DURING EACH GENERATION

During their formative years when values were being shaped, each of the four generations in the workplace inhabited a very different planet Earth. In this section I use my own research from my doctoral thesis in addition to extensive research by my colleague, Claire Raines, who has mentored me about generational issues.

I believe these four generations are appropriately defined in 20-year spans, though some generational scholars use shorter spans. I agree with Raines who defines the World War II generation as those who grew up during the Depression years, the late 1920s and the 1930s. The Baby Boomer generation spans from 1940 to 1960. Generation X was born from 1960 to 1980. And members of the Millennial generation were born from 1980 through 2000. Those born in the early 1940s report that they feel more like Baby Boomers than the World War II generation because they say they were too young to serve in World War II, plus they feel like Baby Boomers because they say they started the fads and trends that the Boomers followed. Those born in the early 1960s feel more like Gen Xers than Boomers because they don't remember the assassination of John F. Kennedy or early events of the 1960s. When scholars speak specifically of the *post–World War II generation*, they are referring to the years 1946 to 1964 when a baby was born every seven seconds. There were approximately 43 million members of the World War II generation, 76 million Baby Boomers, 40 million Gen Xers, and 73 million Millennials. The birth control pill was developed during the birth years for the Gen Xers.

For these four generations, the worlds where they spent their childhood were very different. The family structure, friends, schools, world events, economy, communication methods, language, transportation, music, method of payment for goods and services, heroes, antiheroes, and how work got done were very different in each generation. In many ways, they were raised in different cultures. How these four generations experienced the world as children and teenagers has greatly influenced how they view the world today as well as their core values, motivators, and de-motivators.

Unique Characteristics of Generational Groups

The four generational groups currently in the workforce are:

1. *World War II* includes those born prior to World War II and those whose earliest memories and influences are associated with the Great Depression and World War II;

2. *Baby Boomer* includes those born between 1940 and 1960 and raised in the pro-child era of extreme optimism, opportunity, and progress;

3. *Generation X* includes those born after the Baby Boom (between 1960 and 1980) who came of age deep in the shadow of the Boomers and an anti-child environment; and

4. *Millennial* includes those born after 1980 and raised during a time when children were celebrated and heroes existed.

Exhibit 23.3 shows how the different generations see the world.

World War II Generation (Born Before 1940)

Sociologists refer to the members of the World War II generation as *traditionalists, mature, industrialists, veterans,* and *depression babies.* What was their world like? The family was close-knit, like the famous Norman

EXHIBIT 23.3	Generational Viewpoint Differences			
How each generation sees the world ...				
	World War II	Baby Boomers	Generation Xers	Millennials
Outlook	Practical	Optimistic	Skeptical	Hopeful
Work ethic	Dedicated	Driven	Balanced	Determined
View of authority	Respectful	Love/Hate	Unimpressed	Polite
Leadership by	Hierarchy	Consensus	Competence	Pulling together
Relationships	Personal sacrifice	Personal gratification	Reluctant to commit	Inclusive
Turnoffs	Vulgarity	Political incorrectness	Cliché, hype	Promiscuity
Perspective	Civic minded	Team oriented	Self-reliant	Civic minded

R. Zemke, C. Raines, and B. Filipczak, *Generations at Work: Managing the Clash of Veterans, Boomers, Xers and Nexters in Your Workplace* (New York: AMACOM, 2000), 155. © Claire Raines. Reprinted with permission from Claire Raines and Axzo Press. www.axzopress.com.

Rockwell painting of the family at the dinner table with aunts, uncles, and grandparents present. As a whole, they were very patriotic and had a strong sense of commitment to their country.

Seminal events include the following:

- ▲ 1929: Stock Market Crash leading to the Great Depression
- ▲ 1937: Hindenburg tragedy
- ▲ 1941: Pearl Harbor; the United States enters World War II
- ▲ 1945: World War II ends in Europe and Japan
- ▲ 1950: Korean War

The Great Depression that commenced on Oct. 29, 1929, left an indelible mark, and this significant event changed the World War II generation forever. Their financial security crumbled. "The key to understanding this generation is recognizing the impact of the Great Depression and World War II on their lives. Facing these two immense challenges shaped a generation characterized by discipline, self-denial, financial and social conservatism, and a sense of obligation."[84] Ever since the Great Depression, representatives of the World War II generation have been motivated by money and security. What one grows up without becomes critically important to that person as an adult.[85]

When this generation went to war in World War II, the whole nation got into the act, and there was an unbelievable commitment to win. Women began to work while the men were fighting. War heroes were celebrated with parades and homecomings. Generations catalyze around a *defining moment*, an event so momentous that all members of the generation can tell you forever after where they were when the event took place. These moments are so significant that, until we die, we can remember with precise acuity the weather, the scene, even what we were eating and wearing. For this generation, the defining moment was 7:49 a.m. local time, Dec. 7, 1941, when the Japanese bombed Pearl Harbor.[86]

Values, assets, and liabilities. Some of the predominant core values of most of the World War II generation include hard work, self-sacrifice, honesty, commitment, teamwork (cooperation and mutual support made the sacrifice bearable), respect for authority (looking to the outside for guidance), loyalty and patriotism (essential for teamwork), conformity (following rules and everyone moving in the same direction, united), celebration of victory, payment with cash, leisure (only as a reward for hard work), delayed reward (patience), duty before pleasure, and honor. These remain their present-day values.[87]

Assets that the World War II generation brings to the job market include being detail oriented, thorough, loyal, honest, and hard working. Liabilities that they bring to the job market include ineptness with ambiguity and change, reluctance to buck the system, discomfort with conflict, and reticence when they disagree.

The compelling messages from their formative years include make do or do without, stay in line, sacrifice, be heroic, and consider the common good.

Leadership, motivation, and communication styles. Members of the World War II generation prefer to work for managers who are directive and identify a clear direction; who are logical, fair, consistent, and respectful; and who spell out clear job expectations and set long-term goals. They tend to be motivated when managers connect their actions to the overall good of the organization. The messages that motivate this generation include:

⬥ "Your experience is respected here."

⬥ "It's valuable to the rest of us to hear what has and hasn't worked in the past."

⬥ "Your perseverance is valued and will be rewarded."

The World War II generation values hierarchy, job titles, and recognition for their dedication. Motivating rewards for this generation are tangible symbols of loyalty, commitment, and service, including plaques and certifications. Managers who drive them crazy are indecisive, use profanity and slang, seem too touchy-feely, and use experimental and trendy management styles.

Communication styles that the World War II generation responds to are memos, personal notes, and letters. They respond well to respectful, professional, in-person communication. So it's important to use good grammar, clear diction, and avoid profanity. Relate your leadership messages to the organization's history and long-term goals.

Baby Boomer Generation (1940–1960)

Following the World War II generation, the next generation in the workforce is composed of the Baby Boomers. The Baby Boomer generation grew up and formed its values in a significantly different environment. When this generation was growing up, America was the most powerful, most affluent country in the world. Parents said, "My kids are gonna have it better than I did." And the entire generation was overindulged. This was the largest generation of all time, encompassing approximately 76 million Boomers. Seventy-five percent of families fit the profile of the TV show, *Leave It to Beaver*, with a working dad, stay-at-home mom, and 1.5 children. As children, Boomers started many fads, including hula hoops, poodle skirts, ducktails, and pop beads. Children were in the spotlight.

Seminal events include the following:

⬥ 1960: Birth control pills introduced

⬥ 1963: Martin Luther King leads march in Washington, D.C.

⬥ 1964: President Kennedy assassinated

⬥ 1965: Troops went to Vietnam

⬥ 1969: U.S. astronaut Neil Armstrong lands on the moon

Before World War II, the prevailing wisdom about child-rearing urged a disciplined approach. Many 6-month-olds were strapped to potty seats because the schedule said it was time to potty train. After World War II, Dr. Benjamin Spock told parents to love their children and said that cuddling was not only appropriate but contributed to the healthy development of the child. Permissiveness was in!

Baby Boomers attended schools in a system that had hit its peak; classes were taught by the best and brightest women who had few career options. In school, kids were taught to be good members of a team and received grades for categories such as "works with others" and "shares materials with classmates." There were heroes, including John Wayne, Grace Kelly, presidents, senators, and athletes that the Baby Boomers could admire and emulate. On television, they watched Roy Rogers and Dale Evans, Daniel Boone, Hopalong Cassidy, Gene Autry, Davy Crockett, and the Lone Ranger. By the mid-1950s, there were more than 15 million television sets in the United States.

There was so much hope that *Time* magazine actually gave the "Man of the Year Award" in 1967 to the entire Baby Boomer generation. This was the generation that was supposed to clean up our cities and find a cure for cancer and the common cold. This was a time to "Ask not what your country can do for you, but what you can do for your country."

The Baby Boomers were spoiled and were often called the *me generation*. Boomers remain fixated on self-improvement and individual accomplishment. Boomers wanted to work in a different kind of place; one where they could be involved in decision making, could influence the direction their organizations would take, and could have a voice. This generation was the primary force behind a new way of doing business with participative management, flattened pyramids, employee involvement, quality circles, team building, and empowerment.

When Baby Boomers got to the end of the 1980s, their experience was completely different from their expectations about how life would unfold. Many Baby Boomers found a future filled with contradictions, hardship, and reversals. Now, it appears that the Boomers' career values are shifting. Many have a new yearning for calm and a return to more traditional standards of family.

Values, assets, and liabilities. Baby Boomer core values include optimism, team orientation, personal gratification, health and wellness, personal growth, youthfulness, work, and involvement.[88] They have pursued their own personal gratification, uncompromisingly, and often at a high price to themselves and others; have searched their souls repeatedly, obsessively, and recreationally; have always been "cool … and they'll never, never grow up, grow old, or die."[89]

Assets that Baby Boomers bring to the job include being service oriented, driven, and willing to *go the extra mile*. They are good at relationships, want to please, and are good team players.[90] Liabilities that Baby Boomers bring to the job include being uncomfortable with conflict, reluctant to go against peers, and not being naturally budget minded. They may be overly sensitive to feedback, judgmental of those who see things differently, self-centered, and may put process ahead of result.

Leadership, motivation, and communication styles. Baby Boomers prefer to work for managers who are consensual, caring, democratic, and treat them as equals. Boomers like visions and missions, and want to be assured they are making a difference. They are motivated by leaders who get them involved and show them how they can make a difference. The messages that motivate include:

- ⬆ "Your opinion is valued."
- ⬆ "You can work as long as you want to."
- ⬆ "Your contribution will be recognized."
- ⬆ "We need you."

The rewards that the Baby Boomers respond to are personal appreciation, promotion, and recognition. They want to be included, so providing them with a lot of information makes them feel important and powerful. Managers who drive them crazy aren't open to input, are bureaucratic, are brusque and send a "my way or the highway" message, don't show interest in them, and practice one-upmanship.

Communication styles Baby Boomers respond to are phone calls and personal interaction. Relationships and business are intertwined, so ask about the Baby Boomer's family or other areas of mutual interest. Ask for input on issues and link your message to the vision, mission, and values of the organization.

Generation X (1960–1980)
The third generation in the workforce today has been named *Generation X*. This generation has been frequently defined in negative terms: post-Boomers, baby busters, slackers, the shadow generation, disillusioned generation, repair generation, the "why me?" generation, twenty-somethings, and the

thirteenth generation (born since the American Revolution). Generation X is a term first coined by Canadian novelist Douglas Coupland to describe his own cohort, a generation that he believes defies labels.[91]

Seminal events include the following:

▲ 1973: Global energy crisis
▲ 1976: Tandy and Apple market the personal computers
▲ 1980: John Lennon killed
▲ 1981: Acquired Immune Deficiency Syndrome (AIDS) identified
▲ 1986: *Challenger* disaster
▲ 1989: Berlin Wall falls

There are approximately one-half as many Gen Xers as there are Baby Boomers (40 million vs. 76 million).[92] Although Baby Boomers were indulged as kids, adults in the 1970s often rated cars ahead of children as necessary for the good life. The parents of Gen Xers were some of the first babies whom adults took birth control pills to prevent.

During the 1970s and 1980s, it was an unpopular time to be a child. The school system had grown outdated. Angry community leaders refused to support the schools with more tax dollars, as opposed to the GI Bill for Boomers. In the 1940s, teachers were disturbed when students chewed gum in class, ran in the hallways, passed notes to one another, and were generally disruptive. Today, teachers are disturbed about cheating, guns and knives in school, drugs, and gangs.

Many significant events were occurring during Gen X's childhood that influenced their value formation, including Watergate and Jonestown. The war in Vietnam was grinding down, and those who fought for the United States were often ostracized in their communities — very different than the treatment of returned soldiers after World War II. Economically, times were tough as the stock market dropped 22 percent, interest rates climbed, and unemployment increased. Cars formed lines around the block at gas stations during the fuel crisis, and to conserve energy, President Jimmy Carter decided to forgo lighting the national Christmas tree.

The family picture had changed. As the family shifts, so does the society.[93] Virtually every member of Gen X was deeply affected by divorce. Fifty percent watched their own parents' divorce; the others watched helplessly as their favorite aunt and uncle — or their best friend's parents — got divorced. Many Gen Xers report that they still feel that pain today.

More than 50 percent of the Gen Xers were *latchkey* children. When they opened the door to their home after school, there was silence, and no one was waiting at home with milk and cookies. There was a note on the refrigerator with instructions to put snacks in the microwave, and then they turned on their good friend, the computer. Gen Xers played computer games for hours, learning to be autonomous and taking care of themselves.

Researchers believe this is why many Gen Xers on the job see themselves as free agents or contractors.[94] Teaching themselves computer skills assisted them in learning how to learn on their own, through trial and error, and in developing their creativity and ability to experiment. This is how many Gen Xers learn best today.

Television became a foster parent for Gen Xers, providing cable television, MTV, talk shows, Court TV, C-SPAN, and 75 stations to choose from. Characters in these shows had values that were inconsistent with the values that teachers and parents tried to instill in them. Researchers believe this is an extremely important factor in value formation for this generation. These contradictions led many Gen Xers to be cynical, distrusting, and having little respect for authority. Television programs included *Dynasty*, *Dallas*, and cops-and-robbers programs. By the time they were 16 years of age, Gen Xers had watched more than 16,000 murders on TV and in the movies. Idols and heroes crumbled. In the family, where the parents had been the heroes, there was divorce. Evangelists Jim Bakker and Jimmy Swaggart demonstrated they were evil after all. Richard Nixon became the first U.S. president to resign from office, and then his pardon sent the message to Gen Xers that it is okay to do bad things; just don't get caught!

Perhaps the most important thing about the first 10 to 15 years of Gen X was the change in expectations surrounding them. Whereas in the 1950s and 1960s, Baby Boomers were told "You can be anything you want to be — even the president," the message of the 1970s and 1980s was "Be careful out there." This is the first generation that has been told it probably will not be able to improve on — even to replicate — their parents' lifestyle.

The literature indicates that Gen Xers want a lifestyle with more balance; they want to work to live, not live to work. Many Gen Xers are reluctant to make a commitment, both personally and professionally. Fifty percent were children of divorce. They watched their parents plod through 60-hour workweeks, struggle with difficult bosses, bring work home on the weekends — and then get laid off. Gen Xers decided to give away their personal commitment very carefully. The average age for first marriages has climbed to 25 for women and 27 for men.

Among themes that appear to emerge from Gen X are entrepreneurship and independence, belonging, learning, and security.[95] For many, belonging and security were areas never satisfied in childhood. Learning is a way to keep their skills current because they often do not believe they can depend on others to support them.

Values, assets, and liabilities. The core values of the Gen Xers include diversity, thinking globally, balance, technoliteracy, fun, informality, self-reliance, and pragmatism. The personality traits of this generation are that they are self-reliant, seek a sense of family, want work–life balance, have a nontraditional orientation about time and space, like informality, and approach authority casually. They are skeptical, attracted to the edge, and technologically savvy. Another interesting characteristic of this generation is that many Gen Xers declare that they have no heroes, no one whom they admire.

Assets that Gen Xers bring to the job include the ability to be adaptable, technoliteracy, and independence; they are unintimidated by authority and are creative. The liability characteristics of Gen Xers include impatience, poor people skills, lack of experience, and the fact that many are cynical.

Leadership, motivation, and communication styles. Gen Xers prefer to work for managers who are competent, direct, straightforward, trustworthy, genuine, flexible, and informal. They won't tolerate being micromanaged. Gen Xers want managers who are results oriented, who will give them a deadline and turn them loose to meet it. Gen Xers want training and growth opportunities. They want frequent, accurate, specific, and timely (FAST) feedback. Messages that motivate them are:

- ▲ "Do it your way."
- ▲ "We've got the newest hardware and software."
- ▲ "We aren't very corporate and there aren't a lot of rules."

Rewards that motivate them are free time, opportunities for development, certifications to add to their resumes, and opportunities to achieve results.

Communication styles that Gen Xers respond to are voice mail, e-mail, and text messages. Be direct and straightforward — Gen Xers don't want you to waste their time. State clearly what you want, how it will serve the Gen Xer, and when you want it.

Millennials (1980–2000)

The Millennial generation is often referred to as the generation who was "digital in diapers."[96] Two-thirds of those in this generation used a computer before they turned five. Other monikers for this generation include *Generation Y, echo Boomers, Internet generation,* and *Nexters.*

Seminal events include the following:

- ▲ 1997: Princess Diana dies
- ▲ 1999: Columbine High School shootings
- ▲ 2001: World Trade Center and Pentagon attacks
- ▲ 2002: Enron, WorldCom, and corporate scandals
- ▲ 2003: War begins in Iraq
- ▲ 2004: Tsunami in the Asian Ocean
- ▲ 2005: Hurricane Katrina

The planet where the Millennials grew up is very different from that of their predecessors. Their parents are the most diverse group yet, ranging in age from adolescents to Boomers in their forties when they gave birth to this generation. Although most researchers considered Gen X to be an anti-child era; the Millennial generation is a pro-child era. Parents take kids everywhere — to fine restaurants, on vacations to Club Med, to work. Club Med, which had been synonymous with swinging singles, reports that their family villages now account for nearly half of annual sales.[97] What we grow up without becomes critically important in adulthood. Gen Xers have become very attentive parents.

Radio was the new technology of the World War II generation; TV was the new technology for the Baby Boomer generation; personal computers were the technology for the Gen Xers; and digital technology and the Internet are the technology for the Millennials. Today, as always, parents know more about most things, but Millennials know more about technology, and they're teaching their parents. Many organizations are encouraging their Millennial team members to reverse mentor their older colleagues.

Whereas many Gen Xers were told by their parents that they were *mistakes* due to lack of familiarity with birth control pills, most of the Millennial kids were planned and welcomed. "Baby on board" signs signaled a return of a national concern for children. Soccer moms were in. In a 1995 national survey of preteens called KidsPeace, 93 percent of 10-to-13-year-old Millennials said they always feel loved by their parents.[98] Many colleges are now conducting classes on the topic of "Letting Go of Your Child" for parents of freshmen. This love and protection by parents has translated to some interesting behavior by the Millennials on the job. A *Fast Company* article from 2006 reported that when one of the Millennial employees received a poor performance review from his manager, the following day the employee's parents came to work to confront the manager. They couldn't believe that their child had received a poor performance appraisal!

Millennials are very savvy, sophisticated, and streetwise. They talk with parents and teachers about AIDS, divorce, marital infidelity, gangs, and guns. In school they've studied environmental issues and have already become advocates for rainforests, recycling, and clean air. For many Millennials, diversity is second nature with acceptance of differences in ethnicity, religions, gender, and sexual orientation.

According to a study by Northwestern Mutual Life, researching the attitudes and behaviors of a graduating class of 2,001 college students at 101 colleges, Millennials identify more closely with the World War II generation than with the Gen Xers or Baby Boomers. Millennials are proving to have high integrity and morals, be hard workers, and be more optimistic than recent generations. Heroes exist for Millennials, and researchers see this as a positive change from the viewpoint of Gen Xers who saw all their heroes fall from grace.

Values, assets, and liabilities. The Millennials believe in goal-setting, hard work, and expect to work more than 40 hours per week to achieve the lifestyle they want. They believe in teamwork and collective action, and enjoy working with smart, creative people. Millennials have a strong sense of social responsibility and carefully select the organization where they will work — many want *green* and civic-minded organizations. They have an optimistic outlook and a strong sense of self-esteem. Millennials are very technologically savvy, and both men and women appear able to multitask successfully.

Millennials' liabilities include their inexperience, although they resent any condescension from more experienced workers. They need supervision, coaching, and structure. Their *free agent* mindset makes them more loyal to people than to organizations. Communication skills and good grammar often suffer because so much communication is done via e-mail, text messaging, and voice mail.

Leadership, motivation, and communication styles. Millennials prefer to work for managers who are positive and collaborative, good coaches who teach and support them, and who are achievement oriented. They tend to be motivated when their manager connects their actions to their personal and professional goals. They want to know how they fit into the big picture. They thrive on short-term goals, deadlines, and continuous feedback like they received at home and school. Messages that motivate include:

▲ "You'll be working with other bright, creative people."

▲ "You can be a hero here."

▲ "You and your colleagues can help turn this company around."

Rewards that motivate Millennials include awards, certificates, and tangible evidence of credibility.

Communication styles that Millennials respond to are in-person meetings, instant messages, text messages, e-mails, and blogs. Be positive in your communications — avoid cynicism and sarcasm, and don't be condescending.

What Do the Generations Have in Common?

It's easy to identify differences in these generations. There are many similarities as well, and successful leaders are creating work environments that support them. Recent research conducted by the Center for Creative Leadership®[99] and Randstad[100] has found interesting similarities among employees across the generations:

▲ Work is a vehicle for personal fulfillment and satisfaction, not just a paycheck;

▲ Workplace culture is very important;

▲ Ninety-one percent of employees agree that being trusted to get the job done is the top factor defining job satisfaction;

▲ Eighty-six percent of employees say they need to feel valued by their employer to be happy at work;

▲ More than 6 of 10 employees want career planning;

▲ Sixty-seven percent seek flexibility in workplace schedules; and

▲ All generations define success as finding a company they can stay with for a long time.

RECRUITMENT AND RETENTION

It's imperative that healthcare organizations create recruitment and retention strategies designed with the Gen Xer and Millennial physicians in mind.

Generation X and Millennial Physicians[101]

These younger physicians are less willing to pay their dues to an organization or take on additional responsibilities without promises of higher compensation or partnership. They demand flex time and seek work–life balance. Married male physicians are expecting more family involvement than previous generations. Many Gen Xer and Millennial physicians want to continuously develop skills so they can have options and opportunities to move to other organizations if a better situation presents itself.

Dissatisfaction with their choice of medical career is evident in recent statistics: 39 percent of physicians are doubtful or negative regarding their choice of profession and 41 percent of physicians are interested in working outside the healthcare sector. The first three years of practice are critical for new physicians and hold the greatest likelihood for turnover. Poor cultural fit with the practice and the community as well as a desire to be near family members were most frequently mentioned when asked the reasons for the turnover.

Attracting Young Physicians

To attract and retain young physicians, employers need to provide:

- ▲ A values-driven, relationship-oriented culture;
- ▲ Strong orientation and mentoring programs (61 percent of practices assign a mentor to new recruits);
- ▲ Continuing development of marketable, manageable skill sets;
- ▲ Flexibility in scheduling (9 of 10 groups offer part-time or flexible work options);
- ▲ Emphasis on work–life balance;
- ▲ Prompt attention during recruitment phase and when employed;
- ▲ Prompt response to calls, e-mails, and text messages;
- ▲ Formal development of a physician retention program (only 40 percent have one currently);

▲ Clear expectations about compensation and long-term potential before the physician start date;

▲ Development of interpersonal connections with new physician and peers from start date to initial 90 days;

▲ Regular feedback and performance reviews (a very important retention factor for physicians after initial 90 days);

▲ Partnership and ownership opportunities; and

▲ Spouse relocation assistance during recruitment process.

All Four Generations[102]

There are several ideas that can support the recruitment and retention of your team members by generation. Consider the following strategies for your organization.

To recruit and retain the World War II generation:

▲ Be mindful of age and experience. Show that experience is an asset vs. a liability;

▲ Develop a mature worker strategy;

▲ Review job descriptions and interviewing, hiring, and promoting practices;

▲ Remove age bias;

▲ Capitalize on experience and set up mentoring relationships with younger team members; and

▲ Consider options for career deceleration, phased retirement, and alumni return.

To recruit and retain the Baby Boomers:

▲ Offer flexible work arrangements, telecommuting, adjustable scheduling, and personal time for family and caregiving;

▲ Provide challenging work opportunities, horizontal movement, and learning opportunities;

▲ Offer phased retirement;

▲ Expand and accelerate leadership development; and

▲ Develop systems for knowledge sharing.

To recruit and retain Gen Xers:

▲ Show them lots of options;

▲ Allow them to work autonomously;

▲ Tap into their adaptability, flexibility, and independence; and

▲ Give FAST feedback to build skills and resumes.

To recruit and retain Millennials:

▲ Tap outstanding Millennial team members to talk to new candidates about the company;

▲ Make accommodations for family and personal life and provide flexibility for other interests;

▲ Become community oriented and support volunteer efforts;

▲ Offer benefits such as 401(k) plans so the team members can start saving in their twenties;

▲ Look for ways to involve parents in important decisions;

▲ Pair Millennials with older mentors (reverse mentoring on technological issues);

▲ Focus on Day 1 and poll new hires about their on-boarding experiences; and

▲ Make exit interviews work and ask and welcome people back after leaving.

Six Principles for Successfully Mixing Generations

Six principles can be implemented for mixing the generations successfully:[103]

1. **Initiate conversations about generations.** We often make judgments about each other without realizing those judgments are generational in nature. And we tend to keep those judgments under the table. When we get them out in the open, the issues become less personalized and more generalized. They become easier — and sometimes fun — to talk about.

2. **Ask people about their needs and preferences.** Out of the best intentions, we often project our preferences onto others. The only way to know for certain what someone else's needs and preferences are is to ask!

3. **Offer options.** Working successfully with a mix of generations means being flexible, offering as many choices as possible to suit the needs and preferences of a diverse workforce.

4. **Personalize your style.** Be flexible. Practice the Titanium Rule: Learn about preferences of others on your team and find creative ways to meet their expectations.

EXHIBIT 23.4 | **Tool Kit for Successfully Managing Across Generations**

TEST YOUR CULTURE: IS YOUR WORK GROUP GENERATIONS-FRIENDLY?

Diagnose the effectiveness of your work group, team, department, or organization at creating a culture where all generations can thrive by placing a check mark next to each statement that accurately reflects the culture of your work group.

___ There's not just one type of person who is successful here.

___ When we put a project team together, we consciously include a variety of perspectives.

___ We treat employees like customers, courteously and by honoring their perspectives.

___ We talk about — sometimes even joke about — different viewpoints.

___ We talk openly about what we want from our jobs.

___ Our policies are based on what customers and employees want.

___ We have a minimum of bureaucracy and red tape.

___ We enjoy working together.

___ The people who work here have the big picture along with specific goals and measures, and feel free to find their own best way of reaching them. We recognize that people have different styles and approaches to reaching the organizational and job-specific goals.

___ We're clear about our expectations and show employees how their contributions benefit the company.

___ Our work assignments are broad, providing variety and challenge, and allowing each employee to use and develop a range of skills.

___ We offer health and wellness program options that are tailored to meet the needs of employees at different stages of life.

___ We survey our employees to learn how well we are meeting their needs and to learn whether there are differences in responses for different groups.

___ We offer promotions to employees from all generations and consider employees from all generations in succession plans.

___ We offer a wide array of training and professional development opportunities to all employees to help them increase skills and further their education.

RESPONSE SCALE:

▲ If you marked 14 or more items, congratulations! From bloggers to technophobes, everyone feels welcome in your organization!

▲ If you marked 11 to 13 items, you're making progress. Keep up the good work!

▲ If marked 10 or fewer items, it's time to collect data about your customers and employees and start building a generations-friendly workplace. The results for your organization will be well worth your time and effort!

C. Raines, *Connecting Generations* (Menlo Park, CA: Crisp Publications, 2003); and S. Murphy and A. Arnsparger, *4genR8tns: Succeeding with Colleagues, Cohorts & Customers* (Colorado Print and Digital: Claire Raines Associates, 2008). Adapted with permission from C. Raines and Axzo Press. www.axzopress.com.

5. **Build on strengths.** The best mixed-generation work teams recognize the unique strengths of each individual. Urge people who are different to become more of who they already are, rather than trying to blend in with the rest of the team.

6. **Pursue different perspectives.** Many work teams would tell you that they tolerate differences, but the mixed-generation ones that truly succeed go far beyond tolerance. Choose people with varied backgrounds and perspectives to work together on projects.

The tool kit in Exhibit 23.4 is a great resource to help manage team members from across the generations.

CHAPTER PRESCRIPTIONS

- The workplace is now, more than ever, a hotbed of generational mixing. Be aware that there are now four generations who need to interact with each other and also be served as customers.
- Highly engaged, respected, and valued team members are much more likely to remain working for you — do your best to keep them there.
- A multigenerational workplace is susceptible to becoming counterproductive and conflict driven, so use the various people to your advantage. Engage in open discussions of different perspectives and create high-performing teams of talented people from all backgrounds.

ENDNOTES

1   Pat Kane, *The Play Ethic: A Manifesto for a Different Way of Living* (London: Pan Books, 2005), 128.

2   C. Watson and R. Hoffman, "Managers as Negotiators," *Leadership Quarterly 7*, no. 1 (1996).

3   R. Brim, "Firms, Employees Forsake Court for Win–Win Option: Mediation," *Knight Ridder Newspapers*, 2001.

4   J.R. Gibb, "Defensive Communication," *Journal of Communication* 11 (September, 1961) 141–148.

5   P. Heim, S. Murphy, with S. Golant, *In the Company of Women: Indirect Aggression Among Women: Why We Hurt Each Other and How to Stop* (New York: Tarcher/Putnam, 2003).

6   A. Mehrabian, "Communication Without Words," *Psychology Today* (September 1968), 52.

7   Heim et al., *In the Company of Women.*

8   Heim et al., *In the Company of Women.*

9   D. Stone, B. Patton, and S. Heen, *Difficult Conversations: How to Discuss What Matters Most* (New York: Penguin, 2000).

10 K. Patterson, J. Grenny, R. McMillan, and A. Switzler, *Crucial Conversations: Tools for Talking When Stakes Are High* (New York: McGraw-Hill, 2002).

11 Barbara D. Mathews and Catharine A. Larkin, *Type in Action! Activities for Enriching MBTI Training in Organizations* (Sunnyvale, CA: CPP, 2002).

12 Heim et al., *In the Company of Women.*

13 K.W. Thomas and R.H. Kilmann, *Thomas–Kilmann Conflict Mode Instrument* (Palo Alto, CA: Xicom, 1974), www.cpp.com.

14 Thomas and Kilmann, *Thomas–Kilmann Conflict Mode Instrument.*

15 Thomas and Kilmann, *Thomas–Kilmann Conflict Mode Instrument.*

16 Thomas and Kilmann, *Thomas–Kilmann Conflict Mode Instrument.*

17 Thomas and Kilmann, *Thomas–Kilmann Conflict Mode Instrument.*

18 Thomas and Kilmann, *Thomas–Kilmann Conflict Mode Instrument.*

19 B.W. Tuckman, "Developmental Sequence in Small Groups," *Psychological Bulletin* 63 (1965) 384–399.

20 Tuckman, "Developmental Sequence in Small Groups," 384–399.

21 C. Gersick, "Time and Transition in Work Teams: Toward a New Model of Group Development," *Academy of Management Journal* 31 (1988), 9–41.

22 Heim et al., *In the Company of Women.*

23 Tuckman, "Developmental Sequence in Small Groups," 384–399.

24 Heim et al., *In the Company of Women.*

25 W.H. Whyte, "Groupthink," *Fortune* (March 1952).

26 K. Cherry, "What Is Groupthink?" About.com, accessed June 26, 2015, http://psychology.about.com/od/gindex/g/groupthink.htm.

27 Cherry, "What Is Groupthink?"

28 "Groupthink: Definitions & Examples," *Business 101: Principles of Management*, ch. 8, lesson 5, accessed Nov. 18, 2015, http://study.com/academy/lesson/group-think-definition-examples.html.

29 S. Sorscher, "Group-Think Caused the Market to Fail." *Huff Post Business* (blog), *Huffington Post*, June 9, 2010, www.huffingtonpost.com/stan-sorscher/group-think-caused-the-ma_b_604810.html.

30 Irving L. Janis, *Victims of Groupthink: A Psychological Study of Foreign-Policy Decisions and Fiascoes* (Boston: Houghton, Mifflin, 1972).

31 *Holmes Leaflets: Poems and Prose Passages from the Works of Oliver Wendell Holmes for Reading and Recitation*, compiled by Josephine E. Hodgdon, Riverside Literature Series (New York: Houghton, Mifflin, 1881), 91.

32 R.M. Bramson, *Coping with Difficult People* (Garden City, NY: Anchor Press/Doubleday, 1981).

33 Bramson, *Coping with Difficult People.*

34 Bramson, *Coping with Difficult People*; Heim et al., *In the Company of Women.*

35 Heim et al., *In the Company of Women.*

36 Bramson, *Coping with Difficult People.*

37 Bramson, *Coping with Difficult People*; Heim et al., *In the Company of Women.*

38 "Total Number of Medical School Graduates," The Henry J. Kaiser Family Foundation, 2014, accessed Nov. 18, 2015, http://kff.org/other/state-indicator/total-medical-school-graduates/.

39 P. Heim, with S.K. Golant, *Hardball for Women: Winning at the Game of Business*, rev. ed. (New York: Plume, 2015).

40 Heim et al., *In the Company of Women.*

41 Heim et al., *In the Company of Women*, 21.

42 Heim et al., *In the Company of Women*, 51.

43 Susan Applegarth Murphy, "A Study of Career Values by Generation and Gender" (PhD diss., Fielding Institute, 2000).

44 A. Moir and D. Jessel, *Brain Sex: The Real Difference Between Men and Women* (New York: Dell, 1991), 48.

45 Moir and Jessel, *Brain Sex*, 48.

46 Moir and Jessel, *Brain Sex*, 48.

47 Moir and Jessel, *Brain Sex*, 48.

48 Heim et al., *In the Company of Women.*

49 S.B. Hardy and C.S. Carter, "Hormonal Cocktails for Two," *Natural History* 104 (Dec. 1995), 34.

50 Hardy and Carter, "Hormonal Cocktails," 34.

51 M.M. McCarthy, "Estrogen Modulation of Oxytocin and Its Relation to Behavior," in *Oxytocin: Cellular and Molecular Approaches in Medicine and Research*, ed. R. Ivell and J. Russell (New York: Plenum Press, 1995) 235–242; D. Jezova, E. Jurankova, A. Mosnarova, M. Kriska, and I. Skultetyova, "Neuroendocrine Response During Stress with Relation to Gender Differences," *Acta Neurobiologae Experimentalis* 56 (1996) 779–785.

52 Heim et al., *In the Company of Women.*

53 S.E. Taylor, L. Cousin-Klein, B.P. Lewis, et al. "Bio-Behavioral Responses to Stress in Females: Tend-and-Befriend, Not Fight-or-Flight" *Psychological Review* 107 (July 2000), 28.

54 Heim and Golant, *Hardball for Women.*

55 Heim et al., *In the Company of Women*, 70.

56   S.B. Hardy, "Natural Born Mothers," *Natural History* 104 (Dec. 1995).

57   Heim et al., *In the Company of Women*.

58   L.A. Roggman and J.C. Peery, "Parent–Infant Social Play in Brief Encounters: Early Gender Differences," *Child Study Journal* 19 (1989) 65–77.

59   Heim et al., *In the Company of Women*.

60   Heim et al., *In the Company of Women*.

61   Heim et al., *In the Company of Women*.

62   Heim and Golant, *Hardball for Women*.

63   Heim and Golant, *Hardball for Women*.

64   Heim et al., *In the Company of Women*.

65   Heim et al., *In the Company of Women*.

66   Heim et al., *In the Company of Women*.

67   M.R. Perrault and J.K. Irwin, *Gender Differences at Work: Are Men and Women Really That Different?* (Agoura Hills: Advanced Teamware, 1996).

68   H. Collingwood, "Women as Managers: Not Just Different — Better," *Working Woman* (Nov. 1995), 14.

69   Heim et al., *In the Company of Women*.

70   K. Minich-Purshadi, "Strategic Physician Recruiting," *HealthLeaders Magazine* (March 13, 2012), accessed June 26, 2015, www.healthleadersmedia.com/print/MAG-277560/Strategic-Physician-Recruiting.

71   "Patients, Physicians and Employees: Satisfaction Trifecta Brings Bottom Line Results" (white paper, Press Ganey Associates, South Bend, IN, 2005).

72   Susan A. Murphy, *Leading a Multigenerational Workforce* (Washington, DC: AARP, 2007).

73   P. Buerhaus, "Implications of an Aging Registered Nurse Workforce," *Journal of American Medical Association* 283, no. 22 (June 14, 2000), 2948–2954.

74   Cejka Search and America Medical Group Association (AMGA), *2006 Physician Retention Survey* (St. Louis, MO: Cejka Search; and Alexandria, VA: AMGA, 2007).

75   Cejka Search and AMGA, *2006 Physician Retention Survey*.

76   Cejka Search and AMGA, *2006 Physician Retention Survey*. In March 2015, the economic modeling and forecasting firm IHS Inc. released a new study, "The Complexities of Physician Supply and Demand: Projections from 2013 to 2025," at the request of the Association of American Medical Colleges (AAMC). This study can be accessed at https://www.aamc.org/download/426260/data/physiciansupplyanddemandthrough2025keyfindings.pdf.

77   Deloitte and the Manufacturing Institute, "The Skills Gap in U.S. Manufacturing: 2015 and Beyond," (Deloitte Development LLC, 2015), 4, www.themanufacturinginstitute.org/~/media/827DBC76533942679A15EF7067A704CD.ashx.

78   S. Murphy and A. Arnsparger, *4genR8tns: Succeeding with Colleagues, Cohorts & Customers* (Colorado Print and Digital: Claire Raines Associates, 2008).

79   Murphy and Arnsparger, *4genR8tns*.

80   Murphy and Arnsparger, *4genR8tns*, 20.

81   Gallup, "Employee Engagement Index," *Gallup Management Journal* (2006).

82   Murphy and Arnsparger, *4genR8tns*, 20.

83 R. Zemke, C. Raines, B. Filipczak, *Generations at Work: Managing the Clash of Veterans, Boomers, Xers and Nexters in Your Workplace* (New York: AMACOM, 2000), 17.

84 J.W. Smith and A. Clurman, *Rocking the Ages: The Yankelovich Report on Generational Marketing* (New York: HarperCollins, 1998).

85 M. Massey, *You Are What You Were When* (Schaumburg, IL: Video Publishing House, 1976), video.

86 Zemke et al., *Generations at Work*, 33.

87 Smith and Clurman, *Rocking the Ages*; G. Barna, *Baby Busters: The Disillusioned Generation* (Chicago: Northfield, 1992); C. Raines, *Beyond Generation X* (Menlo Park: Crisp Publications, 1997); B. Tulgan, *Managing Generation X* (Santa Monica, CT: Merritt, 1995); W. Strauss and N. Howe, *The Fourth Turning* (New York: Broadway Books, 1997).

88 Zemke et al., *Generations at Work*, 68.

89 Zemke et al., *Generations at Work*, 65.

90 Zemke et al., *Generations at Work*, 76.

91 D. Coupland, *Generation X: Tales for an Accelerated Culture* (New York: St. Martin's Press, 1991).

92 Murphy, *Leading a Multigenerational Workforce*.

93 Massey, *You Are What You Were When*.

94 Smith and Clurman, *Rocking the Ages*; Barna, *Baby Busters*; Raines, *Beyond Generation X*; Tulgan, *Managing Generation X*.

95 Tulgan, *Managing Generation X*.

96 Murphy and Arnsparger, *4genR8tns*, 14.

97 "Club Med Has Refurbished and Upgraded Its Ixtapa Pacific Resort," Travel Tribe, accessed Nov. 18, 2015, http://www.traveltribe.com/Destination/ArticleDetail/central-america/belize/Club-Med-has-refurbished-and-upgraded-its-Ixtapa-Pacific-resort.

98 Zemke et al., *Generations at Work*, 130.

99 R. Plettnix, *Emerging Leader: Implications for Engagement and Retention* (Brussels, Belgium: Center for Creative Leadership, 2006).

100 Randstad USA, "The World of Work 2007" and "2006 Employee Review," www.randstad.com.

101 Cejka Search and AMGA, *2006 Physician Retention Survey*; IHS, "The Complexities of Physician Supply and Demand."

102 Murphy and Arnsparger, *4genR8tns*.

103 C. Raines, *Connecting Generations* (Menlo Park, CA: Crisp Publications, 2003), 44.

How to Access the Electronic Files

Access the electronic files by visiting mgma.org/maximizingperformance and completing the form.

Case Studies, Tools, and Helping Mechanisms

CASE STUDIES

The Emory Clinic, Inc. – Atlanta, GA

Emory Healthcare, Primary Care Practice – Smyrna, GA

Floyd Primary Care – Rome, GA

John Muir Medical Center – Walnut Creek, CA

Kaiser Permanente – Northern California Perform

Kaiser Permanente – Northern California Strategy

Press Ganey Best Practices

Providence Health and Services

St. Mary's Nell J. Redfield Health Centers – Reno, NV

UCI Medical Center, UCI Medical Group and UCI Clinics – Irvine, CA

TOOLS AND HELPING MECHANISMS

Index

Note: *ex.* indicates exhibit